MW00795926

THE DARK SIDE OF TWILIGHT:
A True Story of Murder and Texas Justice

Jean Lasell

Sundown Publications

THE DARK SIDE OF TWILIGHT:
A True Story of Murder and Texas Justice

Jean Lasell

Sundown Publications

Sundown Publications
Copyright © 1996 by Jean Lasell
All rights reserved
ISBN 0-9651536-0-6

Additional copies of this book may be purchased at bookstores or by writing to: Sundown Publications, P. O. Box 472381, Garland, Texas. 75047-2381

Author's Note

Patricia Crocker was my younger sister. A bright and beautiful girl, a high school cheerleader back in the fifties during the hey day of rock-and-roll music, poodle skirts, pony tails and drive-in movies. But an early marriage and twenty-six years changed her life into a never ending nightmare of domestic violence.

Writing this book was a long and emotional process, to the point that, several times, I backed out of writing it at all. But each time I tried to put it away, it stayed with me, tugging at my heart, refusing to let go until the last word was written. There were long days and nights when I imagined her presence and the fragrance of her favorite perfume. And at times when I was stuck in paragraphs needing a particular word, suddenly the words were there. I became convinced that she wanted me to write it, and write it with hope that in some way it will help others learn the things that for her came too late. I hope I have done that.

In writing this book I have endeavored to render the truth accurately.

Quotes and phrases used in the story were said to me or in my presence by people I trust. While it is possible that not every word is exactly the same as theirs, my interpretation has been to the best of my remembrance. Other information in this book is authenticated by police reports and court records. In order to protect the privacy of the people who deserve it, and for some who do not deserve it, I have chosen fictitious names and disguises for them. I have used real names of family and law enforcement.

All photographs appearing in this book were either taken by the author, or given for publication with this particular story. Special thanks to Mrs. Erwin G. Ernst and Mrs. Brian D. Taylor for the photographs of Judge Erwin G. Ernst and Texas Ranger Brian D. Taylor.

Jean Lasell

ACKNOWLEDGMENTS

My debt of gratitude to the people in Law Enforcement in Grimes County, is far more than I can state publicly. But in my attempt to do so, I wish to express my sincere thanks and appreciation to: Judge Bobby McNew, Judge Erwin Ernst, Latham Boone, David Barron, Brian Taylor, Larry Adams, Tracy Wright, Jackie Siracusa, Glenn Hightower, John Sebastian, Willie Love, Bill Foster, Wayne Rucker and Tuck McLain.

Thanks also to the following persons, many of whom are also in law enforcement throughout the state of Texas, and who were either involved in the case, or contributed to this book, or both: Dr. Arial Espanola, Dr. Mac Leon Bennett, Bill Smith, Tommy Wright, Ed Jordan, Troy Roberts, Bobby Connell, Ray Nutt, Chuck Thomas, Ann Craddock, Brenda Williams, Ricky Brewer, Sandra Vega, Sharon Smith, Lloyd Mason, Donald Ashmore, Rodney Welsh, Richard Bertrand, Sr., Warren Hirsch, Opal Holmes, Billy Dixon, Edwin Marek, Lillie Edwards, Tina Kapchinski, Clifford James, Lambert Laskowski, Carlton White, John Price and Ruby Mason. And, of course, I must also thank my best friend and sister, Carol Gully.

If I have failed to mention anyone who worked on the case, it was not my intention to forget them. I extend my thanks to them, also.

—Jean Lasell

THE DARK SIDE OF TWILIGHT:
A True Story of Murder and Texas Justice

by

Jean Lasell

For Patricia, in loving memory.
And for all other battered women.

I don't know why, but I have a thing about twilight time.
I want to be outside and smell the burning leaves and grass
when it's almost dark. You know, after the sun has gone down
and it's twilight time. That's my time of day.

(excerpt from a letter written by Patricia Crocker, dated August 4, 1975)

In writing this book, I chose to give fictitious names to many people and places who were involved in the story. Each one played an important part, and although a few do not deserve a fictitious name, I have, nevertheless, tried to protect their privacy.

The fictitious names are as follows, in alphabetical order:

Cynthia Ann
Aunt Clara
Lenny Compton
Dottie
Elena
Bob Gordon
Don and Hillary
Clarence Hudson
Betty Hutchins
Claude Hutchins
Arthur Johnson
Tyrone Jones
Charlie Lancaster
Lucille Mayes
Carmen Mitchell
Walter Mitchell
Marcell Nelson
Pauline Nicholson
Fred's Place
Jim Pierce Ranch
Doris Rawlins
Mary Sallonger
Monica Stevens
Bonnie Sue
Jack Thompson
Lily Tyler
Beverly Webb
Mack Wilson
Rosa Wilson

Any resemblance of these names to actual people not involved in this story is purely coincidental. All other names and places appearing in the story are real, to the best of my remembrance.

—Jean Lasell

CHAPTER 1

I awoke to the sounds of thunder rumbling in the distance and hard rain hitting the pavement beneath my window. But in the grogginess of my sleep, what must have been seconds seemed like minutes until I remembered I was still in a motel room in southeast Texas. I had awakened in this room for the past seven mornings, switching on the bedside light and glancing at my watch hoping I had not missed my early wake up calls.

I glanced at the bed across the room, half expecting to see my sister, Carol, still sleeping in it. But this morning its cover was as smooth as it had been the night before. I stared at the empty closet space where her clothes had hung, and then it all came back: The trial had ended, the outburst when the verdict was read, the pickup waiting on the side of the road, the police escorting us to the motel, and later escorting Carol to her home.

Carol and I had been together either by phone or in person for the past seven months seeking justice for our sister, Patricia. Seven months of hell was what we called it. And the past week had been more of the same. But the thought of giving up and backing out of it never crossed our minds. We were determined to see it through to the end. We couldn't let go until then. Regardless of the consequences. We had to be here. We had put our faith and trust in the judicial system, and we had come here to see it work. To us, it was like a gamble in the sense that we had played the game fair and honest and we expected to win.

And, yesterday, at last, the voice of justice had spoken. The judge and jury had had their say. The verdict was read and the trial had ended. For all intents and purposes it was over. And the hell was supposed to end there, too.

There were those who told us to try to forget it and go on with our own lives. But I could not forget the hate and anger or the emptiness I felt in my heart. I would never forget. For the hurt was too great and I had lived with it too long. Now, the most I could hope for was that in years to come, somehow the pain would dull to the point that it would no longer possess me. But still, the past seven months had changed me, and my way of thinking. I was more cautious now. Perhaps overly cautious. I looked at people in a different light and found it easy to distrust them. And I had learned to look behind me, wherever I went, and be aware of what was going on around me at all times.

The roaring thunder and lightning was so loud that I thought it had struck the motel or one of the trees nearby. I walked to the window and pulled the heavy curtains aside, then looked out into the dark morning trying to see if there were broken tree limbs or light poles on the parking lot. But I saw only fog, and heavy rain splattering on the pavement. I stood there a few minutes longer watching the reflection of the rain falling on the tall lights. Judging from the cars and pickup trucks, the motel was full. Yet, it was eerily quiet. Quiet like death, I thought. And my anger was like the raging storm.

On the highway, the neon sign which read: "Best Western," was barely visible. Then I glanced across the parking lot to the manager's office to see if my car was still there. For, upon learning the outcome of the trial, the motel manager suggested that I park my car near hers, where it couldn't be seen from the highway. She had offered to watch it for me, and screen my phone calls.

Looking at the rain made me cold all over. Finally, I closed the curtains and turned the heating system to a warmer temperature. Then, suddenly, the phone rang, and I was relieved that it was my wake up call. I thanked the manager and told her I would be leaving that morning. Then we talked a few minutes about the weather. She said it was snowing in Dallas, and freezing rain would be here by noon, and that I was welcome to keep my room for another day, or as long as I liked.

I told her I needed to leave as soon as possible, but I would wait a few hours until the storm was over.

I turned on the television hoping for more news about the weather, then made coffee in the small electric coffee pot I had brought with me. A few moments later, I poured a cup and climbed back into bed.

I began reading a brochure I had found in the drawer of the bedside table. Of course, I knew I was in a small town called Navasota, in Grimes County, Texas. And I had driven through here many times on my way to visit my parents. But I knew nothing about the town or its people.

While reading the brochure, I learned that it was primarily an agricultural town but that it had several railroads and some industry. It was an old historical town with many historical homes. Some of the homes were Victorian style trimmed in delicate art work. Others were Classic Greek Revival homes. There were annual home tours held in May of each year when art work, homemade quilts and other crafts were displayed to the public. It also boasted of its chili and barbecue cook-offs, hay hauling contests and parades. And, in the middle of Main Street, there was a tall statue of a French Cavalier who was murdered by his own exploration party back in 1687. And in the 1800's it had been a stagecoach town.

It was still a western town, I thought. A town where cars gave way to pickup trucks, and where Stetson hats, cowboy boots and western clothing were the normal attire. But that was not unusual in any Texas town. For even the most famous Texans were as proud of their boots and hats as they were of their Texas heritage, which dated back to the 1800's when Texas won its independence from Mexico. Boots and hats were signs of grit. And I understood them well.

I placed the brochure back in the drawer. Then I went to the window and looked out again into the cold rain. I left the curtains open a few inches and stood there thinking of Richard, and of the many motels we had stayed in while on vacations in the mountain states. I thought of the years when our children were young and the faraway places we took them to see. And of our vacations together after the children were grown. I recalled another storm, of several years ago, while we were vacationing in Taos, New Mexico. It had been a vicious storm causing our motel to be without electrical power for a day, and we had spent the day playing cards by candlelight. Such happy memories.

But the circumstances of this trip to Grimes County, had been that of horror and disbelief. And I had never felt so lonely. I wanted to see Richard and my children. I wanted to feel the comfort of my home. And I wanted to erase from the deepest depths of my mind all that had happened since last summer.

Finally, the rain appeared to have stopped, although the skies were still dark and misting. Then I quickly closed the curtains, grabbed my purse, and ran across the parking lot to my car. I waved to the manager, then got in my car and drove back to my room.

By the time I loaded my luggage and changed clothes, the rain had gotten worse, but I decided to leave anyway. However, after I checked out of the motel, I wondered if I would regret it. For the rain came in torrents as I turned onto the highway and headed toward the town of Anderson, nine miles away. I knew the motel in Navasota would be the last one until I arrived in Madisonville, sixty miles northeast of Navasota. But I had to leave, I thought. I couldn't bear to stay there another day. And surely, if I drove far enough, I would drive through the storm and leave it behind me.

The cold heavy rain continued as I drove on toward Anderson. Dark and dreary, more like late evening than early morning. I shuddered again and asked myself what I was doing in this part of the country this time of morning. I should be home in Dallas having breakfast or talking on the phone to my children or planning a day of leisure. I wanted to be home. I wanted to awake from the nightmare. To blink my eyes and suddenly realize the past seven months had never happened. But in reality, I knew that was only wishful thinking. The way a small child might think. Still, sometimes when adults are hurting, they tend to become as children reaching out for anything to comfort them. But yet, when the hurt is caused by murder, only time can be the comforter.

The highway going to Anderson was a two lane blacktopped road, slick and hilly, like so many others in that part of south Texas. About three miles from the outskirts of Navasota, I heard sirens blaring in the distance, behind me. I slowed down and pulled over to the edge of the highway giving the ambulances room to pass, then after a few minutes, I drove on. Then, a few miles further, I saw policemen in yellow raincoats directing traffic around two mangled pickup trucks as bodies were being lifted into the ambulances.

I shuddered as I drove by and I wondered about the people involved in the wreck. Were they young men on their way to work in the city or perhaps they were older men on their way to check on their livestock in the pastures. I wondered about their families and the hurt and loneliness they would feel upon learning they had lost a loved one. Although I would never meet them, I felt sympathy for them, for I knew very well about that kind of hurting. And of the emptiness and helplessness that would follow.

At the city limits sign in Anderson, I noticed the small white church, again. It had probably been there as long as the town. Or at least longer than I could remember. Its white paint was now gray and peeling, and under the gray morning skies, it appeared even darker. It had always looked deserted, and each time I saw it, I wondered if it was.

The town of Anderson was built on seven hills and named for Kenneth Anderson, the Vice-President of the Republic of Texas. And in 1838, it was named the County Seat of Grimes County. Like Navasota, Anderson also had many old Victorian and Classic Greek Revival homes. And, it was once a stagecoach town with several hotels and considerable industry. But as the years came and went, newer and larger towns were built, within driving distance, leaving Anderson as a small town of picturesque beauty with a population of less than five hundred.

The huge old red brick courthouse trimmed in white dominates the entire landscape of Anderson. Its Victorian three structure is topped by a large square cupola which gives a towering appearance that can be seen for miles from the winding highways leading into the town. It was build in 1894 and has the honor of being listed in the Guiness

Book of World Records as the only recorded courthouse in the world built in the middle of a street.

Although I had driven through the town more than a hundred times in years gone by, I never knew anyone who lived there. And, for no reason that I can remember, I had never even stopped in the town except for traffic lights and school buses. For I was always in a hurry, on my way to visit my parents who lived northwest of Houston. However, each time I drove through Anderson, I admired the old courthouse. It was indeed a significant landmark. And each time I saw it, I knew Mother was waiting for me.

But this time, the courthouse had been my reason for being here. I had spent the past week within its powerful walls. I had walked its hallways lined with photographs of past judges and other important people of years gone by. I had welcomed the strong coffee the clerks offered me. And I appreciated the kindness of many people. Whether it was the words they spoke or merely the expressions on their faces, I would not forget them. Each day I had climbed the stairs to the second floor courtroom, and I admired the intricate design of its tall round ceiling. But I was not there to admire its beauty. My reasons for being there were the same as the thousands of people who had come there before me. I was there to seek justice for those I loved. Justice for Patricia.

Now, as I drove out of the town, I glanced back at the towering old courthouse in my rearview mirror. It would always be a reminder of what had been. The nightmare was real. It had all been true. The seven months of hell had really happened. And nothing could change it.

Hot angry tears rolled down my cheeks, and I pulled over to the edge of the highway to wipe them away. Oh, damn, I thought. Then I cried some more.

I knew this stretch of road would be painful for me. Patricia had lived in Grimes County, and had driven this road several times a week for many years.

"Oh, Patricia. My precious little sister. What I'd give to see you again. Do you know I'm here? Do you know how much I love you?"

The narrow highway that I was now on would take me to Bedias, to Patricia's home, and then to Madisonville and the Interstate to Dallas.

The road soon became crowded with horse trailers and hay trucks, no doubt on their way to care for cattle and horses. For in winter, especially after a storm, ranchers always checked on their livestock making sure there was plenty of food for them. Some ranchers also raised thoroughbred horses, and thunder and lightning could easily spook them.

Several trucks and horse trailers passed around me throwing more rain upon my windshield. And I listened as the windshield wipers worked full speed keeping time with the swishing sounds of the tires on the wet pavement. And at a distance I watched windmills turning in rhythm with the wind. I drove past mile after mile of pasture land cold and brown from the winter, and watched cattle huddled in bunches without shelter. But this was ranch country. Texas ranch country, with miles of rail and barbed-wire fences. Ranches that were large and stretched for miles. Where one ranch ended, another began. Most ranch owners had signs posted advertising different breeds of cattle and horses. And many of the ranchers raised Brahma cattle. Brahma cattle always reminded me of cowboys who rode wild Brahma bulls in rodeos.

The Jim Pierce ranch was one of the largest in the county. It was known as a working ranch and specialized in many things, including Brahma cattle. The ranch reminded me of a small community all its own. The entrance to it was a white gravel road which led through tall black wrought iron gates, then branched off into a winding road that led further back into a deep thickness of woods. A large two story white brick home with tall porch columns stood on a hill to the left side of the main gate. On the right side of the gate, there were several small houses, a long bunkhouse, barns and stables. The tall oak and pine trees which shaded the landscape in summer now looked like dark wintry lace hovering above the near freezing ground. And in the distance, several stock ponds glistened with ice.

The weather report on my car radio said it was still snowing in

Dallas. A late winter storm, they called it. Well, it wasn't really late I thought. After all, this was only the first week in March. And Texas often had some of its worst winter weather this time of year.

CHAPTER 2

As I drove past the ranch, I thought of how different today's weather was compared to last summer when I drove through this area on a sweltering hot Saturday afternoon in late June, on my way to visit Patricia. And it was on that day that I first heard of the Jim Pierce ranch. Patricia's husband, Lewis, had recently become employed there, as a welder.

Last June, I was on my way home after visiting Mother. Mother had been ill. She asked me to stop at Patricia's house and tell her about it.

Patricia and Lewis had bought a home the year before, in the small farming town of Bedias. Mother didn't know their address, but I told her I'd try to find it.

It was mid-afternoon when I arrived in Bedias, on that Saturday in June. I knew my visit was unexpected and it had been a year since I last saw Patricia..

I stopped at the traffic light in Bedias, then turned onto a street that led into the residential area. The house shouldn't be hard to find, I thought. The business section consisted of only one stop light, two gas stations, a bank and a grocery store. It was a quiet town. Quiet and sleepy. Where trees of elm, oak and mulberry shaded the homes on its narrow winding streets. And where gnarled rose bushes bloomed in various colors in front yards, and pink hydrangeas and purple wisteria grew along fences, light poles and porches.

Finally, I saw Patricia's car in front of a white frame house at the end of a long graveled street. And as I drove toward it, I noticed one of her neighbors watering a vegetable garden. Further down the street, an elderly couple sat in rocking chairs on their front porch, probably talking about the heat or politics. Or about the little boy who was playing Frisbee in their yard.

Well, this was a good neighborhood for Patricia, I thought. She liked elderly people. There was a special kindness about her that made her want to help them.

As I pulled into her driveway, I noticed the old brown school bus. Patricia and Lewis had bought it when the girls were young. It was used for camping trips and deer hunting. Now, a new fishing boat was parked behind it.

I stopped and got out, walked upon the porch and knocked on the door. Then Patricia came almost running to meet me.

"Well, look who's here," she said, hugging me. "This is a pleasant surprise. It's about time for it, too. Come in and sit down. And don't tell me you're in a hurry, either. You know, it's been a year since we've seen each other."

"Yes, I know," I replied. "And I've missed you. I think of you every day."

"I've missed you, too. I've been intending to call you."

We hugged each other again and walked into her living room.

"It's so good to see you. And you're cooking something that smells delicious."

"Oh, that's not my cooking," she laughed. "Rhonda and Virginia are cooking today ."

"But you're the cooking expert in the family," I teased. "You're the only one in the family with official cooking certificates, not to mention the awards you've won."

Rhonda and Virginia then came into the room to say hello. They were the second and fourth of Patricia's five daughters. Both were in their twenties now and married. Tammie, the oldest daughter was also married. Kimberly was to begin college in September, and five-year old Jennifer was ready for kindergarten. The girls were tall, blonde and thin with wide set eyes like Lewis. Except for Rhonda, who had brown hair and eyes like Patricia.

"We're cooking steak and chicken, with all the trimmings. You'll have to stay for dinner," said Virginia.

"I'd love to but Aunt Margaret is expecting me for dinner at her

18

house."

Jennifer came into the room holding a toy up to me. She said it was a birthday present and that today was her birthday. As I hugged her and admired the toy, I felt embarrassed that I had forgotten her birthday. I glanced at Patricia with a questioning look on my face.

"Oh yes, she's five years old today. And she's quick to tell me that she's not a baby anymore. She wants to go everywhere with the older girls. In fact, sometimes I think I'm lucky when I can keep her at home. She spends so much time with Rhonda while I work. There's times when I wish I could quit my job and just stay home with her. We're having her birthday party later today but she has already opened most of her presents. But, of course, I'll go back into town and buy her some more so she'll have presents to open at her party."

Patricia motioned to two chairs placed close together. "Here, let's sit down and visit awhile. You know you don't come to see me often enough," she declared. "So tell me, Sis, what brings you to this neck of the woods? Are you on vacation or business?"

When I explained about Mother being ill, Patricia's facial expression saddened. "I've been worried about Mama," she said. "I try to go see her as often as I can, but I feel that it's not often enough. I'll try to go again next week."

"Well, don't feel guilty. After all, you go more often than I do, or any of her other children, for that matter. Carol and I talked to her doctor. He said she's doing pretty well considering that she's seventy-six years old. Her doctor thinks she doesn't take her medicine like she should. You may want to talk to her about that."

Our conversation then changed as Patricia began showing me several mementoes and photographs that were special to her. And I admired her new living room drapes. Rose had always been her favorite color.

We continued our light conversation about other things. Girl talk we called it. And soon we were giggling like teenagers. She was fun to be with. She had a pretty smile. And today she looked younger than she had in years, all trim and tan. Her shoulder length hair along with the green blouse and blue-jean shorts she was wearing made her look almost as young as her daughters.

"I must say you're looking pretty these days," I went on. 'You've lost weight and you're tan. You've got to tell me your secret."

I could see the compliment meant a lot to her. "Well, I just decided to lose weight, and I did," she said. "You know physical fitness is the thing these days. I have a good doctor and he has helped me with it. I now weigh one hundred-twenty. Of course, I'm also getting a little conscious of my age. You know I have another birthday coming up next month. I can't believe I'm going to be forty-two years old, already."

"Please don't mention age to me," I laughed. "I'm older than you, remember. But you look great, and if you won't tell our ages, I won't either. I wish you'd come visit me for a few days before summer is over."

"I'd like to, but there's so many other things going on right now. I've thought about resigning my job at the school. I'd like to go to college."

"Well, I'm proud of you for that. But you could still come visit me for a weekend sometime this summer."

Suddenly, I heard a door slam with a loud bang. I looked behind me and saw Lewis walk out of a bedroom into the hallway and then hit the bathroom door with his fist. I had not known he was in the house, and now I thought maybe he had been sleeping and our laughing had awakened him.

When he came out of the bathroom he walked through the living room past where we were sitting and hit the living room door with his hand. I thought he must be angry because I was there, and I stood up to leave. But before I could say good-bye to Patricia, Lewis came back inside and walked over to me putting his arms around me pretending to cry.

"We've all got to go sometime," he said.

I didn't know what to say and I stood there wondering if he thought I was there to tell Patricia that Mother was dead.

Patricia put her arm around him and assured him that Mother was fine and that I had just dropped by for a visit. He then stood up straight and smoothed back his hair, and called to one of the girls to bring him 'a beer'.

His mood changed immediately as he took the can of beer and sat down in a chair next to Patricia and me. But I noticed that Patricia suddenly seemed on edge. I could see the nervousness in her eyes. My mind wandered for a moment as old thoughts flooded back but I sat there and pretended not to notice the same old signs of Lewis' behavior.

I turned to Lewis and said, cheerfully, "I was just telling Patricia how pretty she looks."

"Yeah, she got up to where she weighed one hundred-eighty pounds and I was about ready to run her ass off," he replied.

I quickly changed the subject and commented on the new fishing boat in their driveway. Patricia glanced at me and smiled. She knew I had picked a good subject. Lewis then leaned back in his chair and crossed his legs.

"Yeah, it's a good boat," he said. "And we've used it a lot this summer. We go fishing at Lake Fairfield just about every weekend." Then he went on to tell me about the many fish he had caught, how big they were and about other fishing lakes in the area. It was plain that he was enjoying the conversation. He told Patricia to bring him another beer. And when she returned with the beer, he pulled her down to sit in his lap. Then they talked about their trips to Florida and Las Vegas.

"It sounds like you're having a lot of fun these days," I commented. "I'm really happy for both of you."

Patricia then asked about Richard and our sons.

"Well, in chronological order, Richard is planning to retire in a few years. John is still in the Army, stationed at Ft. Sill, Oklahoma, hoping to stay there for a while. William is still in Alaska, working as an engineer, and fishing and moose hunting in his spare time. And Harold is still stationed in England with the Air Force, flying planes and living off base in a haunted house."

We laughed about Harold's haunted house and of my vacation there. And of my chasing a ptarmigan in Alaska. The tension was now gone from the conversation, and it was heartwarming to see them sitting there together as they should be.

In years past, he had abused Patricia, both mentally and physically. And she had left him many times and gone to family members seeking refuge. But each time, within a few days, he always found her and by pleading or threats, or both, she always returned to him hoping he would change his ways.

Lewis was born into a generation where many men, more or less, considered their wives as their personal property, as something to be owned not unlike owning a pair of shoes. And to many such men, especially those born in poverty, formal education seemed unimportant. As they struggled to grow up, their priorities were placed on other things, such as guns, fast cars, and women; and their headstrong desire was to control them. And for many, the end result was a life of alcohol and violence.

Through all the years of their marriage, Lewis never once said an unkind word to me. Nor I to him. And always at family gatherings we spoke and exchanged a few words with each other. A family member once told me that Lewis had said he didn't like me, but he respected me. I was sorry I couldn't return the compliment. For I neither liked him or respected him. I had no reason to. And he knew it was because of the way he treated Patricia.

There was something about him I couldn't understand. Something I didn't care to understand. Patricia was my sister and it was hard to hide my resentment of the way he abused her. Each time I shook hands with him, I was reminded that his hands had blacked her eyes and bruised her body. And when we spoke to each other, I was reminded of the many times he had cursed her and threatened her life, and how sad she looked when she tried to smile when her mouth was bruised.

But sitting in their home that Saturday afternoon last June, things appeared to be different. Perhaps it was because they were older now, I thought. And their children were grown, except for Jennifer. But as we talked on, the nervousness in Patricia's eyes returned and at times her voice grew tense.

Rhonda walked through the living room and told Patricia she was going to run an errand. Then I glanced at the clock and realized it was almost five o'clock.

"Oh, I didn't know it was getting so late," I said reaching for my purse. "Aunt Margaret is expecting me, and I'm running late again."

I hugged Jennifer good-bye and gave her some money for her birthday. I told her I'd like to stay for her party but it was getting late and I had to go.

As I stood up to leave, Patricia asked me to wait a moment while she went into the kitchen. And while she was there, Virginia's two year old son found a small piece of paper on the living room floor, and placed it in his mouth. Virginia saw the paper in his mouth and started toward him to remove it. But before she could reach him, Lewis slapped the child so hard that he fell to the floor, crying. I quickly glanced at Virginia, wondering what she would say. Patricia came running from the kitchen and stared coldly at Lewis. Then, without a word spoken, Virginia picked up the child and held him in her arms. Patricia and I walked out on the porch and then across the yard to the driveway. Lewis' behavior had obviously embarrassed her. However, she didn't mention it, and neither did I.

"You know you're welcome to stay for dinner," she said.

"I know, honey, and I appreciate the offer. But it's getting late and Aunt Margaret is expecting me for dinner. I'll see you again next time I'm down this way and we'll be sure to have dinner together then."

Suddenly, Lewis called to me from the porch. "Jean, you and Richard come down some weekend," he said. "We'll take the boat to the lake."

"Thanks. We'll do that, the first chance we get," I answered.

Then Patricia and I held hands as we walked out to the curb to my car. The air was a little cooler now and I noticed leaves gently falling from a tall tree in the yard. As we walked under it, I commented about their autumn colors.

"I think it's the heat that causes them to fall so early," said Patricia. "And this time tomorrow, I'll probably be raking them. It's too bad you can't stay and help me. Maybe we could have a wiener roast and roasted marshmallows for dessert. Remember when we were kids, my marshmallows would always fall off the sticks and you kept putting more on."

"Oh yes, 1 remember," I laughed.

"And when it got dark, you told us stories. I used to wonder how you knew so many stories. I tried to remember them all, but by the time my girls came along, I had forgotten most of them. But I never forgot the funny little rhymes, and I told them all at least a hundred times."

Both of us were suddenly in a mood of nostalgia. Looking back, it was as though we wanted to remember, within minutes, all the closeness we shared together when we were young. She asked again about my sons, and recalled several of her childhood memories with them.

"They've been gone a long time haven't they?"

"Yes. Too long for me," I replied.

"It seems like only yesterday that I used to come visit you during my school vacations," she went on. "I still remember the woods behind your house and the picnics and the boys' tree house. I'd sure like to see those kids."

"Well, maybe we can all get together sometime when they're home," I said.

"You know, I worry a lot about Mama and Daddy," she went on. "They're getting so old. And I think of Merle, and Frances and Carol. There's times when I wish we could all go home again and spend a day together. Just us five kids and Mama and Daddy. It's hard to realize that Daddy is going to be seventy-six in August. I always try to go see him on his birthday. It's on a Monday this year. But if I'm working, I'll probably go see him on the seventh, the Sunday before his birthday."

"Well, I know he'll like that," I said. "Tell him I'll call him as usual. And in the meantime, maybe you and Lewis can come to see us some weekend before then. We'll have a barbecue and I'll make a chocolate cake."

"I'd like to do that but Lewis has taken a new job at the Jim Pierce Ranch and I don't know yet just how it's going to work out. Making a living is hard in this part of the country. I know I'm lucky to have a good job with the school district, and the pay is good. But I still have to work extra jobs in the summer to make ends meet. And I just feel there's a better way to make a living. That's why I want to go to college. But whether I go or not will depend a lot on Lewis' job at the ranch."

"I don't think I've heard of the Jim Pierce ranch. Is it close by ?"

"No. It's one of the big ranches near Anderson."

"Well, maybe things will work out, and you can go to college after all."

She didn't comment on that, but she looked out into the distance, as though she wanted to tell me something and decided not to. Then as I glanced around, Lewis came outside again and walked toward the side of the house.

"Well, honey, I've got to go," I said hugging her. We hugged each other again and she said, "I love you, Sis."

As I opened the car door, tears welled in my eyes, and I turned toward her.

"I want you to always remember I love you. And I'll love you always."

"I'll always love you, too," she said tearfully.

I started my car and drove a few feet, then stopped and we waved to each other again. Then she turned and walked back toward the house. And through my rearview mirror, I watched her walk up the front steps. That was the last time I saw her.

As I drove down the street leaving the sleepy little town of Bedias, several of Patricia's neighbors were sitting on their porches, passing the time of day, enjoying the faint cool breeze of the evening. Some of her other neighbors were watering vegetable gardens and flowers, and the little boy was still playing Frisbee.

Like many other small Texas towns, Bedias was a town that commercial progress had long forgotten. A town where people were born and lived until they were old and died, and nothing ever changed. Except time. Everyone knew everyone else and very rarely did they lock their doors. Even at night. But then perhaps that was the reason the people stayed there. Perhaps it was the quietness of it all.

As I turned onto the highway and headed north for the fifteen mile drive to Madisonville, I kept thinking of Patricia. And soon I started shaking. There was something about our visit that disturbed me. Something I couldn't put my finger on. It wasn't anything she said or did. It was just something. It was an uneasy feeling. And, in my mind, I kept seeing her walking up her porch steps.

There was something about this whole atmosphere, I thought. The late afternoon traffic, the area between Bedias and Madisonville, my visit with Patricia, the closeness we felt, our waving good-bye and her walking up her porch steps. It was something about the look on her face. No, it was the look in her eyes. No, it was when we waved good-bye. No, it was when I looked through my rearview mirror and saw her walking up the steps.

I began shaking so hard, I wondered what was wrong with me. And for a fleeting moment, I thought of turning around and going back to Patricia's house. But if I did, what would I say? Would I tell her I was shaking for some unknown reason? But that it had something to do with her? Would she comfort me and say, "But Sis, you don't have to worry about me, I'm fine." Would she think I was just being foolish?

Maybe I'm just nervous, I thought. After all, it had been a long day and I had spent most of the day on the road. I was tired and it was late in the day. Besides that, it would be foolish to go back. She was probably busy now with Jennifer's party and I wouldn't want to say or do anything to upset that. And, then too, Aunt Margaret was expecting me and I was running late again.

The traffic on the highway was getting a little heavier now. There were pickup trucks of all shapes, sizes and colors weaving in and out of traffic.

I had just come over a hill when I suddenly realized that I was behind a large slow moving truck loaded with hay, leaving me with no choice but to hit my brakes and head for the shoulder of the road. It was then that I decided that for my own safety I needed to slow down and not throw all caution to the wind. After that, I drove slowly on toward Madisonville, still shaking and wondering why.

THE DARK SIDE OF TWILIGHT:

CHAPTER 3

Madisonville was my old home town and I felt a sort of comfort just being there. The downtown square still looked the same as it did when I was a young girl. Except that the courthouse had burned twenty years ago. The new courthouse was a modern two-story red brick structure which stood in the middle of the square. But somehow, it had always looked out of place in comparison to the old buildings around it.

Many of my earliest memories were of being here with my parents and grandparents. Back then, Madisonville was a farming town, and on Saturdays, the area farmers congregated on the courthouse lawn conducting business while the women and children shopped in the stores or saw movies at the theater.

We lived on a farm, twelve miles from Madisonville, and 'going into town' was a weekly event. My brother and I looked forward to the ice cream cones at Burtis' Drugstore on the square. And, more often than not, we sat on the courthouse lawn and listened to a tall Texas boy who frequently visited our town in a flat-bed truck, and sang country music until dark. He later became a legend in Nashville and throughout the world.

Now, on this Saturday afternoon, I drove on through the town and headed north on the long country road that would take me by the church and the old home place and then to Aunt Margaret's.

The cloud of red dust swirling steadily behind my car was an old familiar sight to me, for even as far back as I could remember the road had never been paved.

I drove for miles past what was once grazing pasture land filled with cows and horses, and past old farm houses that had long ago been torn down or had partially fallen to the ground. But, in my mind, I could still see them as they once were.

I suppose it was during World War Two that the area began to change. Back when many of the young farmers either enlisted or were drafted to go fight in the war. Some were lost in the war. And most of those who had returned, moved away to various cities for better opportunities.

But after the years came and went, it was now evident that a few had returned here to live out their retirement years in the quietness of country life. Some had returned and built new brick homes. Others preferred mobile homes. Then there were others who had never left at all. They just re-built their homes and stayed.

Driving along the old familiar country road seemed to relax me, and I was thankful for that. I concluded that it was just what I needed. A quiet drive in the country. However, the road had sharp curves in it every mile or so and I soon found myself trying to remember which curve was which and counting the distance between them.

The trees on both sides of the road were tall and dusty. And along the heavy wooded sections, they leaned toward the center of the road, resembling long green canopies with only traces of sunlight filtering through their branches.

People who were familiar with the road knew to drive slowly, for it was covered with rocks that could easily cause glass breakage or paint damage. The local folks called it a 'washboard road.' It was hard to handle and there was the never ending cloud of red dust that followed. But always when I drove down the old road, a wave of nostalgia rode beside me. It was good for me, I thought. It made me remember where I came from. And I drew strength from my memories.

Like many other families who had once lived here, my parents and my brother, Merle, and I moved to Houston after World War Two began. And my father worked in a Defense plant there until he was drafted into the Army. Then, during the war years, my sister Frances was born. And after the war, my sister Patricia and my sister Carol were born. Then, several years later, we moved to a small town northwest of Houston. But it was always Madisonville that I called home.

And now I was home, again.

The old home church stood just beyond the next curve and when I came to it I slowed down almost to a stop. Its name, Rock Prairie Baptist Church, painted in black letters stood out clearly against the stark white paint on the building. The church was now more than a hundred years old and there had been talk of building a new one.

The thick oak trees nestled around the church had been there as long as I could remember. And the flowers in the cemetery reminded me of more old memories. Back when my mother and aunts used to place flowers on the graves. And my cousins and I placed colorful shells and figurines of birds and swans.

The church had played a significant part of my childhood. My first remembrance of life was of sitting on the second row trying to figure out who God was. Then when I reached the age of four, I tried my luck at singing.

I looked forward to each church service just so I could sing with the congregation. And I especially liked the hymn with the words, 'I'll fly away in the morning.' It was my all-time favorite. In fact I thought it was absolutely hilarious when the men who sang bass, sang the words, 'in the morning.' That alone, was worth going to church for, I thought. And while I couldn't remember the rest of the words to the song, when they sang, 'in the morning,' I was right on cue. And I sang with them in my deepest loudest voice.

During those years the Pastor of the church, whose name I can't recall, was an 'old time hell fire and brimstone' kind of preacher. And when he preached everyone paid attention. Including me.

Some folks said the preacher could be heard for a country mile. Others said he could be heard further than that. My grandfather was one of the folks who talked about how loud the preacher could preach. He lived approximately one mile directly behind the church, and on late summer evenings he said he could stand in his backyard and listen to the church services.

But the Pastor was a good preacher and well liked in the community. And when he preached about sin and the ways of the world, we knew it was serious business.

Before he began each sermon, he removed a white handkerchief from his pocket. Then with his Bible firmly grasped in his hand he preached about hell and damnation, the paths of righteousness and the way to get to all of them.

I gathered that Hell must be a terrible place because the harder the Pastor preached, the faster he wiped his face and the congregation fanned themselves with cardboard fans. And every few minutes someone would say, 'Amen.' I listened carefully and before long I was also saying, 'Amen.'

Then there was Mrs. Prescott who played the church piano. She and her husband and their two sons formed a quartet and sang beautifully together. But I especially liked Mrs. Prescott's piano playing because when she sat down to play, she placed her feet on the pedals and played as though she was determined to play us all into Heaven.

I liked the tithing part of the church service, too. And I insisted on having my own few coins to give to the church. Mother or Daddy would give me the coins and I would wrap them in my handkerchief. Then when the men walked down the aisle with the collection plates, I stood up and proudly put my coins in the plate. I wanted everyone to know that I had given something to the church for the Lord's good works.

During the summers, on late quiet evenings there were ice cream suppers out under the oak trees where the men took turns cranking the old ice cream freezers and the women served freshly baked cakes and cookies.

As time went by, there were many more fond memories of the church and its people before the war came and we moved away. And as I grew into adulthood, I kept them all close to my heart, and drew strength from them.

Now, today, as I drove away from the old church, my thoughts were of Aunt Margaret. I was aware that she often worried about me when I was on these long drives back and forth visiting Mother. She knew how long it took for me to drive from one place to the other and when she was certain that I was on the road, she said she timed me by her clock. Now, I was running late again and I saw visions of her tiny feet pacing the floor.

She was my father's younger sister. A tiny lady barely five-feet tall with white tightly permed hair and brown eyes. But if she was short in height, she was tall when it came to inner strength and character.

I was the first grandchild and her first niece, and I suppose I must have seemed to her like a live baby doll complete with wet tears and diapers. For she became more like an older sister rather than an aunt.

She took me for long walks in the woods behind my grandfather's farm where we walked the creek banks and picked wild violets and wood fern. And in summer, we picked huge bouquets of wild daisies and Indian paint brush along the roadsides.

We also picked berries and wild grapes for homemade pies and jelly. But each time we went berry picking or grape picking, she always carried a garden hoe. She said it was for killing snakes. And one day it proved useful.

We were picking grapes on a hillside partially covered with rock, when I stumbled upon a large snake coiled and ready to strike. I screamed and Aunt Margaret grabbed the hoe. Then she chopped the snake into pieces while I stood there mystified. After than, I thought there wasn't much in the whole world that she was afraid of.

However, she almost broke my heart when she was nineteen and decided to get married. It wasn't that I didn't like A. J. Harrison. I just didn't want her to marry anyone, because she would move away. But she married him anyway. And they were married forty years, and raised six children. Then Uncle A. J. died of cancer. A few years later, Aunt Margaret had a new home built near the old home place and married Uncle Bill.

Now, the old wooden bridge creaked as loud as thunder as I crossed it and turned the last curve before Aunt Margaret's house, and when I drove into her driveway, she was waiting.

"I was beginning to think I was going to have to come find you," she called as she and Bill came out to meet me.

After we hugged each other, I explained that I had stopped to see Patricia and was late leaving there. And that I almost ran into a hay truck.

"Well, thank goodness, you're alright ," she said, looking for any bruises I might have. "Come on in. Dinner is ready to be put on the table."

While we were setting plates on the dining table, Aunt Margaret asked about my visit with Patricia and I told her about it. She didn't say much except that she felt sorry for Patricia. But there was something in the tone of her voice that let me know that she suspicioned things she didn't really want to tell me. I knew it was useless to ask questions, but as we finished setting dinner on the table I tried to study her thoughts. Finally, I decided that she wanted to think about whatever it was and tell me at a later time.

We sat down to a country dinner of steak, fresh garden vegetables, iced tea and banana pudding. And the conversation turned to recipes for making pickles, jams and jellies, and Bill was taking credit for his part in helping with them.

He was a large man, tall with graying hair and a sincere expression on his face. He earned his living clearing land, cutting and selling firewood, and building fences. But when he talked about making pickles, I couldn't help smiling, thinking of his large hands packing tiny cucumbers into pickle jars.

It was good to be with Aunt Margaret and Bill. Sitting at their table, visiting and watching the sunset through the kitchen windows was almost like being home.

After dinner, Bill went for a walk while Aunt Margaret and I cleared the table.

We were at the sink washing dishes when she mentioned that Lewis had bought some firewood from Bill but never paid for it.

"And, if it hadn't been for Patricia being my niece, we wouldn't have sold him the firewood, to begin with," said Aunt Margaret. "But you know I'd do anything for you girls. And I like to visit with you. I'd like to see Patricia more often, but Lewis drinks and he don't care what he says. So, occasionally when I see Patricia in town, we visit there."

"Have you seen her lately?"

"I saw her about three weeks ago, on the parking lot at the mall.

She was getting into her car and acted like she was in a hurry. We waved to each other but that was all."

"Did she know Lewis owed you for the firewood?"

"Oh, she paid me part of the money for that, last winter. I figured she thought Lewis had paid the rest. And I've never told her that he didn't. I doubt that he knew she paid me anything. But he knew he owed it."

"Well, you know Patricia is honest."

Yes, I know. But she married a scoundrel. Once when we were coming back from your mother's we stopped by Patricia's house. I thought it would be nice to visit for an hour or so. Patricia met us on the front porch and she was glad to see us. But we heard a lot of noise and Lewis came outside acting like he was drunk so we didn't go in the house. We just stood on the porch and visited with Patricia for a few minutes. And we didn't mention anything about the wood. And I hope you won't tell her that I said anything about it."

"There was something about my visit with Patricia, today, that disturbed me," I said. "And it was more than Lewis hitting the little boy. I'm worried about Patricia. Of course, she was very sweet to me, but I sensed that something was bothering her. Something she didn't want to talk about in front of Lewis. I think that's why I started shaking. I even thought about going back."

"Well, let's try to relax, now that you're here. Come on, let's walk down to the chicken house. I've got some of the prettiest little baby chicks you ever saw. But first I want to show you my garden."

We walked across the back yard and toward the chicken houses. And on the way, I followed her down the rows of her garden, looking at prize tomatoes, corn, beans, peas, potatoes and zucchini.

The sunset across the fields was breathtaking, the way I had always remembered it. My parents and I once lived on this land, back when I was four years old. My brother, Merle, was born here. In later years, I often wished that Frances, Patricia and Carol could have shared our early memories here. And that all of us could have played in the fields and picked wild violets along the creek banks as children together.

The sunset was gone by the time Aunt Margaret and I walked back to the house that evening. Then in comfortable chairs, we sat up late talking about how our lives had changed with the years.

"I have an appointment in Navasota next week," she said. "And I'll be going through Bedias. I think I'll stop and see Patricia. Of course, I don't expect her to tell me any of her problems. But you can learn a lot over a cup of coffee."

The next morning as I was leaving, Bill carried sacks of fresh vegetables to my car, and Aunt Margaret gave me several special recipes.

"Now I want you to come back next month and I'll have some more vegetables," Aunt Margaret said. "I'm tired of canning and freezing, and I don't like to waste. But you can come before then, too. In fact, tell Richard that you're both invited to our Fourth of July barbecue."

"We'd love to, but we'll be going to Oklahoma for the Fourth of July holiday. We'll try to see you in August." Then I thanked her again as we hugged good-bye.

It was a typical June Sunday morning for that part of Texas, as I began the drive back to Madisonville. The hot sun was already blaring down upon the parched earth beneath a clear and cloudless sky. It was the time of year when church congregations prayed for rain and water wells became almost sacred. Only a farmer can understand the importance of a good water well.

Back in the old days, several oil companies sent their representatives into the area seeking permission to drill for oil. Some of the farmers were skeptical about that because of water wells. But eventually the oil companies won, and now oil rigs dotted the land.

By the time I rounded a few more curves, I was at the church again. Cars were beginning to gather there for morning services, parking under the trees for shade. I especially noticed the children and young people walking across the church yard. That was good, I thought. For here, they would learn many of their most important values. And, as I drove by, I found myself wishing I had time to join them. But the long drive to Dallas was still ahead of me.

As I drove past the square in Madisonville, on my way to the Interstate, I thought of turning back and taking the highway to Bedias. But what would I say to Patricia about my sudden return? I didn't want to appear more inquisitive than I should. But I was still bothered by yesterday's visit. Patricia's facial expressions always showed her feelings. And her eyes had looked so sad. But then they had looked that way for many years. She had been happy to see me, and our good-bye was very emotional. But I felt there was something she wanted to tell me and never got the chance. Now, this morning, she was probably already on her way to church in Bedias, and my next opportunity to talk to her would be at Mother's on Thanksgiving Day.

The drive from Madisonville to Dallas was always tiring for me. In fact, during the many trips I had made back and forth, there were times when I thought I had reached a borderline state of paranoia. For the traffic was heavy with cattle and oil field trucks, semi's and freight, bullying their way along the highway, their drivers talking on CBs, ignoring the speed limit. And it was not unusual to see a truck loaded with squawking chickens scattering feathers across my windshield. Then, in lesser populated areas, the odor of dead skunks and armadillos filtered strongly through my car air conditioner.

Patricia would laugh if she were riding along with me now, I thought. And, what fun we would have. I tried to imagine what she would be doing on July Fourth. In my mind, I could see her water skiing on the lake, and later having a picnic under the tall pine trees with all her family there. Water skiing was probably how she got that pretty tan.

The next day after I returned home from Madisonville, I phoned Mother. I told her I had visited with Patricia.

"Yes, I know," she answered. "Patricia called me. She said she enjoyed your visit and wished you could have stayed longer. She's coming down to see me next weekend. I haven't seen her since the church homecoming back in May. Patricia and Lewis went with us this year."

"Oh, I didn't know that."

"Yes, they did. And they seemed to enjoy it. Or at least Patricia

THE DARK SIDE OF TWILIGHT:

did."

"That's nice. By the way, how are things going with them these days?"

She paused for a moment, and then said, "Well, I'm not real sure."

Mother was good at keeping secrets. So, I prodded some more.

"I think they're having some trouble," she went on. "Patricia acted like there was something she wanted to tell me."

"Do you have any idea what it might have been?"

"No. But that afternoon, after lunch was over, she said she had rather not go in for the 'singing.' She said she just wanted to walk around for a while and talk. So, she and I walked out across the cemetery there at the church. And we were talking about several things. Then her face turned red and she looked like she was going to cry. I asked her what was wrong. And she said, 'Mama, Lewis has a girl-friend.' We walked on and I asked her how she knew he had a girl-friend. She said, 'Mama, I know.' Then she went on to tell me that Lewis had some gambling debts he couldn't pay, and that people were after him trying to collect their money. She started to tell me something else, but before she could tell me what it was, Lewis walked over to where we were standing and told her that he was ready to go home. And I never did find out what it was that she wanted to tell me."

"Have you talked to her since then?" I asked.

"No. But the next time she comes to see me, I'm going to ask her what it was."

"Why don't you just call her up some morning and gently work it into the conversation?"

"There's no way to call her. Her phone has been disconnected. She usually comes down every few weeks. Most of the time it's on a Sunday afternoon, and she doesn't get to stay long. But she knows I always look for her on a Sunday."

"I wish she would leave that man," I said.

"She's left him before," Mother went on. "And he always finds her. He won't leave her alone. He always hunts around until he finds her, no matter where she goes."

"Well, why don't you write to her and invite her for Sunday dinner, next Sunday. And while she's there, make some sort of excuse to have her drive you somewhere for an hour or so. That would give you some privacy to talk."

"I think I'll do that," Mother replied.

So, that was it, I thought. Lewis had a girlfriend. But the question I asked myself was: What else did Patricia want to tell Mother?

THE DARK SIDE OF TWILIGHT:

CHAPTER 4

On the Fourth of July, the skies over Ft. Sill, Oklahoma were as bright as the combat boots worn by the thousands of soldiers who marched in the downtown early morning parade. To me, there was always something special about a military parade. Flags blowing in the wind, soldiers marching, bands playing, cannons and tanks rolling behind them, all blending together in a profound surge of pride and patriotism. Then there were the families and veterans, both young and old, who stood at attention watching with pride, waving flags and holding babies, all proud to be Americans. Indeed, there was a lot one could say about a military parade. And with three sons, two of which had military careers, I had seen my share. John, our oldest son, had served eighteen years in the Army, and had made all of his promotions. He had recently been approved for the rank of Sergeant Major.

After the morning parade, it was customary for the soldiers and their families to gather in the mountains for picnics, music, games and sack races until dark. Then there was the magnificent fireworks show and ice cream until midnight.

The Fourth of July weekend came and went. And Richard and I returned home with crayon drawings and photographs of John's family, and pleasant memories.

Now, the month of July was almost over. The long mid-summer days were hot and dry. And, like most people, I stayed out of the daytime heat as much as possible. But at night, when the air was cooler, I enjoyed sitting on the patio, listening to the night sounds of summer. That was my time of night. The time when I thought of my loved ones. The time when I let my mind wander.

Tonight I sat watching a full moon as it slowly drifted beyond the trees. There was something about a full moon on a quiet summer night. To me, it was one of the most beautiful and mysterious sights the eyes could see. As a child, I thought its restful glow must be like God. Quiet and peaceful. I wondered how it could be everywhere and if it knew things and held dark secrets.

Tonight, as it drifted, my thoughts drifted with it. Thoughts of Mother and Patricia.

Several days ago, I had called Mother to inquire again about her health. And in the conversation, I asked about Patricia.

"Let me think a minute," said Mother. "Patricia came to see me a few weeks ago, and she stayed almost all day. She helped me clean house, you know the heavy cleaning that I'm not able to do anymore. Poor child worked so hard, I can't remember everything she did. I finally persuaded her to stop and sit with me in the kitchen while I cooked dinner."

"Was Lewis there, too?"

"Yes, he was here," replied Mother. "He sprayed the yard for fire ants."

"How is Patricia?" I asked.

"Well, Patricia said she caught Lewis with another woman. A woman whom she thought was her best friend. She told the woman that she could have Lewis, that she was more than welcome to him. And she told Lewis to take his clothes and leave. But Lewis has refused to move out of the house. Patricia said if he didn't leave, she was going to leave him."

"But he was with her, at your house that day?"

"Yes. But I could tell something was wrong between them, even before she told me what she did."

"Well, it will probably blow over. Have you talked to her since then?"

"Yes. She and Lewis came back again last week. But they didn't stay long. Just a couple of hours. Lewis sat on the porch most of the time they were here, and he didn't have much to say. I asked him if his knee still bothered him, and he said it did."

"What about Patricia?"

Mother paused for a moment, the way she usually did when she was getting ready to tell something she didn't want to.

"Patricia said she was going to resign from the school. She wants to take part of her retirement money and go to college this fall.

"Well, I think we should be proud of her for wanting to further her education."

"I am proud of her," Mother went on. She has worked hard for a lot of years. And now, she's starting to think about her age. When she was here, she said, 'Mama, do you realize that I'm going to be forty-two years old next week?' I told her I did. And we laughed. Then I reminded her that I'll be seventy-seven in November."

"Well, tell her I wish her luck and I'll be at her college graduation."

"Patricia said she is definitely going to leave Lewis this time," Mother said. She says she's leaving for good, and getting a divorce. She says she has 'had it' with him. She said, 'Mama, all he wants to do is drink and beat on me and run around, and I've had enough of it.' "

"Did she tell you where she plans to go?"

"No. She just said she was going where he couldn't find her."

"But you know he'll find her wherever she goes," I said. "He always has. Every time she has left him before, he has always hunted until he found her. But besides that, what about her children? You know she's not going to leave Jennifer."

"I asked her about that, too. And she said, 'Mama, Tammie and Rhonda and Virginia are all busy with their own families. And Kimberly is going to college in Galveston this fall. Rhonda has agreed to keep Jennifer for a while. And if I let Jennifer stay with Rhonda, Lewis won't have any reason to look for me.' "

"It sounds like she's got it pretty well planned out," I said.

"I think so. But I couldn't help crying when she told me about it. I asked her to stay in touch with me, and she promised she would."

"I'm sure she will," I replied, consolingly. "Mother, you know Patricia would never desert her children or the rest of her family. She loves them too much. Look at it this way, she's a grown woman who has gone through hell in a marriage that has lasted nearly 27 years. And now, she wants a better life for herself. No one can blame her for wanting a better life. How many times have you seen her beat up? She didn't do that to herself. Lewis Crocker gave her those black eyes and bruises. I think he's damn lucky that she stayed with him as long as she has. She has suffered so much. I think we should wish her well, and let her know that we'll be there for her if she needs us."

"I do wish her well," Mother went on. "And while you girls know that I'm against divorce, I know that there are times when it's best for all concerned."

"Patricia will be fine, Mother. But I'll be worried about you and Daddy. You know Lewis will be coming to your home, drunk, looking for her."

"He had better not start bringing his guns down here," Mother said. "Daddy and I are old and we can't stand that sort of thing."

"By the way, Mother, where was Lewis when Patricia was telling you all of this?"

"He was sitting on the front porch."

"Do you think he may have been listening and heard anything she told you?"

"I don't know. Probably not. Because, later, we walked outside and around the yard looking at the flowers. When we walked by the porch, Lewis was still sitting there and he didn't say anything."

"But Mother, just because he didn't say anything doesn't mean that he didn't hear it. If he heard it, he probably would have waited and confronted her with it later. He always was a sneaky bastard."

"Well, anyway, Patricia and I walked to the pink rose bush, and stood there a few minutes, admiring the roses. She said she wanted to plant some cuttings from it when the weather got cooler."

"She must be planning to keep the house in Bedias."

"No, I don't believe she will. All I know is that she was very upset."

She just wants to be free. She said, 'Mama, Lewis has called me every dirty name in the book. He has squandered away everything I've worked for. He has beat me, pulled guns on me, and threatened to kill me. And I'm tired of it. I just can't take it anymore.'

I told her I knew he had mistreated her. And that he had always

44

had everything the way he wanted it. And she said, 'Yes, he has. But that's going to change.' "

"I don't think anyone could blame her for feeling that way," I said. "I just hope that wherever she goes, he doesn't find her."

"Maybe he won't. Maybe he'll be too busy with his girlfriend. The way I feel about it is that Patricia gave him five daughters. She worked and helped raise them, and she showed a lot of love for them. I think she would have divorced Lewis years ago, had it not been for them. She was also a good wife to Lewis, and I think she loved him for a long time."

"And he was mean as hell to her," I said. "He treated her like dirt."

"I know that," said Mother. "And every time she left him, he'd hunt around until he found her, then he'd go to her, and put on his best pitiful look and promise never to hurt her again. And, of course, the girls would cry and want to go home. And Patricia would always take him back. A woman will put up with a lot to keep her children together and have a home for them."

"But abusive husbands often prey on the love of their children and use it as a weapon. Number one, they don't have to pay child support. Number two, more often than not, they have the privilege of whatever earnings the wife may have. And number three, they have someone they can knock around when they feel like it, as long as the wife will take it. It's unhealthy for all concerned. And it also takes its toll on the rest of the family."

"I know," said Mother. "We've all tried to help her."

"Then let go and wish her well. She's not a little girl anymore, Mother. And she's already been through hell."

"But you know I've never believed in divorce," Mother went on.

"But Mother it's not your marriage. You've never had black eyes and bruises, or a gun pointed at your head. Think about that. And besides that, remember there have been other divorces in the family for a lot less reason.

It's true that none of us kids see each other very often, because we're all caught up with our own families. But we love each other.

And when one of us is hurt, we all hurt.

I'll never forget the times Patricia came to my house, years ago, all black and blue, when Lewis almost beat her eyes out. She looked so sad, standing at my door with her little girls. After I invited her in and got her settled, I went to my bathroom and cried."

"Yes, I remember," Mother said. "I paid for her bus tickets and put her on the bus. I didn't think Lewis would come around you and Richard after he beat her like that. Richard would have showed him what it felt like."

"Yes, but after about a week, Lewis started calling my home. At first, Patricia wouldn't talk to him. But the girls were sick, and he continued calling. Finally, she talked to him. And he made promises to her that he knew damn well he didn't intend to keep. The next day, he sent her money to go home on. I tried to talk her out of going, but she said maybe things would be different. I told her I thought that was foolish thinking. But she went home, anyway."

"I remember that," said Mother. "And I think the next time I saw her, she had bruises on her again."

"Well, that particular time after she left, I was so upset, I wrote a letter to the Sheriff of Waller County. I didn't know his name, but I wrote it anyway, and I mailed it. In the letter, I told him I was afraid for Patricia, and I pleaded with him to keep an 'eye' on Lewis. I was so angry, I even wrote a letter to Lewis' parents and asked them to talk to Lewis about his behavior toward Patricia. Well, to make a long story short, I never received a reply from the Sheriff. But I did get a letter from Lewis' sister, telling me to mind my own business. That was twenty years ago. And he's still abusing her."

"And look how many times Patricia has left him since then," Mother went on. "A couple of years ago, during the summer, she left him and came down here. She got a job and planned to stay. Then, he came down here 'carrying on.' "

"She was sitting on the bed in the back bedroom and I heard them arguing. He sounded like he was getting ready to hit her. And when I opened the door, I saw him jerking her hair. I told him to stop it that instant. Then he muttered something to me. I asked him to repeat it, but he didn't answer. Then I told him that he was not going to behave that way in my house. And he got up and walked outside."

"But Patricia went back home, didn't she?"

"Yes, she did," Mother went on. "She went home that night. I told her to stay right where she was, but she didn't. She said, 'Mama, I'm going home. He won't leave me alone, and I don't want him here worrying you and Daddy.' So, she left with him. And I didn't see them for a long time after that. But finally, when they did come back, they seemed to be getting along allright."

The longer Mother and I talked, the more angry I became as I thought of the hell Patricia had endured throughout her twenty-six years of marriage to Lewis. Just who did that bastard think he was that he could treat her that way, and why? What right did he think he had to abuse any human being the way he abused her? Why couldn't he realize that she wasn't something he owned like an old pair of boots that he could kick around? Why couldn't he be man enough to leave her alone?

"Now, it's two years later, and he's still abusing her," I said, angrily.

"But not for long," Mother replied. "Patricia said she's going to leave him, once and for all, this time."

"When did she tell you that?"

"The last time she was here. The last time I saw her. When we said good-bye, she said, 'Mama, don't worry about me. I'll be allright, and I'll keep in touch with you. But I'm going where he'll never find me."

After Mother and I ended our conversation, I thought of Patricia's last words to her. She was going to leave Lewis. She was going where he would never find her.

It was now the first week of August. Hot and dry. The dog days of summer. And, again, in the quietness of the nights, I continued sitting on my patio, watching the moon slowly drift across the cloudless sky. The leaves on the trees where the squirrels played in the mornings were now folded in sleep, and the flowers beneath them were bathed in moonlight.

Somehow, my deepest thoughts always managed to surface on quiet nights like this. And, tonight, I thought of Patricia. And the dream. The old dream I had tried so hard to forget, but yet had stayed with me. Now, it returned again as clear as the night I had dreamed it, more than thirteen years ago.

The night of the dream was like any other ordinary night. At that time, it had been a month or more since I last heard from Patricia. And it had been several weeks since I last talked to Mother or the rest of the family. There was no special reason for not contacting them. It was just that we were all busy with our own lives. Just ordinary days and ordinary nights. But the dream came.

In the dream, I was in Madisonville walking across the street to the funeral home. The street was wet with rain and I saw several beer cans laying near the curb of the street. As I walked across the street, I was angry and I kicked the cans into the gutters. Then I walked across the front lawn of the funeral home and up the steps and opened the front door. I walked into the funeral parlor and then into a large room where a casket lay ready for burial. The casket was closed, beneath a wreath of white and yellow flowers. It was Patricia's casket.

I was alone in the room with the casket, but as I stood there crying and looking at it, an unknown voice said to me, 'You know who killed her.' And the voice told me the name of her murderer. 'But the Laws have him now,' the voice continued. Then I was surrounded by a dark wave labeled, 'lies and deceit.' And in the distance, someone was laughing.

I awoke from the dream crying and switched on the lamp beside the bed.

"Tell me she's not dead," I cried, shaking Richard. "Tell me she's not dead!"

"What are you talking about?" he asked.

I then explained the dream to him, as he walked with me to the kitchen for a glass of water. "Honey, it's just a dream," he said. "Patricia's okay. It's just a dream."

"But it was so real," I went on. "Oh, God, it was so real."

"Well, try to calm down. It was just a bad dream. Why don't you call your Mother in the morning? She'll tell you Patricia's allright. She sees her a lot."

"But I can't tell Mother about something like that."

"You don't have to tell her about it. Just call and visit a while. Ask about the family. That should put your mind at ease."

After Richard returned to bed, I went out into the den and turned on the television hoping to find a late night movie that would help me forget about the dream. I sat there for an hour or so, switching channels, neither hearing or remembering anything, except the dream. Nothing could take it away. It kept happening over and over. Each horrible detail more vivid than before. I couldn't forget it. I would never forget it.

The next morning, determined to forget the dream and be as cheerful as possible, I called Mother. Then after we exchanged the usual pleasantries, I asked about Carol and Frances.

"And, how is Patricia?" I asked, trying to sound lighthearted.

"Oh, she's doing fine," Mother replied. "She and Lewis and the girls were here last weekend. They're all doing well. The girls are growing like weeds and Patricia has been busy sewing, trying to keep them in dresses. And Lewis is going into business for himself. He's opening up a mechanic shop. He said he was tired of working for other people and he wants to be his own boss for a change. They all seemed just as happy as can be."

"That's good news," I replied. "I'm glad to hear it."

As the conversation continued about other things, I decided not to tell Mother about the dream. It would be silly to mention it, I thought. In fact, I would feel embarrassed to talk about it. Even to Mother. People just didn't talk about dreams like that. Maybe sometime later when I was visiting her, I'd tell her then. But most likely, I would never tell her. After all, why should I? There was no reason why I should.

However, in the dark recesses of my mind, I knew it was more than a bad dream. But I wondered what could be accomplished by telling Mother about it, other than I hoped she would tell Patricia and perhaps it would be taken as a warning. But then Patricia might worry, needlessly. I didn't want that. The whole thing was crazy, I thought. I won't tell her. But what if I don't tell her? Suppose it was a warning, and I knew about it, and didn't tell her?

And so it was that before our conversation ended that morning, I told Mother about the dream. She paused for a few moments. She had not taken it lightly.

"Well, let's just pray that it never happens," she said. "God knows it would kill all of us if it did."

At that moment, I wished I had not told her. Then I tried to make light of it by saying that I had probably been worried about Patricia, and that was the reason for the dream. Then I changed the subject, talking about old time things that I knew would please her. We talked for a long time about happy things Mother had recalled to me about her childhood, and mine. And by the time our conversation ended, I hoped she had forgotten the dream. But I knew I would remember it. No matter how hard I tried to forget it, it would stay with me. In my darkest moments, I would remember it for the next thirteen years. And forever.

I was seven years old when I first noticed that I would have certain dreams that came true. But at that tender age, I thought it must be a natural thing. For everyone I knew had dreams. And I had happy dreams as well as the others. I thought it was fun to know beforehand when we would be going to Grandmother's and who we might see there. And I dreamed of school and new friends and the games we would play. It never occurred to me that that may have been unusual. And, in looking back, perhaps it wasn't. For I was a reasonably happy child. I liked people, I liked school, I took the Bible seriously, and I vowed to grow up as a person who would care for others.

But, as a child, after I had dreamed a bad dream, I was quiet and withdrawn. And, whenever possible I would go to a small wooded area near our home to be alone. I thought of it as my secret place. A place I did not share, not even with my friends. From the outside it looked like a thicket of small trees woven together. Trees so thick that at times it was difficult to find the opening I had made for an entrance. But inside the thicket, there were no trees at all. Only sunshine, grass and wildflowers. It was the most unusual place I had ever seen. And I would sit there for what seemed like hours, thinking about life, wondering what the future would hold for me. And child that I was, I wanted a future of happiness without pain or sorrow. And without bad dreams.

I had always felt a closeness with my grandmother. And as a child, I was especially happy when I visited her. Her name was Martha. She was my father's mother, and I was her oldest granddaughter. I thought she understood me, completely.

She liked flowers and peach trees, baking and sewing. Gardening and fishing. And the wild turkeys that lived in a grassy field behind her home. She also taught me to know the trees by looking at their leaves. And there wasn't anything that I couldn't tell her.

One day she mentioned something about dreams. And I told her I had dreams. I had happy dreams and, sometimes, I had bad dreams.

"Everyone has bad dreams," she said, consolingly. "But if you tell them early in the morning, they won't come true. Just walk outside and tell them to the morning wind, and it will blow them far away."

I thought about those words and wondered if that was all I had to do. Just tell the bad dreams to the wind and it would blow them far away.

But, throughout the years, on into my adulthood, there were many more dreams. Some were happy. Some were sad. And, in conversations, I sometimes heard the words: 'psychic or clairvoyant.' But I never thought of myself as either. For when I thought of those words, I thought of people with mysterious powers which enabled them to see into the future. And I only had my dreams.

It was during the late fifties when one of my dreams foretold a tragedy that happened in my family. Although it was not clear and did not happen until the year after. In that dream, I saw a baby's coffin on a highway and there were broken bones around it.

In September, the following year, Frances was driving Patricia and Carol to a high school football game. Patricia was sitting on the passenger side of the front seat holding Frances' baby daughter in her lap. The car stalled on the highway and was hit by a moving van. The baby was killed instantly. Frances had scrapes and bruises. Patricia's right arm was broken. Her left knee and ankle were also broken, requiring plastic pins to be placed in them. Both of Carol's legs were broken and she wore a cast for months afterwards.

Years later, there was the dream about my grandmother. In that dream, we were at a large family reunion. And all of the aunts and uncles, and other relatives were there. It was a happy day. We laughed and ate tons of food as the day went on. But there was a brown canopy hanging over us.

I dreamed the dream three times. Then in September of that year, I was invited to attend Grandmother's birthday dinner. All the family was there, just like in the dream, and it was a happy day for everyone. And when I started to leave to come home, late that evening, Grandmother took my hand and walked with me to my car. Holding her hand, I was a little girl again. Life was good, and our memories would last forever.

When we came to the car, she put her arms around me and said, "This will be the last time I'll get to see you." I cried and hugged her close. "No, it won't be the last time," I assured her. "I'll see you again. I'll be back soon. You'll see."

Afterward, when I thought about the dream, I discarded the part about the canopy. After all, it had been a cloudy day on her birthday. But Grandmother was right. We did not see each other again. But there was more to come of the dream. For when I attended her funeral, the following June, the canopy was there just as I had seen it in my dream.

In years to come, there would be dreams of my sons as they joined the military and left for faraway places in other parts of the world.

When my son, John, was stationed with the Army in Panama, I dreamed that he was in a hospital there, and very ill. I could hear his voice clearly as he spoke to me on the phone, telling me he was ill.

I awoke crying and told Richard about the dream. Then exactly three weeks later, John called from his hospital room in Panama to tell me he was ill with hepatitis.

Several years after that, I had another dream about John having a motorcycle accident. This time he was stationed in Oklahoma, near the mountains. In the dream, I saw his face covered with blood, and his motorcycle was wrecked on a narrow mountain road.

A few weeks later, his wife, Imogene, phoned to tell me that John had been driving on a mountain road and someone ran him into the side of a mountain. His face had been cut and he was in a hospital.

Back during the Vietnam War, our son, William served in the U.S. Marines. He left in April 1972 for his second tour to Okinawa to await duty in Vietnam. He was gone less than two months when I dreamed that he would be sent home on a hospital plane in October of that year. He would come to a place where there was sand and palm trees and then he would come to Dallas.

I told Richard about the dream.

"I don't see how that could be," he said. "You know he's over there on a thirteen month tour. And he's got eleven months to go, yet."

"No," I replied. "He's only going to stay six months this time. But he's going to be okay. And he will be home around the end of October."

"Well, maybe so," Richard went on. "But they have hospitals on all military bases. It seems to me that if he gets sick, he would be in a hospital in Okinawa. Or if they sent him back to the States, they would send him to California. That would be closer to Okinawa than Texas."

The months passed on until late October. Then one night William called me from Okinawa to tell me that he had been in the base hospital there, but was being transferred to a military hospital in Corpus Christi, Texas. Three days later, when Richard and I arrived in Corpus Christi, the first thing I noticed were palm trees and sand. And two weeks later, William came home on a weekend pass.

During those years, when I went to bed at night, I prayed not to dream at all. For my dreams, both old and new, had left a sadness within the depths of my mind that was increasingly difficult to cope with. But, finally, I devised a plan where at night, I would think only of large green meadows in beautiful faraway places.

Then one night I dreamed of being in England riding in a car with my son, Harold. In the dream, we were going through several small villages in northern England, and I was admiring the structures of the century old buildings. I could see them clearly as the narrow winding roads passed through one village after another. Harold and I were laughing and talking about me flying on a 747 jet all the way across the Atlantic just to visit him.

"I wondered if you'd really do it, Mom," he laughed. "What I mean is that I didn't think you'd make a trip like that without Dad. But I'm glad you're here."

Almost a year later, the time came when I did make a trip to England, alone.

On a late June afternoon I boarded a 747 jet in Dallas for the long non-stop night flight to London. And as we flew over Oklahoma, I thought the sunset had never been more beautiful, nor had it ever set so low. Then the night came quickly as did the hours as we crossed the Canadian seaboard on our way out over the Atlantic, until at last we became a small flickering light in total darkness.

I welcomed the blanket and pillows the stewardess brought to me, for the air in the plane was colder now that we were flying over the ocean. During the next several hours I drifted in and out of a restless sleep dreaming of narrow winding roads and villages with centuries old buildings. Then I awoke when we were over Ireland, and watched the rays of a new sunrise filter light into the plane's cabin. An hour later, we were flying beneath the clouds over London. And as we approached Gatwick Airport, I saw miles upon miles of long hedgerows and beautiful green meadows.

"So, you really did it, Mom," Harold said, hugging me as I got off the plane. "I didn't think you would. Are you sure Dad is not on the plane?"

That was a happy morning for both of us, and almost before I realized it, we had driven through the busy city of London and were on our way to Huntington. And as we drove through the small villages in northern England, I recognized many of the centuries old buildings, for I had already seen them in my dreams.

CHAPTER 5

Now, as I sat on my patio, watching the moon drift through the trees, other dreams of my family continually flashed through my mind. Dreams that I prayed had long been 'forgotten.' Especially the dream about Patricia.

It had now been thirteen years since I dreamed of Patricia's murder. Surely by now, it had been 'forgotten.' But, still in the deep recesses of my mind, from time to time. it had returned to haunt me. And, like a child, I would tell it to go away. To stay away. It was too horrible to think about. But no matter how hard I tried, I could not forget it. It still stayed with me.

Almost from the beginning Patricia had known about the dream. And I still had the letter that she wrote to me the day after Mother told her about it.

It was a nice cheery letter, typical of the kind of letters she always wrote. She wrote of her visit to see Mother and Daddy, the day before, and that they were well, and Daddy was happy with his new car. Then she wrote of how busy she had been. Her four daughters had entered the local FFA Princess Contest and she had made all of their dresses and how pretty they looked in the contest. And that she had also made their dresses for the Homecoming Parade. And she had taken pictures of them and enclosed several with the letter. She went on to say that she was working part-time at a grocery store, the only store in town, and that Lewis was busy with his new mechanic shop. She asked about Richard and our children and wished us well. Then toward the end of the letter she wrote in a more serious frame of mind:

"Mama said you had a dream about me, and I have had you on my mind for the last couple of weeks. Do you realize it's been almost a year since I've seen you? A lot has happened since then and time has passed by. You know every day I get older and it seems that I learn more every day. I wonder if we ever stop learning in life. I hope you will be at Mother's on Thanksgiving Day. I would love to see you. May God bless you and yours, and remember me in your prayers."

Thanksgiving Day at Mother's that year was a happy occasion. Mother and Daddy seemed twenty years younger when all their children came home. And, that day, their small home was crowded with children and grandchildren. There was Merle and Nelda and their children, Frances and Ben and their children, Patricia and Lewis and their children, Carol and Emil and their children, and Richard and I. What a crowd we were when we were together. And what fun we had.

The men played dominoes and talked of hunting and fishing. The children played outside in the bright cool sunshine while Mother and my sisters and I prepared tons of food and set up extra tables in the dining room. Mother's face beamed and gleamed as Frances, Patricia, Carol and I hurried around in the kitchen, cooking, laughing and talking, and recalling old times.

Mother said we looked like peas in a pod. For all four of us girls had dark brown hair and brown eyes and our facial features strongly resembled each other. However, Frances and Patricia were several inches taller than Carol and me. Which was a subject that they often teased us about. But it was all in fun, and Carol and I usually had a few pert answers for them. Then we would giggle like small children. And our love for each other knew no bounds.

The amount of food we set on the table could have fed an Army Brigade, I thought. Several baked turkeys, smoked turkeys, hams, roasts, and venison, with all the trimmings plus at least a dozen different kinds of desserts.

Among the other covered dishes that Patricia and Lewis brought was a large pan of barbecued venison. Lewis fancied himself an expert in deer hunting. He enjoyed talking about his hunting trips, how big the deer were and how many antlers or points they had. And he invited the men in the family to go with him so he could show them just how and where to find and kill the largest deer. Personally, I found the subject of killing deer revolting.

However, back then, thirteen years ago, it was still a family tradition that my brother, sisters and I, and our families spend our Thanksgiving holiday with Mother and Daddy. But as the years went by and the families grew, it became more difficult for all of us to be together on that special day.

I suppose I missed more Thanksgiving Days at Mother's than any of her children. For at that time of year, my sons were usually on military leave, flying home from faraway places, or I traveled to their homes to be with them. Then the years seemed to pass as quickly as autumn leaves on an Indian summer day. Now, my brother and sisters and I did most of our visiting by phone or letters. But, occasionally, we still managed to take time away from our busy schedules for family visits.

It was now the middle of August, and as I listened to the quiet sounds of the warm summer night, my thoughts returned again to Patricia. I thought of our last visit and, for a fleeting moment, I imagined her presence, sitting beside me.

Last week, on August 8th, I had phoned Daddy to wish him a happy birthday. He laughed about being seventy-six years old, and said he guessed he was too old to go out on the town with his grandsons. Then he talked about birthday cards and phone calls he had received from Merle, Frances and Carol.

"How about Patricia?" I asked.

"Well, I haven't heard from her yet," he replied. "But she'll be here this afternoon. She always comes to see me on my birthday."

"Well, tell her I said hello, and tell her to write to me."

"I'll tell her to write or call you," Daddy went on. "She was here a couple of weeks ago, one afternoon. She said she had a new job she was starting in a week or so. So, she's probably busy. But I'll give her your message and she'll be calling you."

However, the week had passed without hearing from her. And as I thought of my last conversation with Mother, I decided to call again.

Perhaps tomorrow.

But for now, the hour was late and the moon had drifted far beyond the trees. I straightened the chair cushion and walked toward the back door. Then I walked up the steps, shuddering in the gentle breeze blowing around my shoulders. The night was almost gone now, and morning was waiting.

The next day began like any other August Sunday morning in Texas. A bright sun shining down upon the earth and air conditioning units struggling against it. The highways were crowded with cars, boats and trailers headed for the nearest lake or picnic grounds; while in the cities, people gathered in church for the morning services. Others were hurrying to the sailboat regatta that would begin in early afternoon. And there were those in pickup trucks hauling hay to cattle in pastures. And there were those in love beginning their married life together. And then there were others who sat in dark places remembering bad things. Evil things; trying to justify them and knowing they could not.

Richard and I were at home watching a special church program on television. And when it ended he began watching a sports game while I cut out various newspaper articles for my collection.

Saving newspaper clippings was something I had been doing for many years and by now there were several boxes of them stacked in a corner in the attic. I suppose I saved them because I thought that someday the grandchildren would enjoy reading them. But then again, perhaps I saved them merely out of habit, the way I saved old cards and letters from years gone by.

I had finished cutting the clippings for the day and was writing the date on them when the phone rang. It was Patricia's daughter, Tammie.

"What a pleasant surprise," I answered. "How are you doing these days? And how is your new baby?"

"Oh, he's fine and growing. He's almost two months old now," she said.

"That's nice. And how is the rest of your family?"

"Well, Aunt Jean, that's the main reason I called you. I was wondering if you have seen my mother lately?"

"No, I haven't. Not since I was at her home back in June. Why? Is there something wrong?"

"Well, we don't know. Daddy said Mama got mad at him and just walked off down toward the grocery store and never came back."

"That doesn't sound like anything your mother would do," I said.

"But you know she's left him several times before," Tammie went on.

"Yes. But he has always known, within a day or two, where she was. What happened? Did he hit her?"

"No. I asked him if they had a fight and he said they didn't. He said he and Mama went to a lounge last Sunday afternoon with some of their friends and while they were there, Mama got sick and waited outside in the car. Later, when he got ready to go home, she was still sick. And she lay with her head on his lap all the way home."

"Well, if she was that sick, how could she feel like walking to the grocery store?"

"I don't know. But anyway, Daddy said that when they got home, Mama went into their bedroom and laid down. Then later she got up and changed clothes and told him she was leaving. He said she told him that she was fed up with him and she didn't want him or his kids or anything he had ever given her. She just wanted to be free. Then when he saw that she really meant what she said, he went outside and disconnected the coil wire on her car to prevent her from leaving. But she came out on the porch and saw him doing that, and she really became angry. That's when she started walking off, and now we can't find her."

"Exactly when did all of this happen?" I asked.

"A week ago today. On the seventh of August."

"Have you talked to your grandmother and Aunt Frances and Aunt Carol?"

"Yes. I've called everyone I can think of who might possibly know where Mama is. But no one has seen her."

"Well, that's strange," I went on. "By the way what is your daddy's reaction to all of this?"

"Oh, he wants her to come home. But he said that this is one time he is not going to look for her. He says he is just going to give her her own space and let her get her shit together, once and for all. He said Mama told him that she has a boyfriend named Bill, and he thinks she probably called Bill to come pick her up and they're together somewhere."

As I continued listening to Tammie, I became acutely aware that Lewis had lied to her, and through no fault of her own, she was now repeating those lies to me. For every word she said sounded exactly like something Lewis Crocker would say, and everything he had told her about Patricia severely contradicted Patricia's character.

As I paused for a moment to collect my thoughts about everything Tammie had told me, it seemed as though someone else was listening, and saying to me: "It's not true. Don't believe her. Remember, a sister knows a sister."

I knew Patricia might leave Lewis. But she was a very good mother, and she would never desert her children. And Lewis' story that Patricia was supposed to have said that she 'didn't want anything he had ever given her,' made no sense at all. For what had he ever given her that was so great? It was she who had provided the major financial support for her family. And, there was also Patricia's consideration for Mother and Daddy. Mother was seventy-seven years old, and ill. Patricia wouldn't do anything that would cause them to worry. Then, there was Daddy's birthday, last week. He was expecting her to visit him that day. But she had disappeared the day before, and no one had heard from her.

But the part of Lewis' story that upset me the most was when he said he was 'not going to look for Patricia *this time*. He was going to give her her own space. And that she had probably run away with a boyfriend.'

I wondered who he thought would believe that story. Surely not our family. For we knew as well as he that every time Patricia had left him in years gone by, he always hunted until he found her. He was extremely jealous of her. And if he had even suspected that there was another man involved, he would have stayed on the road with his guns until he tracked them down.

In many ways, Lewis had always reminded me of a sly fox waiting for his prey. He was of medium height, with reddish blond hair, a long face and wide set eyes. And it was hard to tell what he was thinking. But it was no secret to all who knew him that he could be violent. Especially to Patricia.

"Tammie, I want you to listen to me. I want you to go immediately and file a missing persons report on your mother. Since she was last seen walking, someone may have kidnapped her. If the Sheriff's Department in Anderson is not open on Sundays, by all means go there first thing in the morning."

"Well, I guess we could do that. I don't see that it would hurt anything if we did. But Daddy said he's not going to look for her."

"Trust me, Tammie. You won't be hurting anything. Just tell the Sheriff that your mother has been gone for a week and her family is worried about her. Make sure you tell the Sheriff what kind of clothes she was wearing. Do you know if she carried any money or a change of clothing with her?"

"No. But Daddy said when he saw her last, she was wearing a tan colored blouse and tan shorts and white tennis shoes. And she didn't take any extra clothes. But Daddy said she stole a hundred dollars out of his billfold before she left. And she could go a long way on that."

"Tammie, listen to me. Don't worry about the money. She can't get in trouble for that. Just go file the missing persons report."

"But Aunt Jean, Mama's left before and we think that somebody in the family or some of her friends knows where she is. Or she may be with her boyfriend. Daddy says this 'Bill guy' has got a lot of money."

"Do you have any idea where this 'Bill' lives? Or where he works?"

"I don't know anything about him except what Daddy has told me."

"Tammie, trust me on this. I want you to file a missing persons report. If you'd like, I'll come down and go with you."

"Well, we'll think about it. We may go down to the Sheriff's office tomorrow and talk to them about it. I have to go now. My baby is crying."

After the conversation was over I walked back into the den where Richard was watching television and sat on the sofa beside him.

"What was that about Patricia and a missing persons report?"

I explained that she was missing and the rest of what Tammie had told me.

"But you shouldn't get too upset about it," he said. "It's happened before."

"Not like this. I think there's something very wrong this time. And I'm going to try to find her."

Mother answered her phone almost immediately. I told her I was looking for Patricia, and asked if she had heard from her, or her daughters, and if she knew Patricia was missing.

"I know she left Lewis," Mother replied. "Tammie has called every day trying to find her. But I don't know where she is."

"What else did Tammie tell you?"

"She said Patricia and Lewis went to a turkey shoot last Sunday afternoon, and Patricia got sick, and they came home around four-thirty. Then she got mad at Lewis and walked to the grocery store. Lewis took the coil wire off the car so she couldn't leave in it, but she left anyway, and he hasn't seen her since."

"But they have two cars. Why didn't she take the other car?"

"It was at Tammie's house."

"Well, Patricia must have called a friend, from the grocery store, to come get her. I know she wouldn't walk down the highway wearing a blouse and shorts. She is not a hitchhiker."

"She wasn't wearing shorts. She was wearing blue jeans and a shirt."

"But Mother, Lewis said she was wearing a tan colored blouse, tan shorts and white tennis shoes the last time he saw her."

"Well, he and Tammie were here last week and talked to me about it. He wanted me to help find her. He said he loved her. I told him if he loved her, he should find her and he should be good to her. He said he would. He said he thinks she is at Frances' house, because a woman named Martha who lives in Madisonville sent word to him that she had seen Patricia and talked to her the day after she disappeared. And Martha said Patricia told her that she was going to her sister's house."

"Who is Martha? Is she a friend of the family?"

"I don't know anything about her," Mother replied. "But I think Patricia walked to a friend's house and she is either still with her friends or she is at Frances' and she doesn't want anyone to know where she is. And Lewis thinks the same thing."

"I don't believe that. Because she wouldn't leave Jennifer for that long."

"By the way, where was Jennifer when Patricia disappeared?"

"She was with Rhonda. She wanted to go play with Rhonda's little girl, so Lewis and Patricia took her over there earlier that day."

"Where were Kimberly and Virginia? Do they still live with Patricia?"

"Yes. But they were gone that Sunday afternoon. Kimberly was at Tammie's. I don't know where Virginia was."

"Did Lewis tell you what time Patricia left? Was it around four-thirty?"

"No, it was later than that. They left again after they came home that evening, and came home again around six-thirty. Then Patricia left around seven-thirty that evening."

"Okay. Now, why would Lewis say he saw her leave wearing a blouse, shorts and tennis shoes, and then later say she left wearing a shirt and blue jeans?"

"Maybe she changed clothes before she left. She probably did. All I know about it is what they have told me."

"Maybe she went to visit Carol," I said. "She's gone there before."

"No, I don't think so. I talked to Carol a couple of days ago and she didn't say anything about Patricia being there."

"Did you tell her Patricia was missing?"

"No. But if she had been there, Carol would have said something about it."

I could tell by the tone of Mother's voice that she wanted to tell me something else and was trying to decide whether she would or not.

"Mother, is there something else you'd like to tell me?"

"Well, I don't know if I should talk about it or not. It happened back in July. On the eleventh, I think. When Patricia and Lewis got into an argument and he got his gun after her. She ran and got in her car and headed toward Anderson. He got in the other car and chased her. One of the girls called the Sheriff, and a State highway patrol car met Patricia at a gas station in Roans Prairie near Anderson. When Lewis saw the patrol car, he ran to a store across the parking lot and gave the gun to one of his friends to hide for him so the patrolman couldn't find it. The patrolman said Patricia had been drinking and he arrested her. I don't know whether he took her in for drinking or for her own safety. But Lewis stayed inside the store with his gun hidden, so he was not arrested. Lewis told his friends that he wasn't trying to kill Patricia, he was just trying to shoot the tires off of her car."

"And she went back to that bastard after that?"

"No, she didn't. The next morning Lewis went to the jail to bring her home, but she refused to go home with him. I think she realized how dangerous the situation really was. And she was so humiliated about the arrest. It really hurt her pride. So, she stayed with one of her girlfriends, for a while."

"I wonder if the patrolman took the time to check out the situation before he arrested her. You know Lewis was drinking. He's the one who should have been arrested. Think about it, Mother. What kind of a damn fool would chase his wife down a highway with a loaded gun in his hand, trying to get close enough to shoot her tires out? That is attempted murder. And he had the nerve to go to the jail the next morning?"

"But Patricia didn't go home with him," Mother went on. "She stayed a week or so with her girlfriend. Lewis tried to get her to come home, but she refused. Finally, she told him the only way she would come home was if he moved out of the house. Lewis agreed, and promised to move out. So, she went back. And then he said he couldn't find a place to move to."

"I know she was planning to leave him again. She was so battered and humiliated, she knew she had to get out. So, she resigned her job at the school and filed the papers to collect her retirement. She was expecting to receive the money the week she disappeared."

"Do you know if she received it?"

"No. But she went ahead and started a new job as a hostess in a new restaurant, the week before she left. Patty Lynn saw her there the day before she left. Patty was on her way to visit me, and she stopped at the restaurant and ate dinner with Patricia."

"Did Patty notice anything unusual about Patricia?"

"No, not at all. She said Patricia was so happy to see her and they had a nice visit, and Patricia gave her some photographs to bring to me. Patty was supposed to go by Patricia's house the next day, on her way home. And she did. But Patricia wasn't home. I thought Patty may have met her in Madisonville, and maybe Patricia went home with her."

"Mother, you said Patty's visit with Patricia at the restaurant was on the day before she disappeared. And Patricia seemed happy with her work. You know Patricia is not the type to work one week on a job and quit without notice."

"No, she wouldn't. In fact, she mentioned that she had to work Monday."

"Mother, tell me where you think Patricia is at this moment."

"I don't know. Lewis says she is with Frances, or Frances is hiding her somewhere."

"Mother, you also know that Lewis Crocker has been known to be a damn liar."

When I thought of Patty Lynn and her sister, Darlene, I liked to remember them as little girls in starched and ironed dresses with colorful bows in their hair. They were Frances' oldest daughters, and as children they had visited me often. They were both in their twenties now, both married with children and more beautiful than ever. Darlene was a tall willowy brunette with dark curly hair and blue eyes. Patty was also dark haired, blue eyed and very beautiful. They were both serious and determined young women.

As I dialed Darlene's phone number, I looked forward to hearing her soft voice with its broad Texas accent. And after we exchanged our usual pleasantries, I asked if she knew Patricia was missing.

"Grandmother told me about it," Darlene replied. "And Tammie did, too. But Aunt Jean, I have no idea where Aunt Pat is. No one in our family has seen or heard from her. I told Tammie that, but she acted like she didn't believe me."

"Did your grandmother mention to you that a woman named Martha said she saw Patricia in Madisonville and she told this Martha that she was going to her sister's? We don't know which sister she was referring to."

"Yes, I heard that, too. But Mama hasn't seen her. None of our family has seen her. Patty hasn't seen her, either. Patty went by Aunt Pat's house on her way home. But Aunt Pat was gone. Kimberly was raking leaves in the yard. She told Patty that Aunt Pat and Lewis had gone to buy some hay. Patty told Kimberly to tell Aunt Pat that she would see her the next time she was down that way. Aunt Jean, we're all so worried. I hope nothing has happened to her. You know I would tell you if I knew where she was."

After our conversation ended, I thought of other family members Patricia might possibly be with. I thought of our brother, Merle, who lived in Odessa. But common sense told me she wouldn't be there, because he worked out of state most of the time. Besides that, she would have called me if she was there.

But I wondered about the guy named 'Bill' that Lewis had talked about. And I tried to analyze Patricia's thoughts. She would know that in a town as small as Bedias, the people were very observant and well kept secrets were few. But perhaps after she walked to the store and saw that it was closed, she walked to a neighbor's house to use a phone. But since the store was the only one in town, Patricia would have known beforehand whether or not it was closed on Sundays. And as for her neighbors, they would surely know by now that she was missing. It would have been a topic in most conversations. And, too, she had disappeared late on a Sunday afternoon. Some of her neighbors had to have been sitting on their porches or watering their gardens. Or driving along the streets on their way to church. Besides that, there were houses along the highway going in and out of town. The people all knew each other, and the cars and trucks they drove. If someone had picked her up, she would have been seen. It wasn't dark when she left. It was still twilight.

The more I thought about it, the more I kept coming to the same conclusion: Patricia was not a foolish school girl nor would she behave like one. She would never deliberately vanish. She couldn't just vanish, even if she tried. Someone had to have seen her.

I also wondered about the woman named Martha, who supposedly had seen Patricia in Madisonville. If Patricia didn't want anyone to know where she was going, why would she tell Martha? For obviously, Martha knew her and had given that information to the family the next day. Why would she choose to tell Martha of her plans and no one else?

Then there was the question about Patricia's other car at Tammie's house the evening of the disappearance. Lewis had called Tammie later that night and asked if Patricia had taken the car. But the car was still there. I wondered why Patricia would leave without taking the car, but then perhaps she had been afraid Lewis would find her and once again chase her down the highway trying to shoot her tires out.

I wondered how she got to Madisonville. It was fifteen miles from Bedias, and much too far to walk on a hot August night. Besides that, Lewis said she was sick. I could not imagine her being sick and standing on the highway trying to hitchhike to Madisonville. But if she had, someone would have seen her and most likely they would have known her.

I thought of my conversations with Tammie, Mother and Darlene. None of them really knew anything about Patricia's whereabouts. So far, only the woman named Martha supposedly had seen Patricia since she left, and she had given her information to Lewis' family. But yet, no one knew Martha. It didn't add up.

THE DARK SIDE OF TWILIGHT:

CHAPTER 6

I had barely finished my first cup of coffee the next morning when the phone rang. It was Carol, wanting to know about Patricia. I told her about Tammie's phone call telling me Patricia was missing, and that I had advised her to file a missing person's report at the Sheriff's office in Anderson.

"You know, I keep thinking about Lewis and his damn guns," said Carol. "I'll never forget the first time I saw him pull a gun on Patricia. It happened when Tammie was only a few weeks old. Lewis had beat Patricia, blacking her eye and bruising her body. And she left him and came home to live with Mother and Daddy. She had been home about a week when Lewis showed up one afternoon and wanted her to go back with him. Patricia was sitting in a chair nursing Tammie. Lewis was half drunk as usual. He said to her, 'I told you to get your God damned ass up and get in the car.' But she refused. Then suddenly, he pulled out a silver plated pistol and threatened to kill her. It scared me so bad, I ran as fast as I could down to where Mother was working. I guess Lewis knew what I was going to do, because he jumped into his car and started following me. I was absolutely terrified. I ran through yards, gates and jumped fences trying to get away from him. Finally I saw the Deputy Sheriff's wife who was working in her front yard and I stopped and told her what was going on. She rushed me into her house and locked the door behind us. Then she called the Sheriff's office. Lewis drove toward the highway and headed for Hempstead. And by the time the Sheriff stopped him, he had already disposed of the pistol. But the Sheriff knew me and Patricia. And he gave Lewis a warning. I had never been so scared in my life. For until then, I had never even seen a real pistol. Just seeing him stand over her and point that thing at her head made my blood run cold. And I never had any use for him whatsoever after that."

"That must have been just the beginning. From what I hear, he continued to pull guns on her for many years. In fact, a month ago, he chased her down the highway trying to shoot her tires out. Absolutely nothing he would do, would surprise me. And I think he's lying through his teeth about Patricia's disappearance. Number one, he changed his story about what she wore when she left. Number two, he says he's not going to look for her this time. I think he's got a good reason for not looking for her this time, a reason that has nothing to do with a boyfriend. And furthermore, if there is not a missing persons report filed on her this week, I intend to go down there and do it myself."

Two days later, Carol called to tell me that the report had been filed by Tammie's husband, Garvin. Carol had also spoken with Detective Larry Adams, the investigating officer assigned to the case. He said the information on the report had gone to other police departments throughout the state, and that he also expected television stations to show Patricia's photograph on their news broadcasts.

"Has Adams talked to Lewis?"

"Yes, he did. And Lewis told him pretty much the same story as we've heard. He said Patricia left home hitchhiking. He said she was wearing shorts and a blouse and tennis shoes, and that she had a hundred dollars in her purse. He said he looked for her but couldn't find her."

"If he didn't find her, how did he know she was hitchhiking? How did he know how much money she had? Besides that, he told Mother that Patricia was wearing blue jeans and a shirt. And don't forget, he also said Patricia was sick. He's lying, Carol. I can feel it.

Carol, since you live closer to Grimes County than I do, I wish you'd try to locate the girlfriend that Patricia stayed with the week after she was arrested. Mother said the lady owned a dress shop. Look in the phone book and check out the dress shops in Navasota. Also, I think it would be interesting to learn whether or not Patricia's retirement check came after she left. And if she picked up her last paycheck from the restaurant."

"That's another thing Adams told me. He said Patricia's retirement check came in the mail four days after she left, and that Tammie has the check. He also talked to Patricia's employer at the restaurant. She said Patricia's last day of work was August sixth, and she has not returned to pick up her paycheck."

Later that day, I called Mother to see if she had learned anything new about the situation.

"No, I haven't heard much more about it," she said. "Everyone still seems to think Patricia is with Frances. Lewis says she is."

I told Mother I didn't give a damn what 'everyone' said. Patricia was not with Frances. Frances had not seen her, nor had Frances' family seen her. And that I was tired of hearing that lie.

"Well, don't start jumping on me about it," Mother said.

"Tell me, Mother, how is Lewis taking it?"

"Well, he's upset and he's worried about her. He wants her to come home."

"Mother, think about it. You know Lewis is insanely jealous. And if that sonofabitch really thought she was with any member of our family, he'd be parking his ass on their doorstep. And if he thought she was with a boyfriend, he would have already burned the roads up trying to find them. By the way, why don't you tell Patricia's daughters to go to Frances' house and see for themselves whether Patricia is there."

"Lewis has already said he's going out there this weekend. But he says it will be up to her whether she comes back or not."

"Well, I won't hold my breath until he gets there. Another thing, have you heard any more about the guy named Bill?"

"No. Nobody knows anything about the guy named Bill. But there was another man named Charlie Lancaster. He disappeared the same time as Patricia did, and they think she left with him."

I hung up the phone. I couldn't talk to Mother anymore. It was obvious that she believed everything Lewis and his daughters told her, and nothing I said sunk in or made a difference. And that was the way Lewis had expected it to be, I thought. But I had news for him. I could play a few games of my own, and throw it back at him. The first thing would be to tell Carol that it would be in our best interest not to tell Mother anything significant that we learned until the situation was over.

I called Darlene again. This time she was crying because Tammie wouldn't believe her when she said she hadn't seen 'Aunt Pat.' I told her I believed her. I also told her Lewis was supposed to come to Frances' house the coming weekend, and I asked her to let me know what he said when he got there. I also asked Darlene if Patricia had in previous years when she left Lewis, ever come to see Frances.

"Yes, she did. She came to Mama's last summer. Lewis had beat her up and she left him. She stayed out here about a week, and she found a job in Corsicana. And she planned to get an apartment for her and Jennifer."

"Did she have Jennifer with her?"

"Of course she did. That's another thing we don't understand about her leaving this time. We know she wouldn't leave Jennifer. Last summer, Mama was going to baby-sit while Aunt Pat worked, but one night Lewis showed up, out of the blue, to take Jennifer. And Aunt Pat knew the only way she could be with her was to go back home. And she did."

I asked Darlene if Patricia had ever mentioned a boyfriend.

"No, she certainly did not. I never heard her talk about other men."

After our conversation was over, I sat down to compose my thoughts about the situation. The whole thing was going around in circles. Just like the sonofabitch planned it. But we would find her. Somehow, we'd find her.

As I dialed Aunt Margaret's phone number, I could almost smell the aroma of apple cake and butterscotch cookies in her kitchen.

"I was wondering if you were going to call me," she said. "I have something to tell you. It may not have anything to do with Patricia's disappearance, but then again it might. One of our cousins said she saw Patricia in Madisonville on Wednesday before she disappeared. She said Patricia's face was bruised and she looked like she was sick. But they didn't get to talk to each other because Patricia was in a hurry."

Another thing is that I've been in Madisonville a couple of times this week and I've heard gossip that Patricia ran off with a man. But I acted like I didn't know anything about it. Which, I don't. I think it's just trashy gossip. But then the other day when I was at the gas station where I usually buy gas, another thing happened that I thought was strange. There's two old boys who work at the station and they live in Bedias. They usually speak to me when I stop to buy gas. We never really talk at length about anything but we say hello and comment on the weather. Just small talk. And I know that they know who Patricia is because I've seen her there before. But anyway, the last time I stopped there they acted like they didn't want to talk to me. They just sort of shied away from me. Not that I cared about them acting that way. But I thought there was something odd about it."

"Do they know you're Patricia's aunt?"

"Oh, they probably do. You know how people are in a small town. But I'll be going back there tomorrow and I'll ask a few questions and keep my ears open. I'll let you know what I find out. One more thing: Don't forget you're supposed to come to see me in two weeks."

Later that evening, I told Richard about the conversation. "Somewhere, someone knows where she is," I said for the hundredth time.

"But have you thought that she may not want to be found," he replied. "She told your mother she was going where Lewis couldn't find her. And maybe she did. People disappear every day. You see it on television and read about it in the newspapers. They're gone for years, and sometimes they never come back."

"Well, I know my sister. And you do, too. And she would never do that."

During the next week, I tried several times to reach Detective Adams, by phone. But according to his secretary, he was out of his office, or had left for a meeting, or he was out in 'the field,' or off for the day. However, she continually assured me that he was still working on the Patricia Crocker case.

Then, late one afternoon, I received a call from Carol. Her voice was shaking. She had located two of Patricia's friends and had conversations with both of them. "Neither one of them has seen or heard

75

from Patricia since she left," Carol went on. "But they told me some things that sound interesting. And I want to know what you think about them."

"Who did you talk to?" I asked.

"I first talked to Pauline Nicholson. She has the dress shop in Navasota. She said she has known Patricia for several years and they are close friends. She said she is worried sick about Patricia and she thinks something is terribly wrong."

"Did she tell you why she thinks something is wrong?"

"Well, while we were talking, I told her about the dream you had about Patricia. And she started crying and said, 'I hope there wasn't any fire in it, because there are two witnesses who saw Lewis burning something at the dump shortly after Patricia disappeared.' "

"Which dump was she referring to?"

"I asked her that. And she said it was the dump on the Jim Pierce ranch."

"Who were the witnesses who saw him at the dump, and what was he burning?"

"Pauline said they were two ranch hands who work on the ranch. But she didn't know their names. She said the two ranch hands had gone to the dump late that afternoon, about dark, to burn some boxes. And they happened to drive up at the time Lewis was burning something. They saw him with a five gallon gas can, and they thought it was strange. They said Lewis acted real nervous when he saw them get out of the truck to open the gate going into the dump. And he told them to go back to the ranch and he would burn the boxes for them."

"Did they see what he was burning?"

"No. They said they saw some brush piled on top of something else. And when Lewis offered to burn the boxes, they drove back to the ranch. They said they didn't think too much about it at the time. But later, they wondered about it after they heard Patricia was missing."

"I wonder if Adams knows about that."

"I don't know. But there's more."

"Several days after Patricia left, Virginia called Pauline, looking

76

for Patricia. Virginia told Pauline that there was a lot of blood in the house and a bloody smear on a door. She said she came upon Lewis as he was cleaning up a spot of blood in the kitchen. And when she asked him about it, he said it was blood that had dripped from some meat he had thawed on the kitchen counter.

But that's not all Virginia found. She said that after finding the house in such a mess, she and Kimberly started walking through it looking around. And in the hallway, Kimberly found a bloody wash cloth hidden in a vase. When Kimberly asked Lewis about that, he said he had cut his knuckle and it bled a lot, and he wiped the blood on the wash cloth. We may never know whose blood it was, because Kimberly washed the cloth in the laundry."

"It sounds like he was having all kinds of little accidents."

"Well, brace yourself. There's more," Carol went on. "Virginia told Pauline that some carpet and a mattress is missing from the house. The mattress is missing from Lewis and Patricia's bed, and strips of carpet have been cut out of the bedroom and living room, and all of the carpet in the hallway is missing. Also, Kimberly found a blouse with blood on it, thrown under the bed. It was the blouse Patricia was wearing the day she disappeared.

When the girls confronted Lewis about the missing mattress, he said they were mistaken. But the girls said they had changed the sheets on the bed numerous times, and they know for a fact that there were two mattresses on it. Now, about the carpet. When the girls asked him why he cut out the carpet, he said he and Patricia had been planning for a long time to take all the carpet out of the house. He said she wanted new floor covering, and that she had helped him take out part of the carpet the day she left."

"Oh my God, Carol, that lowlife lying sonofabitch has killed her. She never left the house by herself. The sonofabitch murdered her. And I'll bet that whatever he was burning at the dump had something to do with her murder. That sorry sonofabitch, how could he do that to her, and to her children and her family?"

"I know how you're feeling," Carol replied tearfully. "Believe me, I know."

"But he won't get away with it," I cried. "We'll see him in hell first."

"What else did Pauline tell you?"

"She cried a lot during our conversation. And she thinks something really bad has happened. She said she had seen the violence building up for a long time. Especially this past year. And she said when Virginia told her about the blood in the house, she knew Lewis had beat Patricia again. But when she heard about the carpet and mattress being gone, it upset her so bad that she immediately closed her shop and went home crying."

"I wonder if she reported her suspicions to the Sheriff's office."

"I don't know. But she gave me Rosa Wilson's phone number. She said Rosa saw Patricia on the Sunday of her disappearance. So, after I finished talking to Pauline, I called Rosa. When Rosa answered the phone, I got the impression that she had been expecting me to call, even though I've never met her. Then as soon as I introduced myself, she told me she was a very good friend of Patricia's. In fact, her best friend. She knows Patricia is missing, but she hasn't heard from her. She also said she was Lewis' friend as well as Patricia's. She said that she and her husband, Mack, had seen Lewis and Patricia at the turkey shoot at Fred's Place that Sunday afternoon, and that they had a drink together. She said Patricia complained that she wasn't feeling well, and said she felt faint. Rosa went with her to the restroom and bathed her face. Then Patricia went outside to the car and lay there until Lewis took her home. However, she also said that Lewis and Patricia had argued. Patricia wanted to go home, Lewis didn't."

"I wonder if she knows the condition the house is in?"

"How could she not know it? She said she was Patricia's best friend."

"Rosa's attitude seemed odd to me," Carol went on. "Rosa kept saying she was Patricia's best friend. She said they had been friends for a long time. But yet, she says she feels so sorry for Lewis now that Patricia is gone. She says Lewis is still drinking a lot and he's not eating properly. The way she said it just made me want to throw up."

I had a feeling that Rosa's name would show up again, further down the line. But at the present time, I wanted Detective Adams to know about the missing carpet and mattress and the blood in the house.

"He knows about it," Carol went on. "I told him about it this morning. And I told him about the fire at the dump. But he indicated that he already knew it. However, he said Lewis has changed his story several times about what happened the day Patricia left. Adams also said there were several other leads that he was looking into. He said he thought Patricia was probably with a member of her family. He also asked me if I had ever heard her mention a boyfriend named Bill or Charlie. And I told him no."

By now, Carol had had several conversations with Adams, while my attempts to reach him had all been futile. I thought about driving the two hundred miles to Anderson, and waiting for him at his office, then going to Carol's home, an hour south of Anderson. I knew her safety was well protected. But my presence in the area of the Sheriff's office, if I was recognized, would cause suspicion and could possibly be dangerous.

The next morning, I called Adams again. And, again, he was unavailable. However, late that afternoon, he returned my call.

CHAPTER 7

My first conversation with Detective Adams was the beginning of a series of conversations between us. Most of which would have as many ups and downs as a high-rise roller coaster. He was a professional law man with almost twenty years experience. And I was a persistent woman.

As time went by, we compared notes and ideas concerning Patricia's disappearance, always looking for the truth and trying to find her. And we frequently argued. There were times when I thought he showed symptoms of the 'East Texas Good Ol' Boy' syndrome, which was not meant as flattery. And during one argument, he said he had other things to do besides waste the taxpayers' money talking to me on the phone. But by the time it all was over, there was a better understanding of family loyalty and respect.

In our first conversation, we discussed the missing persons report. I asked if he had talked to Lewis. He said he had. And Lewis' story was the same as what I had heard from Mother and Tammie. He also confirmed that Patricia's retirement check had come in the mail a few days after she left, and one of her daughters was keeping it for her. And that her paycheck had not been picked up. I asked if her prescription for diet pills had been refilled. He said he would find the name of her doctor and check on the prescription.

"Now, let me ask you a question," Adams said. "Did you know your sister had a boyfriend?"

I said I had heard that story and that I didn't believe a word of it. In the first place, as jealous as Lewis was, she couldn't have had a boyfriend even if she had wanted one. If there were any extra-marital affairs going on, Lewis was having them, not Patricia.

"Allright, another question: Did you ever hear her mention Bill or Charlie?"

"No. Who are they?"

"Well, around here, people call Bill, 'Billy Gigilo.' The other one is Charlie Lancaster. They both like pretty women, especially women with money. Charlie is an old ex-con."

I felt my face turning redder by the minute. There was only one person who would have supplied Adams with such lowlife information. Lewis Crocker. It had all the earmarks of his personality.

"Well, have you found this Bill and Charlie?"

"No. But we're trying to locate them. We have information that Charlie is in the Wichita Falls area. Now, another question: Have you talked to your sister, Frances?"

"No. But I've talked to her daughter, and Patricia is not there. Why don't you ask Lewis to go see for himself. Or why don't you send an officer out there?"

"Lewis said he was going last weekend, but his car broke down. He says he's going this weekend. But he still thinks the family is covering up for her."

It was the same song and dance, and I was tired of hearing it. I wanted to know about the fire, the missing mattress, the cut-out carpet and the blood. I asked Adams what he knew about all of that.

"Allright. I can tell you that I searched the dump and all I found was ashes. And Lewis said there weren't any mattresses missing. And the blood came from his cut finger. As for the carpet, he said he and Patricia removed it before she left."

"You're dealing with a man who is a mean drunk," I said. "And he usually carries a gun. He has beat his wife numerous times and she has left him numerous times. But he always knew where she was. And he always brought her back home because he is too jealous to stay away from her. Now, we are expected to believe that this is the one time that he's willing to let her stay. And this is the one time that he says she has not one but two or more boyfriends. And he is not jealous. We're supposed to believe that she just left walking toward the highway. She took no extra clothes or cosmetics. She took very little money, even though she was expecting to receive a large check in the mail. And even her paycheck is still at the restaurant. Besides

A True Story of Murder and Texas Justice

all of this, we know that only a few hours before she left, she was so sick, she could hardly hold her head up. But yet, we're expected to believe that she had the strength to get out of bed, engage in a heated argument with Lewis, and then walk to the highway and hitch a ride to Frances' house, which is at least a hundred miles away."

"Basically, that's the way it happened according to Lewis," Adams went on.

"Detective Adams, I hope your tape recorder is on because I want to go on record, here and now, as saying that I think Lewis knows exactly where Patricia is. I think he murdered her and hid her body. I think he has told you nothing but lies, and I think he's doing everything he can to cover his dirty tracks. And that is my official statement."

"And I think you may be exactly one hundred percent right," said Adams. "But at the present time, I don't have the evidence to prove it. And I have to follow up on the leads that come in. Can you think of anything else that might help us?"

"I'm not sure if it will help, but I have a couple of ideas. I keep thinking about deer leases and trees. I don't even know what a deer lease is. But I know that Lewis is a hunter. He knows the woods and all about deer leases."

"Do you know the location of any that he may have mentioned?"

"He once had a deer lease in Llano. But I don't think he would risk taking her that far. But I've heard of one near Iola."

"Well, if he's got one near Iola, I'll find it. I'm familiar with that area. Do you know who owns the property that the deer lease is on?"

"No, not at all. However, Lewis also made a remark one time about hiding things in water. He said if a person wanted to hide something, he could weight it down in water. But in hot weather, it could easily surface."

"Well, I'll keep that in mind. And if you hear anything else, I'd appreciate it if you'd let me know."

After my conversation with Adams, I poured a cup of coffee and sat in the den, thinking about everything I had told him. I had really done it, I thought. I had given an official statement of my suspicions.

83

And in the end, I may come out looking like a fool. But at least, I hadn't told him about the old dream I had had about Patricia's murder. I had thought about telling him, but I was afraid he would hang up and close the case. After all, he was looking for solid evidence. And premonitional dreams did not make convictions in a courtroom.

Later that night, I went out to the patio, taking a cup of coffee with me, and sat down in my usual old comfortable chair. The night was warm and clear with a crescent moon glowing among the trees. On nights such as this, I could see the lights of the air traffic coming in and leaving DFW Airport north of Dallas. I liked to watch the planes stack into a holding pattern as they waited for clearance to land. I stared at the planes' twinkling lights, wondering about the people inside who were waiting to greet their loved ones. And of the loved ones waiting for them. Soon the planes would land and then leave again. And always somewhere someone would be waiting. People waited for different reasons. Some would wait with excitement. Others may wait in duty. Then there were others, like me, who waited with an unknowing fear.

In the clear starlit night, I thought of Patricia. I prayed she was happy, wherever she was. And secretly, I hoped she had found someone who loved her. Someone who would show her the happiness she deserved. I wanted her to be free of the hurt. I wanted her to be loved. But although I wanted to think she was free and happy, I could not dismiss the thought that she was gone forever. And I felt the dark emptiness of never hearing her voice again, or hugging her. If she was gone, all I had left of her were photographs and a box of old letters.

The next morning, I found the box of letters and sat at my desk to read them. In the box were bundles of birthday cards, valentines and letters dated back as far as fifteen years before. A birthday card on which the number "42" was written lay on top. I read the cards again and then began reading the letters. Patricia wrote of many things. Some of which I had long forgotten.

In several letters, she expressed her appreciation for little things I had done for her in years gone by. In one letter she thanked me for a winter coat. In another letter, it was a necklace. In others she thanked me for clothes and Christmas presents which I now barely remembered.

She wrote about her daughters and their school activities, and about members of our family, always expressing her love for all of them, and for me. And she wrote of birthday cards and valentines and letters we had sent to each other.

But in one letter, she wrote in part: "I don't know. Sometimes I just get tired of living. I guess everybody does. I get tired of clean-cook-wash-iron, and griping. I work all day and then Lewis gripes at the least little thing. I guess all of us have our faults and I know I'm not perfect. But I think sometimes if it wasn't for my kids, I would crawl into a hole and stay there. Don't say anything to anybody about this. It is just between you and me. I want to talk with you when I see you, because I know I can trust you." In another letter, she wrote in part: "Mama said you had a dream about me, and I have had you on my mind for the last couple of weeks. I would love to hear from you."

There was another letter that I could not remember having read before. It was written on lined paper and I could not find the envelope. But the letter was dated August 4, 1975. And it read in part: "I don't know why, but I have a thing about twilight time. I want to be outside and smell the burning leaves and grass when it's almost dark. You know, after the sun has gone down and it's twilight time. That's my time of day."

I read the letters again, over and over, knowing I would never forget them.

Carol and I talked almost daily by phone, comparing information, notes and ideas about Patricia's disappearance, wondering how long it would last and afraid of how it would end. I also worried about Carol. One day, we decided we needed a break, and made plans to meet in Madisonville for the weekend. Aunt Margaret had been expecting us and it was time to visit again.

It was early Friday afternoon when Richard and I arrived in Madisonville and stopped at a restaurant for lunch. The restaurant was crowded and the waitresses were busy. When one of the wait-resses came to our table to refill our tea glasses, she glanced at me several times and asked if I had relatives in Bedias. I explained that my sister, Patricia, lived there but said nothing of her disappearance.

"I just knew you were related to her," she said. "My family and I have known her for years. But we've always called her 'Pat.' I went to school with her daughters. I don't see them much anymore. But I saw Virginia about a week ago, at the Mall. My name is Monica. Monica Stevens. My parents are Carmen and Walter Mitchell. We live on the other side of Bedias, out in the country. Mama takes care of my boys while I work, and it seems like I work all the time."

Monica picked up the tea pitcher and wiped the table with a towel, then leaned over close to me and said, "I've heard gossip that Pat left town with a boyfriend. I don't know whether to believe it or not. It's not true, is it?"

"Well, Monica, I don't believe it. And small town gossip can ruin a person. But tell me, do you know a woman named Martha?"

"Let me think. I know several Marthas. Do you know her last name?"

I told Monica that I didn't know Martha's last name or anything else about her. And that I hoped the wagging tongues wouldn't talk too much until we learned the truth of what really happened.

"Oh, I won't. I always liked Pat. She did some sewing for me."

Monica then went on her way, her red hair bouncing. But we would talk again. And the day would come when Carol and I would know her as a friend.

At the cashier's counter, I waited as Richard handed the money to a plump, middle-aged gray-haired lady, who was not overly friendly. And as she returned his change, she smiled at me knowingly, then abruptly turned her head. I felt like asking her what she thought she knew that would interest me. And I wondered if someone had al-ready spread the word that Patricia Crocker's sister was in the restau-rant.

Back at the motel, I called Aunt Margaret to let her know that we were in town. And I asked if she had heard any interesting talk in town lately.

"No, not really, but I know the gossips are talking," she replied. "The last time I was at the Mall, I overheard two women talking. I couldn't hear what they were saying, but I know they were talking about Patricia, because when they saw me, they got real quiet. Then when I got to the check-out lane, one of them looked at me kind of sheepish. I was nice enough to her, but when I gave her the money, I looked her straight in the eye and told her Patricia was my niece."

"How about the two boys at the gas station?"

"I don't even trade there anymore. But I still say that they know something. Or they suspect something that they don't want anybody to know about."

Aunt Margaret invited us to spend the night with her, but I told her we were expecting Carol and Emil, and their children. And that they had reserved rooms at the motel.

"Well, make everybody get up early and come to my house for breakfast," she said. "I'll have it ready at seven o'clock, including homemade biscuits."

It was good to be with Carol and Emil, and their family. Carol and Emil had been married twenty years, and were the parents of four daughters and one son.

"Well, I brought only half of my family with me this time. Emil, Trey and Priscilla. The three oldest girls had other plans," Carol said, as she entered the door.

Emil was tall and muscular, with white blond hair and a good-natured smile. Their son, Trey, now the awkward age of fifteen, was a nice looking young man with dark hair like Carol. And their baby daughter, Priscilla, age three, was the pride and joy of the family.

Later that night, after we had visited awhile and had dinner, Richard, Emil and Trey watched ball games on television. Carol, Priscilla and I sat in the other room and talked about Patricia's disappearance.

"We drove by Patricia's house this afternoon, on our way here," Carol said. "The house was dark and no cars were there. But if I thought Lewis was there, I think I would have stopped and asked him some questions."

"And that could have been a dangerous situation," I said. "He could have said that you came to his house and attacked him, and he shot you in self-defense. We can't afford to let him know our suspicions. We have to work with the Law."

CHAPTER 8

"I don't think I can stand it much longer, not knowing where she is," Carol went on. "I cry every afternoon when the sun starts going down, because it reminds me of when Patricia and I used to sit on the hay barn and watch the sunsets, back when we were kids. It just brings back all of my childhood memories with her. Our school days and all the fun we had together. Looking back we were such innocent kids. We were especially close after Frances married and moved away. We were the only two kids at home then. And even though Patricia was only four years older than me, she became very protective and she tried to have all the answers to my questions about growing up. We were happy doing the most simple things. We took long walks by the railroad tracks picking berries and wildflowers, and we loved to swim in the rice canals.

"One summer, Mother and Daddy took us for a weekend at the beach in Matagorda. Patricia and I spent hours playing in the sand, building sandcastles and gathering sea shells. And we played in the waves, trying to outrun them as they lashed upon the shore. One of the waves knocked me down and I tasted salt water as I called out to her. Later, I asked her why the water was so salty. She thought about it for a moment and then said she really wasn't sure, but that it was possible that a huge ship loaded with salt had capsized in the ocean, and that was why the water was salty. And I believed it, until years later.

"Another incident happened on a cold snowy day in January. It was so cold, the stock ponds were frozen over. Patricia and I were out walking around, sliding on the frozen grass in the pastures. And when we started back home, I decided to slide across one of the ponds. The ice looked thick enough to slide on so I ran ahead of Patricia. She called out to me but by that time I was already in the pond. The

THE DARK SIDE OF TWILIGHT:

ice broke and I fell in. Patricia jumped in and pulled me out. We were both so scared, we cried and shivered all the way home. Patricia had her arm around me and she kept telling me how foolish I had been for walking into the pond, and that she was so thankful that God had helped her save me.

"She was always popular in school, too. She was a cheerleader for the high school football team. I'll never forget how pretty she was in her red and white uniform, with her hair pulled back in a pony tail. And one year, she was voted 'Valentine Sweetheart' in the high school annual. She also made good grades. Math was her favorite subject and she excelled in trigonometry. Several years later, when I had trigonometry, she tried to help me with it. But it was all I could do to make a passing grade on it.

"She also liked her Home Economics class. That was where she learned home management, and how to cook and sew. The following year, she learned to make some of her school clothes. But best of all, she liked to cook. And she liked recipes with peanuts in them. I would get aggravated at her because she put peanuts in almost everything she cooked, but she said they were nutritious and that I should eat lots of them.

"But that's the way she was when we were growing up. No matter what we disagreed on, or whoever was at fault, she would always put her arm around me and tell me she loved me. And always in the late afternoons, we sat on top of the hay barn and watched the sunset. Watching sunsets were our special times together. That was our time of day. Patricia called it twilight time.

"During those years, rock and roll music was still in its heyday, and we wanted to learn how to dance. Before rock and roll came along, the only kind of dancing we knew was a slow version of the Texas Two-Step and the Waltz. Patricia had good coordination and she could waltz real well. It seemed like she would just glide across the floor when she danced. And how she loved to dance.

"But rock and roll music was the latest and the greatest. We were anxious to learn how to jitterbug and do the bop, and the twist and the stroll. Every Saturday morning, we'd turn on the TV to a rock and roll show and we practiced dancing. After a few weeks of that, we thought we could dance pretty well. We began making plans to ask Mother and Daddy if we could go to the sock hops that had begun to crop up around town on weekends, at the school and the skating rink and at private parties.

"Mother didn't approve of rock and roll music. She said it sounded like music that belonged in a honky tonk. But like the other kids in town, Patricia and I were wild about it. We even hid our radio under the covers at night and listened to it. We learned some of the latest songs the big name groups were singing and we tried to copy them. We knew when to sing, 'do wa do wa,' and 'schooshoobedo,' and other catchy little phrases that were popular in the songs. So we listened to those songs when we were relaxing. But when we were full of energy, we were ready to dance.

"One Saturday morning while Mother was in town, Patricia and I decided to practice dancing on the front porch. The radio was blaring loudly, playing our favorite songs, and our saddle oxfords and penny loafers were keeping time to the music. Our poodle skirts were swinging and we were dancing in high gear when we noticed Iris and Fernella Kosse standing at the front gate. They were two of Patricia's classmates in school.

'Oh, don't stop dancing because of us,', said Fernella, with a wide smile on her face. 'We've been standing here watching you. Haven't we, Iris?'

'Yes, we have,' said Iris. 'We've been trying to figure out what kind of dance you were doing.'

"Patricia explained that we were doing the bop. And that we knew how to do the twist and the jitterbug and the stroll, as well.

'Well, what we saw you doing wasn't no kind of dance,' Fernella said. 'You were just moving your feet, that's all.'

'What do you mean by that?' asked Patricia. 'We've been practicing for a month or more.'

'Tell you what,' said Fernella. 'If you really want to learn to dance, we'll teach you. We'll show you a few of our dance steps.'

"And they did. Those girls were two of the best dancers I ever saw. And they taught us more in an hour than we thought we would ever know about dancing. Daddy drove us to the school that night, to our first rock and roll sock hop. Of course, Fernella and Iris were both there since they were the best dancers in town. But what surprised us most was seeing Reverend Jamieson's daughters, Cynthia and Connie, dancing along with the rest of us.

"All of us kids continued going to church on Sundays and Wednesday nights, and never once did Reverend Jamieson preach against dancing in his sermons.

"Then September came and Patricia and I were back in school. She was a cheerleader again and I was in the school band. Frances was married to Howard and had a new baby daughter, Pamela. Mother was especially happy because Frances and Pamela were visiting us, and Frances and Howard were making plans to move back to town.

"On Friday afternoon, September the eleventh, the high school football team was to play its first game of the season in Tomball, near Houston. On the school bus that afternoon, Patricia said she needed to hurry home and change into her cheerleader uniform, because she had to be back at school in time to catch the bus going to the game. And since I was going, she told me to start getting ready as soon as we got home. She said she couldn't be late.

"Daddy had left his car at home that day and had given Frances permission to drive it. So, Frances offered to drive Patricia and me back to school to catch the bus for the football game.

"Patricia sat in the front seat with Frances, and Pamela was in a car seat between them. I was in the back seat. When we got to the highway we stopped and looked in both directions for oncoming traffic. But as we started across the highway, the car stalled. Frances kept trying to start it again, but it was too late. We were in the middle of a busy highway and could not get out. I saw the moving van coming and I knew it was going to hit us. I screamed and tried to brace myself against the car door and back seat. I saw Frances leaning over Pamela. And I saw Patricia put her head between her knees.

"When I regained consciousness, two paramedics were pushing on my ribs. I looked around for Patricia but didn't see her. Then I heard Frances crying. And I saw Pamela lying underneath a large tree. Her tiny body was covered with blood, and I knew she was dead. Then I lost consciousness again.

"The next thing I remembered was being in the ambulance hearing its siren as we were being rushed to the hospital. I knew Patricia was in the ambulance with me, but I couldn't see her. I started crying and glanced around trying to see her. But all I saw was blood trickling down her skirt. I thought she was dead. I started crying again. I couldn't stop crying. Then suddenly, I heard her say, 'Carol, honey. Please don't cry. I know it hurts, but we'll be there soon.' And I stopped crying immediately. I was so happy to hear her voice. I don't think she ever knew that I was crying for her and not for me.

"Patricia's right arm, left knee and ankle were broken. During surgery, the doctors placed several plastic pins in her knee and ankle. And she was in the hospital for two weeks, and wore a cast for many more. I had six broken ribs and both of my legs were broken. I had surgery and spent eight weeks in a hospital in Houston."

"That was a terrible time for all of our family. We felt so helpless. It was hard losing little Pamela. But we were thankful that you and Patricia and Frances survived it."

"Of course, cheerleading and band was out of the question for the rest of the school semester," Carol went on. "But we were more concerned about our grades. And, again, we were fortunate. Our teachers visited us at home and sent homework to us. We worked extra hard to keep our grades up with the rest of our classes. But our convalescence was slow. We spent a lot of time playing jacks and hangman's noose and making up songs and funny rhymes. And when Christmas came our most cherished gifts were new rock and roll albums and a record player. Then by springtime, we had learned to dance again.

"We had also returned to school. And when school ended for summer vacation, Patricia and I set out to do all of the things we had done the summer before.

"We took walks along the railroad tracks again, and gathered bouquets of wildflowers. We sat at the concrete dam and watched the blackbirds and crows in the corn patch. We learned to swim again, and swam in the rice canals almost every day. And we did extra chores at home so Mother would have time to spend with Frances and her new baby daughter, Darlene.

"We went to sock hops, movies and church. And late afternoons still found us on top of the old hay barn, watching the sunsets and dreaming of our future."

"I really missed visiting with you that summer," I said. "But that was the year Richard's job transferred us to Colorado."

"And that was the year Patricia met Lewis Crocker," Carol went on.

"I often wondered where she met him. Did she meet him at a dance, or what?"

"Not exactly. You see, Frances met him at a party one night and she let him drive her home, and she dated him a couple of times. But she met Howard and fell head over heels in love. So we didn't see Lewis for a long time."

"But when did Patricia start dating him?"

"That came later. She liked a boy at school. And he liked her, too. He was a real nice boy and came from a good family. They dated a few times, but she didn't want to get serious about him because he was going away to college that fall. And she wanted to finish high school and have a career of her own.

"Then one Friday afternoon as we were riding home on the school bus, Phoebe Garner announced that she was giving a party at her house that night. She invited Patricia and me, and asked that we bring some of our rock and roll albums.

"It was not unusual for us to walk to parties at our neighbor's homes if they lived on the same road as we did, so on that particular night we decided to walk to Phoebe's party.

"It was almost dark when we left home and began walking down the country dirt road to Phoebe's house. Then suddenly the night grew darker and rain clouds rolled swiftly overhead. It was a scary feeling. Patricia and I held hands and walked faster. Then the rain began and we started running. We were still running when we saw car lights coming from behind us. But as they came closer, we stopped and waited on the side of the road. The car was coming fast and we were afraid that whoever was driving wouldn't see us. But he did see us. And when he stopped and opened his car door, we saw that he was Lewis Crocker.

" 'What are you girls doing out on a night like this?' he called.

"Patricia told him we were on our way to Phoebe's party. And that it wasn't raining when we left home.

'Well, I'm on my way there now,' he said. 'Ya'll come on and get in. Don't you know there's a storm coming?'

"We thanked him and climbed into the back seat, trying to brush the rain from our hair and clothes. Lewis handed us a towel. But he didn't say anything else on the way to the party, and neither did we."

"What happened at the party? Did he dance with Patricia, or talk to her?"

"No, he didn't say much of anything to her, or dance with her. But he watched her. It was like he couldn't take his eyes away from her. I'll never forget how he looked standing against the wall with one leg hiked up behind him. He was wearing boots and jeans and a white tee shirt with a package of cigarettes rolled up in the sleeve. And his hair was combed in the style that was called the duck-tail. I don't think Patricia knew he was watching her, because we were busy dancing with the other kids, and he would look away when she turned in his direction.

"When the party was over, it was still raining, and he was waiting with his car keys in his hand and he drove us home. When we stopped in the driveway, we immediately got out of the car and thanked him for bringing us home. And as we walked up on the porch, he called to Patricia. She went back to see what he wanted. A few minutes later, when she came in the house, she said Lewis had asked her for a date, but that she told him she couldn't go. She said she didn't want any of Frances' rejects. I told her Lewis was too old for her. He was twenty years old and she was only fifteen.

"But Lewis was persistent. He began parking his car near the school grounds in the afternoons, and he asked if he could drive us home. Patricia was polite, but she told him we had cheerleader and band practice after our classes, and that we were expected to ride the school bus home after that. Then Lewis worked out a new plan. Mother and his mother attended church together and had known each other for years. So, he delivered messages from Mrs. Crocker to Mother. And sometimes he brought her over to visit Mother. And while they visited, he would sit around and be as charming as he could. It was plain to see that Mrs. Crocker idolized him. And, as time went on, he also charmed Mother into thinking that perhaps she had misunderstood him when he was dating Frances, and that all along he had really been waiting for Patricia. Anyway, his charm and flattery finally paid off. Patricia changed her mind about him. And Mother liked him."

"What did Daddy say about it?"

"He told Mother he didn't want Patricia going with Lewis. He said Lewis was no good. But Mother disagreed. She said she didn't see anything wrong with Patricia dating Lewis, as long as I went on their dates with them. So, there I was, eleven years old and expected to chaperone my sister's dates. I had no choice in the matter. I just did what I was told to do.

"Patricia never said what her reasons were for changing her mind about Lewis. And I guess I was too young at the time to give it much thought, one way or the other. But as their chaperone, I felt that I was pretty much in charge of the situation. I could go to movies free of charge, sit in the back seat of the car and eat hamburgers and drink cokes. And if I saw any hanky-panky going on, it was my job to report it to Mother. So, on their first date, we went to the Starlight Drive-In movie theater in Brenham, to see a double feature movie. We had a nice time. Patricia and I drank soda pop and ate popcorn. Lewis drank a six pack of beer that he had hidden under the front seat. When we got home, I told Mother about it, and she told Patricia that there had better not be any more beer drinking on her dates."

"Did Mother say anything to Lewis about the beer?"

"I don't know whether she did or not. But if she did, it didn't change anything because the dates continued. And Lewis started bringing us home from school every afternoon. At first I didn't mind, but later I began to miss riding home on the school bus with our friends. I think Patricia missed them, too. But there she was, a fifteen year old kid, caught up in a whirlwind of flattery and attention from Lewis. And it seemed that no matter where she was in school or in town, or at home, Lewis was always waiting on the corner. As far as I was concerned, Lewis was getting to be a problem. I could see it coming. I first noticed it one afternoon as he was driving us home from school. Patricia had had cheerleader practice that day and she was still wearing her uniform. When we got in the car, Lewis was nice to her, but then he said he wanted her to give up cheerleading because her skirt was too short and he didn't want other boys looking at her legs. She didn't say anything, but she blushed and tried to pull the skirt down to her knees. Later, I told her that he had no right to tell her what to do. But she said he loved her.

"So, Patricia and Lewis continued dating, and I was still their chaperone. But I got tired of the job, because I didn't like Lewis' attitude. And a few months later, Lewis decided that his sister could be their chaperone. But as it turned out, she wasn't. And at last, Lewis and Patricia were alone on their dates."

THE DARK SIDE OF TWILIGHT:

CHAPTER 9

"Mother had a talk with Lewis. I don't know what was said, but whatever it was didn't change anything, because the dates continued. And the subject of chaperones quietly faded.

"Later Lewis began leaving his car with Patricia while he was at work. However, she was not allowed to drive it to town. She said he wouldn't let her. And he issued other rules for her to follow. He chose the places she could go and the people she could talk to. And she must pick him up from work each day, on time. I told her if love was supposed to be like that, I'd forget it."

"What was Mother and Daddy's reaction to that?"

"Mother soft-pedaled it. She said Patricia would get tired of it and send Lewis packing. Daddy would say he 'didn't want her going with the sonofabitch.' Then to my amazement, Patricia broke up with Lewis. I don't know what it was about, but it happened one afternoon at our house.

"Lewis drove into the driveway real fast and slammed on his brakes. I guess he thought Patricia would run out to meet him. But she didn't. So, he honked the horn. But she ignored him. He kept honking the horn, and she kept ignoring him. Finally, her face turned red and she jumped up and ran outside. And I ran to the door to listen. I couldn't hear all of it, but I heard her yell, 'don't you come back, either.' Then he skidded his tires in the driveway and left in a hurry.

"After that, they didn't see each other for a couple of weeks. But in the meantime, Mrs. Crocker came to visit Mother, and I'm sure they discussed Lewis and Patricia's romance. And a few weeks later, Lewis and Patricia made up and decided to get married."

"I'll never forget the day I received Patricia's wedding invitation," I said. "Or the letter she enclosed with it. She said it would be a small church wedding at seven o'clock on the twenty-ninth of September. And would I please make every effort to be there. She said she realized that my children were in school, but maybe I could hire a housekeeper for the few days it would take to come to her wedding. She said I must be there. She said she wouldn't take 'no' for my answer. And, she said I didn't know Lewis, but that she would introduce us when they met me at the train station in Houston."

I wanted to be happy for her. But I felt let down. She was so young. And I had expected her to accomplish so many great things. I didn't want her to suffer the misery of a young marriage and divorce, and find herself returning to school, years later, trying to rebuild her life back in order.

However, I answered her letter and wished her happiness. I assured her that I would be there, but it would be within hours of the wedding. And I enclosed a copy of the train schedule stating my arrival time in Houston. In later years, I would have made the trip by plane, but in September 1961, jet airplanes in Colorado were still a part of the future.

It was cold and snowing the morning Richard drove me to the train station in downtown Denver. The train was long and crowded and was called the Zephyr Flyer. As Richard handed my luggage to the porter, he commented on the length of the train. The porter said it was the longest train west of Chicago and that it was known as 'The God Of The West Wind.'

The train rolled slowly through the south section of Denver, and the train whistle blew continually as we neared the suburban railroad crossings and small towns. Train whistles always depressed me. But on that day, I thought it was the most lonesome sound in the world. I stared into the distance, watching the heavy snow clouds hanging low, shadowing the Rocky Mountains near Colorado Springs. Then the snow became heavier and large powdery flakes splattered against the train windows. I thought of Richard and the children. And I already missed them. But I had promises to keep. Promises to Patricia.

The train was very fast and the night came quickly. A porter asked if I wished to have dinner in the dining car, but I chose a sandwich and coffee. And while eating, I found myself listening to loose rocks falling away from the train tracks. I couldn't help thinking that had I been on another train, I might have been afraid. But I wasn't. After all, I was on the Zephyr Flyer, 'The God Of The West Wind.' And as I looked out into the cold night, I thought of Patricia. She was so young. What kind of man would she marry? Would she be happy?

Patricia was born on July 26, 1946, a hot sultry day in Houston. She was a beautiful baby with blonde hair and blue eyes, and weighed seven pounds. I was eleven years old and her oldest sister. And I adored her. I bathed her and changed her diapers. I sat her on the vanity chair, brushed her hair and told her how pretty she was. I took her walking and taught her to pick wildflowers. And in first grade she made crayon drawings especially for me. In later years, we shared letters, photographs and summer vacations. And now, I was on my way to her wedding.

When I arrived in Houston, the next afternoon, the weather was hot and humid, the opposite of what I had seen the day before in Denver. My wool skirt and sweater felt uncomfortable, but I forgot about it when I saw Patricia standing on the platform, holding hands with the young man beside her.

"There she is," Patricia called as I stepped off the train. "There's my sister."

We ran and hugged each other, then she turned and introduced me to Lewis. We smiled and said hello. And as we shook hands, he said, "Hello, sister-in-law."

"Hello, brother-in-law," I replied. "I'm glad to meet you."

Patricia and Lewis were married that night in the small church that had been so much a part of her life. She was a beautiful bride. Her wedding dress was aqua blue with a matching lace jacket. Her shoes were white, matching the white flowers in her hair, and her bridal bouquet.

"Yes, she was a beautiful bride," Carol said. "And the fact that you were at her wedding meant a lot to her."

"It meant a lot to me, too," I replied. "But I wondered why Daddy and Frances and Howard didn't come to the wedding."

"Well, you may not have noticed it, but there was a lot of tension at home that evening. While Patricia and Lewis were gone to the train station to meet you, Mother and Daddy had a big argument about the wedding. Daddy was absolutely furious at Mother. He even threatened to leave her. You see, all along Daddy had tried to put an end to Patricia's dating. And he thought it was over. But Mother went to the courthouse and signed the marriage license for Patricia to be married. During their argument, Daddy said to Mother, 'I told you I didn't want her going with the sonofabitch, and now you're letting her marry him.'

"He said Patricia was going to ruin her life. That was why he refused to go to the wedding. I think Frances and Howard felt the same way.

"I really missed Patricia, after she married. Even though she lived close by, I was lonely and I wanted things to be the way they used to be. I constantly dwelled on my memories of all the years we had spent together. But I missed her most at twilight time. I missed sitting on top of the hay barn, holding hands with her, and talking about our future as we watched the sunsets. At that time of day, after she married, I sometimes felt like just running to the barn, climbing to the top and sitting there alone. But I never did, because I knew it wouldn't be the same without her.

"My melancholy mood continued for months after she married. But as time went by, I realized there was nothing I could do about it except try to grow up, and out of it. So, each time I saw her, I would pretend to be happy. And when she came to the house to visit, I clowned around more than ever before.

"She talked about things she wanted to buy for their home and different ways to make it look nice. One day she came over to borrow Mother's sewing machine to make some new curtains. And she asked if I could go home with her and spend the night. Lewis worked nights at the Salt Mine, and she didn't like to be alone while he was gone. So, we loaded the sewing machine into the car, and I went home with her. We laughed and visited as she cut material for the curtains. I told her how much I missed her and all the things we used to do together. She said she missed me too, but that I should start going places with my friends. She said she missed going to the football games with the cheerleaders, and that she missed being in school. I asked if she had seen any of her school friends since she married. She said she saw a few in town, but that she was reluctant to invite them to her home because she was married. She said she had already learned that marriage required a lot of give and take. To hear her say that, hit a sore spot with me. I couldn't help thinking how much she had changed her life by leaving school and all of her friends to marry Lewis. She didn't have to get married and I was still wondering why she did. But I was glad to be with her and we continued talking about the old days while we cooked and ate dinner. Then we sat outside in the cool air until bedtime.

"Patricia said I could sleep on the living room couch. She brought out a pair of brightly flowered sheets and as we began putting them on the couch, she said they were a gift from you. She said they were her best sheets and she had been saving them for a special occasion. We then started talking about you living so far away in Denver and wondering if you would ever move back to Texas. She said you wouldn't. She said the mountains would keep you in Colorado. I had never been to Colorado so I didn't understand what she meant by that. But anyway, we talked on for a while and then went to bed.

"I must have been more tired than I realized, for I slept soundly. I didn't even hear Lewis come home from work. And when I finally awoke, it was morning. I got up and dressed, folded the sheets and put the couch back in place. I didn't want to stir around or make any noise so I just sat on the couch and waited for Patricia. I had been sitting there probably five or ten minutes, when suddenly I heard a loud commotion in the bedroom. Then there was a loud slap, and I heard Patricia moan.

"I jumped up and ran into the bedroom. Lewis and Patricia were standing near the bed, and I noticed that Patricia's mouth was bleeding. Lewis yelled at me and told me to get out of there. But I told him I was not going to leave my sister. Then I picked up a straight-backed chair that was sitting near the door and said I would hit him with it if he hit her again."

"What did he say to you"

"He didn't say anything. He just looked at me and walked out of the room. I guess he was afraid I would tell on him."

"What about Patricia?"

"I stayed with her. I got a cold wet wash cloth for her mouth and I tried to comfort her. She was crying and pleading with me not to tell anyone, especially Mother and Daddy. She kept saying that Lewis had just lost his temper and that he didn't mean to hit her so hard."

"The fact that she didn't want anyone to know about it was her second biggest mistake."

"Yes, and it got worse," Carol went on. "The slapping and pushing her around turned into beatings. When I say pushing, I'm talking about the time he pushed her out of a car, back when she was pregnant with Rhonda. It's a thousand wonders that she didn't lose Rhonda when that happened."

"I never knew that. How did you find out about it? Were you with them?"

"No, I wasn't with them, but I know the people who were. And they remember it well. Mother and Frances knew about it."

"And then there was the time, back in the mid-sixties, when Patricia and Lewis moved to North Carolina. He had relatives there and he thought he could find work with them. I'll never forget the day Patricia and Lewis came by the house to tell us they were leaving. I hardly recognized Patricia when she walked up on the porch. She looked like she had been in a car wreck. Both of her eyes were black, her face, neck and arms were bruised, and patches of her hair had been pulled out.

"I ran into the kitchen and told Mother that something terrible had happened. I had never seen anyone beat up like that before. Mother's face turned red and she was furious. I stood there for a moment wondering what she was going to do about it. She grabbed a dish towel and quickly dried her hands, then reached over and turned the stove off. I knew by the look on her face that she was going outside to confront Lewis and that all hell was going to shake loose.

104

But at that instant, Patricia walked into the kitchen. Mother looked at her and started crying. Patricia walked over and put her arms around Mother. But she offered no explanation for her bruises. She just said she was leaving that day for North Carolina and she had come to tell us good-bye. Mother said, 'What are you going to do? Move out there and let him kill you?' But Patricia said that they would make a new start and things would be better for them.

"Patricia hugged Mother again and asked her not to say anything. Then Patricia and I hugged good-bye. I walked with her to the front door and stood on the porch as she walked toward the car. Then suddenly, Daddy drove into the driveway, stopped and got out. Patricia ran and put her arms around him.

"Daddy hugged her and asked where she was going. Then he stepped back. He looked at her and he looked at Lewis. Then he put his hand in his pocket and said to Lewis, 'If you hit her again, I'll slit your god-damn throat.' Lewis mumbled something, but he wouldn't repeat it. Daddy stepped forward. Lewis grabbed Patricia's hand and they left.

"They didn't stay very long in North Carolina, and I was so glad to see her when she came home. But her appearance had changed. She was still thin as always, but she looked tired. And I noticed premature age lines in her face. Each time I saw her, she almost always looked like she wanted to cry."

"In the spring of 1967, Patricia, Tammie and Rhonda came to my home in Dallas. I was so happy to see them but I couldn't help thinking how sad they looked. Patricia was three months pregnant with Kimberly, and had suffered another of Lewis' beatings. Her eyes were so black and swollen, she could barely see. I got the impression that she was embarrassed for me to see her that way, so I didn't say much about it until she felt more comfortable. But I thought of how humiliating it must have been for her to take the beatings, and then pick up her two little girls and try to find a place of refuge. She showed little resemblance to the happy, carefree sister I had taken to Colorado seven years before. She was now withdrawn and very quiet. And even her little girls were quiet. I noticed that when she held them on her lap, they would look up at her and say, 'Mommy, does it still hurt? Mommy, don't cry any more.' It was like they knew she was hurting and they were wanting to be kind to her. I called Frances and asked that she come for a visit. And she did. But she hadn't been in the house ten minutes until I caught her in the bathroom crying. She kept saying she thought Patricia might lose her eyesight because her eyes were beaten so bad. But still, we knew there was nothing we could do other than try to persuade Patricia to stay with us.

"Patricia, Tammie and Rhonda stayed the next week at my home, and as the days passed by, their stress seemed to disappear. Patricia was more relaxed and the girls played happily. Frances came to visit almost every morning and stayed until mid-afternoon. What fun we three sisters had fixing lunch, recalling old times and laughing together. But of course it was not to last, for Lewis was calling every day, begging Patricia to come home. And finally she did. As she left on the bus to return to him, I wondered why he hadn't come to my home to get her. For when she had left him in the past and had gone to other members of the family, he usually got in his car and went looking for her. He always looked until he found her and brought her back home. But as I thought more about it, I concluded that the fact that she was in my home this time made the situation somewhat different.

"About a month after Patricia returned home to Lewis, Frances and I went to visit Mother, and Patricia came over to be with us. Patricia's eyes were black again, and there were red and blue marks on her neck. When she saw us, she looked like she wanted to cry. I wanted to cry, too. And there were other thoughts going on in my mind when I saw her that way."

"Well, you saw some of the after effects of the abuse," Carol said. "But Emil and I witnessed some of it several times. It was in December, that same year, that we invited Patricia and Lewis to attend a dinner with us at a deer camp, near our home. The dinner was an annual event for Emil's family and friends, and it was always held during deer season. The men usually cooked two or three kinds of barbecue and sausage, and the women fixed baked beans, potato salad, and cole slaw. And we also took jars of homemade pickles and jalapeno peppers to go with it.

"Anyway, we were all at the deer camp getting ready to eat. Patricia and Lewis were with us. The men were standing around talking about hunting, and the women were placing the food on the picnic tables. Lewis walked over to one of the tables and picked up a jar of jalapeno peppers. He asked if they were hot and we told him they were. Then he took one out of the jar and ate it.

"The pepper burned his mouth and he called for Patricia to bring him a beer. She handed a can of beer to him, and after he had taken a drink, she asked if his mouth was still hot. Then he turned the can of beer up and poured it on her head and asked her if it was cold. Then he picked up the jar of peppers and threw them in her face and he began hitting her.

"Several of the men intervened and asked him why he was treating his wife that way. That really made him angry, and he got in his car and left. Patricia was scared of what he might do later, and she said she should also leave. So, Emil and I drove her back to our home. Emil's little brother came with us.

"When we got home Lewis was in his car in the driveway waiting for us. He ordered Patricia to go in the house and get her things together. He said they were going home. As Patricia and I walked inside, I heard Emil ask Lewis what his problem was. Lewis told him to mind his own damn business. When we walked back out on the porch, Emil and I asked Patricia to stay with us. But Lewis was determined not to let her win. He reached beneath the seat of his car and pulled out a pistol. He pointed it at Patricia and then waved it at us. I pleaded with her to stay, but she said it was best for everyone concerned if she went with him. She said she didn't want her problems to become ours."

"You should have filed charges on him for waving the gun at you and Emil," I said.

"Yes, I should have," Carol went on. "But the reason I didn't report him was because I thought he would punish Patricia for it. However, I called Mother and told her what happened. And I asked her to go to Patricia's house and inquire about her well-being.

"For the next several years after that, Patricia didn't come back to my home. And I didn't see her at all except when she came to Mother's while I was there visiting. Of course, we were always happy to see each other and our visits were pleasant. But every time I saw her, I would think about her on my way home, and for weeks afterward. I thought of how her appearance was changing. She looked so sad, she had more misery than she could cope with.

"Then to my surprise, late one Saturday afternoon, several years later, Patricia and Lewis and their children came to visit us again. They now had four daughters. I hardly knew the two youngest girls, for both of them were born during the years since our last visit. And during that time, I had two girls.

"Patricia and I ran and hugged each other with tears in our eyes. And we were talking a mile a minute about our girls, saying whoever would have thought that we would someday be mothers of six little girls. Then we ushered the girls into the house and to the toy room and I made Kool-Aid for them.

"Patricia and I cooked dinner and after everyone had eaten, we sent the children out to play. Then we sat on the porch with Emil and Lewis. Around nine o-clock, I invited Patricia and her family to spend the night. So, we gathered the children and bathed them and put them to bed. Then around ten o'clock, Emil excused himself and went to bed. He was polite about it, but I sensed something was wrong. And, after he was in bed, I asked him why he went to bed so early. He said he got tired of hearing Lewis talk about how many women he had.

"Patricia and I then sat in the kitchen and continued our visit. Lewis sat outside drinking beer. Later, he called Patricia to come out and sit with him. I told her I was going to bed. And I explained that the guest bedroom was prepared for them when they were ready to turn in.

"About an hour later, Patricia came to my bed and started shaking me, asking if I had an ice pack. When I turned the light on, I noticed her mouth was bleeding and there were red marks on her throat. I asked what happened and she said Lewis had tried to kill her. She said he accused her of being down at the creek with Emil, 'screwing.' Then Emil woke up and asked what was going on, and I told him what Lewis had said. Emil was furious. He said, 'that sorry lying sonofabitch.' He jumped out of bed, barely taking time to put his pants on, before he ran outside to confront Lewis. He asked Lewis, 'just what his damn problem was.' Lewis said he was mad at his 'old lady,' and he shoved Emil. Emil slapped him a couple of times and then came back in the house. I was still trying to console Patricia and doctor her wounds when Lewis came inside and walked over to Emil. He put his finger to Emil's face and said, 'you slapped me, you sonofabitch, and if you slap me again, I'll kill you.' Emil got up out of his chair and said to Lewis, 'you've had this coming for a long time.' Then he slapped Lewis all the way through the dining room, out the front door, knocked him through the banister on the porch and out into the yard.

"After Lewis picked himself up, he looked at Emil and said, 'you're in your territory now, but I'm warning you, you'd better not come to mine.' Emil told him to shut his mouth and leave or he would slap him all the way back to his territory, wherever that was.

"And so our visit ended much the same as the one before. We asked Patricia to stay with us, but she said Lewis would just cause problems for us, and she didn't want that to happen.

"I really didn't expect Patricia and Lewis to come to our home again, but several months later, late on a Saturday afternoon, they returned for another visit. We tried to welcome them, but with the memory of their last visit still fresh on my mind, I couldn't help being skeptical that the same thing might happen again.

"However, this time, they brought another couple with them, a man and his wife, Don and Hillary.

"We didn't invite them in, but after we talked a few minutes on the porch, Emil suggested that everyone go around to the back yard and sit in the lawn chairs. I knew what he was thinking when he said that. He had only recently repaired the banister on the front porch, and if he was going to have to slap Lewis again, he didn't want to repair anything else as a result of it.

THE DARK SIDE OF TWILIGHT:

"We visited a while longer, and then I invited them to stay for dinner. Patricia and I cooked a nice fish dinner. After everyone had eaten, and we were sitting in the living room talking, Patricia said she was thirsty. I told her to go in the kitchen and get a soda pop out of the refrigerator. She got up and walked to the kitchen and Lewis followed her.

"We could see the refrigerator from where we were sitting, and all at once, we heard one loud slap after another. As we jumped up to see what was going on, the slapping continued. We saw Patricia's head bounce back a couple of times and I heard Lewis cursing Mother and Daddy for something.

"Emil and I ran into the kitchen. I told Lewis that he was not going to knock my sister around in my house, and I told him to get out. He looked at me, but he saw Emil standing behind me. I thought Emil was going to hit him, and he would have, but I stood between them, and Lewis went out the back door. He went out to Don's pickup and returned with a rifle and cocked it. I told him he'd better not try anything with the gun. He stood there for a moment and by then, Don and Hillary were leaving and he went with them. Emil and I asked Patricia to stay with us because we were in fear for her life. And she did.

"I was surprised that Patricia and her daughters spent the night with us, but I was relieved that she had. But after Lewis left, I became concerned for Mother and Daddy. Lewis was angry with them and since Patricia had refused to leave with him, I thought he might take the gun and confront Mother and Daddy with it. Patricia agreed that it was possible. So, I called the Deputy Sheriff in Waller and asked him to check on Mother and Daddy, and to tell them that Lewis was angry with them and that he had left my house with a gun."

"How long did Patricia stay with you?"

"Just until the next day," Carol went on. "Lewis came the next morning and talked her into going back home with him. And the girls were crying to go home. That was the last time Patricia and Lewis were at our home together.

"However, during the years that followed, she came to us several

110

more times seeking refuge. She always had fresh bruises and black eyes and she was always on the run hoping Lewis wouldn't find her. He had threatened to kill her so many times, she had reached the point where she seriously thought he would. But she said that sometimes he brought her flowers and things after he had beaten her. And sometimes he would apologize to her, but in an instant he would turn mean again. She said she knew she had to get away from him. But she didn't know where to go. I offered to let her live with me, but she said she couldn't. She said that regardless of where she went, Lewis would track her down. And he would punish her and everyone who had helped her.

"I suggested that she call his bluff. She said, 'Carol, I've tried to. But you know what happens every time I leave him. And now that the girls are grown, when I leave him, they always get on the phone and start calling around until they find me and they tell him where I am. Then there's my baby. He knows I won't leave her. And if I take her with me, he won't rest until he finds me.

'Believe me, it's a living hell. I've tried to reason with him. I've tried to be a good wife and mother. I've worked at the school for nearly nine years, to help support my family. And I've given them everything I could. But it's pure hell coming home to a man who packs a gun, and wondering if I'll wake up in the morning beat up, or whether I'll live to wake up at all.

'Not having lived in it yourself, you can't possibly know how I feel when he gets drunk and starts cursing me, calling me every filthy name that he can think of. And while he's doing that, he beats me. Then if that's not enough, he gets one of his guns out and puts it to my head. And there's no reason for any of it. He's just plain damn mean. He's as evil as the devil himself.

'After he's through beating me, I wash the blood off and rinse my mouth out, hoping he hasn't knocked any more of my teeth loose. You know I've lost several teeth already. And while I'm cleaning up the mess, I think to myself: If I call the Sheriff's Department and file charges, when he gets out of jail he'll beat me up again, or worse. And if I try to put him in a hospital for alcohol abuse, he will refuse it, and he may be meaner than ever before. So, I just try to cope with it, hoping that someday he'll change his ways.

'When I get up in the morning after he has beat me the night before, sometimes my eyes are so swollen I can hardly see. I have to hold cold wash cloths on them for a long time until my vision clears. And it's not only my eyes, it's also my throat and ribs. I ache all over and I tell myself that I've got to get out of it. I've got to get away. And the hell of it is that Lewis says it's my fault. He says I make him mad. Then when I ask him what I do that makes him so mad, he won't tell me.

'So, in the meantime while I'm trying to figure out why he was mad at me, I have to remember my responsibilities. My job and my family. So, I bathe and try to cover the bruises with makeup, and I brush my hair gently because my head still hurts. Then I take a couple of aspirin and put on some dark sunglasses and go to my work. Fortunately, my co-workers are too kind to mention anything about my bruises, but I know they can't help but notice them. And they know who put them there.'

"I cried with her when she told me that. I couldn't keep from crying. It was like she knew she was fighting a losing battle. Yet, she was trying her best to hang on, hoping for the best. I tried my best to comfort her. I tried to make her realize that her life was most important. I tried every way I could to help her renew her self-esteem.

"A couple of years ago, she came to my house again. And, she had been beat up again. She had an appointment with the school board for a job in Columbus. So, I kept her youngest daughter for her while she went for the interview.

"Patricia had been gone about an hour when Phoebe called. I don't know where she got my phone number. I hadn't talked to her in years. But she wanted to talk to Patricia, and I said I hadn't seen her. She said Lewis and Tammie were on their way to my house to get Patricia, and that Patricia had better be there. I didn't know what to do. Emil was at work, and I didn't want to be home alone when Lewis got there. So, I grabbed Jennifer and drove into town to find Patricia. And when I found her, she took Jennifer and left again.

"About an hour later, after I returned home, Mother called and wanted to talk to Patricia. I told her that Patricia had left. Mother was crying and very upset. Someone had called and told her that Patricia's mobile home had burned to the ground. I asked how it happened and she said she didn't know.

"We talked a while longer, then suddenly, Mother said, 'Patricia just walked in.' I asked to speak to her, and when she came to the phone, she was crying. She said, 'Oh, Carol, that bastard burned me out. He did it. I know he did it. He told me if I ever left him again, he'd burn it down.' "

"Was there ever any proof that he burned it?" I asked.

"I don't know," Carol replied. "But I believe Patricia. Because that's the way he was. He'd do anything to punish her for leaving him.

"After that, Patricia didn't come to my house any more. But I saw her a few times at Mother's. And, last year, Patricia and Lewis bought the house in Bedias. The last time I saw her was on Thanksgiving Day, last year at Mother's house. She looked so pretty. She wore a pink blouse and designer jeans, and her hair was styled in the latest fashion. She talked about wanting to go to college and said that I should go with her. We joked around about how we could be the two oldest 'teeny boppers' on campus. She said since we had already gone the route of marriage, babies and diapers, we may as well start over and go back to school again. I said she could be the oldest cheerleader. She said I could be the oldest saxophone player. And we laughed at the impression we could make at our ages of forty-one and thirty-seven. Then we laughed about our long ago childhood pranks, many of which were almost forgotten. It seemed as though all of our questions began with 'Remember back when we did this? Remember when we did that? Do you remember so and so? What was her name? Don't you remember? Didn't they get married right after high school? No? Well, I wonder where they are now. Oh, don't you remember?'

"Then suddenly we saw smoke coming from Mother's stove. It wasn't funny but we had to laugh. For it was another reminder of the old times when, as young girls, we liked to cook but would almost always forget to take the dinner rolls out of the oven. And, once again, like history repeating itself, Mother came running to the kitchen reminding us that we had burned the rolls again."

Carol and I cried together. "Carol, we must both hold on to our memories. Patricia would want it that way. She knows we'll always be there for her. Just as she would for us. And I don't know how or when or where we'll find her. But we will. I know you're hurting. I am, too. But until she is found, we can't prove that he murdered her. But we know he's dangerous and I don't think we should confront him with suspicions or go to his home. That could make things worse. Because, number one, if he murdered her, he's not going to admit it. Number two, if he knows we suspect him of that, he may move her body. Remember, deer season will be open in a couple of months. Think what that could do to a body. And Number three, I think he would leave the country. So, I think it's best to learn all we can and then watch him experience the element of surprise."

Suddenly, the phone rang, jarring our already jangled nerves. We had talked the night away. Aunt Margaret was on the phone, and breakfast was ready.

The meal that Aunt Margaret prepared for us could be more aptly described as a small feast rather than a Sunday morning breakfast. But that was typical of her. She knew we enjoyed her home-cooked country breakfasts.

Afterwards, we spent several hours visiting with her. She said the heat had taken most of her vegetable garden but she insisted that we walk out to it so she could show us where and what she planned to grow the next year. When we returned to the house, Carol and I followed as she went to her closets showing us stacks of beautiful crochet and embroidery. Then there was the kitchen pantry filled with jars of beets, homemade pickles, jams and jellies. And there was the trip to two deep freezers which were packed full of meats and vegetables. When I asked where she found the time to do so many things, she laughed and said, 'I do it because I like to keep busy. And if I wasn't doing that, what else would I be doing?' Carol and I couldn't think of an appropriate answer, so we smiled and complimented her ingenuity.

Later, we stood outside under a huge tree and talked again about Patricia's disappearance. Aunt Margaret and Carol talked about the missing persons report, hoping the television stations would continue mentioning it on the news. Richard, Emil and Bill were standing nearby, talking amongst themselves.

I was engrossed in my own thoughts watching leaves falling gently to the ground. I imagined the leaves swirling, telling me not to leave. I was so close, I needed to stay. I could think of nothing but trees. Large trees on a deer lease. Trees with water close by. Trees with leaves falling gently, carpeting a grave that lay beneath them.

"I believe Patricia is on a deer lease," I said to Aunt Margaret and Carol. "I don't know what a deer lease is, but I believe she's there."

"Lewis used to go deer hunting down near Llano," Carol said.

"But there's several deer leases within twenty-five or thirty miles from Bedias," Aunt Margaret said.

"Will you explain to me what a deer lease is?"

"Well, it's a lot of land that has deer on it. And during hunting season, deer hunters will lease the land and hunt the deer."

"Well, I guess that blows my theory, because hunting season is not open yet. But why do I keep thinking about it? Am I losing my mind and don't know it?"

Aunt Margaret never batted an eye. She turned and asked Bill if he knew of any deer leases in the area close to Bedias.

"No. But I can tell you who would know," Bill replied. "His name is Bob Gordon. He owns a big cattle ranch just before you get to Navasota. You can see it from the highway."

"Lewis worked for Bob Gordon, a long time ago," Carol said. "I don't know how long he worked there, but I know where the ranch is. We'll go by there today on our way home and see if Mr. Gordon will talk to us."

THE DARK SIDE OF TWILIGHT:

CHAPTER 10

At home, the next morning, I received a phone call from my brother Merle.

"Hey, Sis, what's going on?" he said. "I tried all weekend to call you, but I couldn't get an answer. What have you been up to lately?"

"Richard and I spent the weekend in Madisonville, with Carol and Emil. We also visited Aunt Margaret and Bill."

"Well, I didn't know where you were," Merle went on. "I thought maybe you were on vacation. I called Mother yesterday morning, and she said she didn't know where you were. I told her I hadn't talked to you lately, and I just wanted to check in with you to see how you're doing. What's this business about Patricia being gone? Mother said she just disappeared and that she's been gone nearly three weeks."

"That's true," I replied. "This is the third week. And we're all worried sick about her. Do you have any idea where she could be? Have you heard from her?"

"No, I haven't. Mother says the story is out that Patricia ran off with a boyfriend. And they're suppose to be somewhere around Graham, Texas. Or Wichita Falls. I told Mother that if Patricia did something like that, she sure must have changed a lot. But Mother said Patricia had told her, about a month ago, that she was planning to leave Lewis."

"Did Mother also tell you that there's a missing persons report out on Patricia?"

"Yes, she mentioned that."

"Merle, you know that you and I have always been close and we have shared our feelings where the family is concerned."

"Yes, I know that. Is there something special that you want to talk about?"

"Well, it's about Patricia. I just don't believe that she left her home willingly."

"What do you mean, willingly?"

"I mean, I don't think she ran off with a boyfriend. I don't think she left on her own. Nor of her own free will. I think Lewis has done something to her. And I've even told a detective about my suspicions."

"Well, now, I don't know whether you should have done that or not. You may be stirring up a hornet's nest."

"But I couldn't help it. I felt I had to tell him. I just know something is dreadfully wrong about the whole thing. I feel it in my bones. I've heard all the stories that are being spread around, and none of them make any sense to me. I know Patricia wouldn't do the things she's being accused of. I know my sisters, and I think I'm a fairly good judge of character."

"I'm sure of that. But you may be making a mountain out of a mole hill, where this is concerned. After all, we both know that Patricia and Lewis have fought for many years. This could have been just another one of their arguments that got out of hand, and maybe she decided she had had enough. I'm surprised she didn't leave him a long time ago. But after all these years, how many has it been, twenty-five or more, I just assumed that maybe things were not as bad between them as they used to be. Of course, I probably know less about it than anybody, because I never see them except when I go to Mother's on Thanksgiving. And you know how that goes. Everybody's busy visiting, and nobody talks about their problems."

"But getting back to now, I'm not only worried about Patricia, I'm also worried about Mother and Daddy."

"Well, maybe I can put your mind at ease, a little," Merle went on. "I didn't get to talk to Daddy. He was taking a nap. But Mother and I had a lengthy conversation. And I got the impression that she was not too concerned about Patricia being gone."

"You must be joking," I said. "She seemed upset about it the last time I talked to her."

"Well, she was in an all around jolly mood Sunday night. She said she didn't think there was anything to worry about. She said she expected to hear from Patricia any day now."

"I wonder if Mother secretly knows where Patricia is."

"I don't know whether she does or not, but she's not overly concerned about it."

"She probably thinks I'm just overreacting," I said.

"Well, maybe I can help you out of it," Merle went on. "I've got a friend who lives close to Navasota. He's lived in that area all his life and he is a retired policeman. It's been about a year since I last saw him, but I know he'll help us out if he can. He gets around, and he knows a lot of people in that area. I'll give him a call tonight, and see what he can come up with. He'll check it out, and as soon as I hear anything from him, I'll let you know."

Two days later, I received another phone call from Carol.

"Wake up sleepy head, it's a beautiful morning," she said. "All the little birds and squirrels have already had their breakfast. And so have I."

"Well, pour yourself another cup of coffee and bring it to the phone," I replied. "We'll have coffee together. We need to talk. I tried to call you yesterday but there was no answer."

"Oh, I had to work overtime, again. Getting ready for the end of the month audit. I intended to call you last night, but I just couldn't break loose long enough to do it. Besides that, I didn't want to broadcast the news that I have to tell you."

"Is it about Patricia?"

"Yes, it is. Mother called me last night, and she was very upset. She had talked to one of Patricia's daughters, she didn't say which one, and she said Kimberly was very upset because her birthday was a couple of days ago and Patricia had not called to wish her a happy birthday. Then Mother said that if I had any idea at all where Patricia was, she wanted me to tell her to call her family. You can imagine how that made me feel. I wanted to scream."

"I know how I feel about it," I said. "It makes me shiver. I think Patricia would have called her, if she could have."

"I know she would have called," Carol went on. "I know how close they were. She and Kimberly went through so much together after Kimberly's motorcycle accident. Patricia even took a month's leave of absence from her work, so she could take care of Kimberly. She didn't want anyone else to do it."

"Have you talked with Detective Adams any more?" I asked.

"No. He said he would call me when there were any new developments on the case."

"Well, at the rate things are going, that could be weeks or even months from now. Or it could be never. Because all we've got, so far, are our suspicions. And that may be all Adams has got.

"Carol, we've got to put our heads together and think a little harder. There's got to be an answer. There's no such thing as a perfect crime. So, we know there's bound to be a loophole in this thing. I think it's something that we have simply overlooked. Is there any way that you could take a few days off, and meet me in Madisonville?"

"I wish I could. But I can't. My manager is on vacation now, and he won't be back until the third week in September. That would be the earliest that I could leave. But we can start making our plans and be ready to go then."

"I'll be ready. Oh, by the way, Merle has a friend who is a retired policeman, and he lives near Navasota. Merle is going to call him and see if he can find out anything for us."

"Well, I hope he can. And be sure to let me know about it."

As we ended the conversation, we promised to keep in touch every day, and share any news that we might have. However, late that same afternoon, Carol phoned again.

"I've just finished talking to Detective Adams a few minutes ago," she said. "And I have some disturbing news. Now it may or may not have anything to do with Patricia's disappearance, but he's checking on it. He called and said that he had received reports of two 'Jane Does,' unidentified bodies. One was found in Livingston County, the other was found near Lake Somerville. He wanted to know if Patricia had any unusual markings, tattoos, scars, or anything that could help identify her. I told him that the only thing I could think of was the plastic pins that were put in her left knee and ankle, back when we had the car wreck in 1959."

"Did he say anything else?"

"No, he was in a hurry. But he said he would give the information to the proper authorities. And he said he'd let me know what they come up with. I'll call when I hear from him."

Later that evening, when the long hot day had ended and night began, I walked out to the patio to sit and think, and wonder. It was now the fourth week of August. A time when Texas nights are at their warmest before quietly fading into September. I looked up through the trees now bathed in moonlight, and again I counted the nights that Patricia had been gone. I thought that time had never before seemed as distressful as when I counted those long fearful nights. For to me, each one was a definite symbol of lost hope. But still I knew I would never give up. For as surely as the long nights turned into mornings, I knew she was out there somewhere, waiting to be found.

I thought about Adams' phone call to Carol, telling her of the two unidentified bodies. And I thought that, most likely, they had died under tragic circumstances. I wondered how many days, weeks, possibly months, their families had prayed and waited for their safe return. I felt sympathy for both the victims and their families, whoever they might be. But in my heart, I knew that neither of the victims was Patricia. Later, Carol called to tell me that both victims had been identified.

It was early one morning when Merle called again.

"Hey, Sis, I'm at work, but I thought I'd take a minute to call and tell you some good news."

"Is it about Patricia?"

"Yes, it is. And she's okay."

"How do you know?"

"I talked to the friend I was telling you about, the retired policeman. And he did a little checking around."

"What did he say?"

"He said Patricia was seen at a gas station in Shiro, Texas. He said an employee there told him that she was with another man, and they stopped at the station to buy gas."

"When was she seen? What day was it?"

"It was on Tuesday morning, the ninth of August. The employee said he remembered the date because it was his daughter's ninth birthday."

"How does he know it was Patricia? And, does he know the man she was with?"

"No. He didn't know the man. But he says he's pretty sure that Patricia was the woman."

"Did he talk to her?"

"No. He said he didn't talk to her. He said she sat in the car while he filled the gas tank. He said she was sitting in the front seat on the passenger side, and he got a good look at her. He said she kind of kept her head down, like maybe she was studying a map, or something. But he noticed that she was real friendly to the guy who was with her, and that they left going toward the Interstate."

"Okay. But listen to this: You know that in small towns, everyone knows everyone else. And they're usually friendly. I think if the gas station employee knew Patricia well enough to recognize her while she was sitting in a car, he probably would have spoken to her."

"But he said she kept her head down, like she was reading something. Maybe he didn't want to interrupt her."

"Well, I think it's logical to assume that the employee has seen the local news on television. And if he has, he knows she is listed as a missing person. So, when he saw her, why didn't he notify the Sheriff's office?"

"Well, you're forgetting that he saw her before the missing persons report was filed."

"But when he heard that she was missing, why didn't he report that he had seen her? Why did he wait until now to say anything about it?"

"I can't answer that. All I know is that the employee said he saw her."

"Do you know his name?"

"No, but I'll call my friend again. And I'll call you back. But I really don't think there's any need to worry. I think she's somewhere in North Texas, trying to get her life straightened out. And I think we'll hear from her soon. She'll call us when she's ready. In the meantime, I've got to go, or I'll be late for work. I'll talk to you later. Call me if you hear anything new."

After our conversation had ended, I poured myself another cup of coffee and took it out to the patio. I sat there for probably half an hour, watching the birds and soaking up the morning sunshine. It was a beautiful morning. The birds were singing, the flowers were in bloom, and for the first time in weeks, I felt that my worries about Patricia would soon be over.

So, she had really done it, after all, I thought. She had finally gotten the courage to stand up and say that she wasn't going to take it anymore. Enough was enough. It was time to move on. Then I smiled to myself, wondering what she was doing at that very moment. Was she looking for a new job? Or perhaps she was busy straightening up a new apartment. Or she could be sitting out on a beach somewhere soaking up the morning sunshine. Who knows, she may call me today and say, "Hey, Sis, is your coffee pot on? Well, put it on because I'm on my way over to see you." Then we would sit and talk for hours and she would explain everything.

I decided to call Carol and tell her the good news. Then I planned to call Detective Adams. Maybe he knew the gas station employee. But as I was thinking about Adams, my thoughts became as dark and cloudy as ever. And try as I might, I could not shake them away. I kept hearing the same words over and over: *Trust your thoughts, Jean. Remember the oak tree last Sunday. Remember the deer lease. Remember your thoughts. Trust your thoughts. Trust your thoughts.* Suddenly my phone was ringing again, and I rushed back inside to answer it.

"I was beginning to think you weren't home," said Carol.

"Oh, yes, I'm here. I was sitting out on the patio. I was just getting ready to come in and call you. Merle called earlier with some good news about Patricia. Or perhaps I should say that it could be good news. We don't know for sure. But it sounds hopeful."

"Well, tell me your news first," Carol went on. "Because I've got a lot to tell you. And what I've learned doesn't sound all that good to me."

After I repeated to Carol everything that Merle told me, she paused for a moment without comment.

"Are you still there?" I asked.

"Yes, I'm here," she replied. "I was just wondering why the gas station attendant hasn't shared his information with anyone else. Surely, by now most everyone in the county knows Patricia is missing. And her picture has been on the news. To be honest with you, I don't know if I would believe the gas attendant's story or not. It sounds like he may be like a lot of other people about things like this. He may want others to think he knows something when actually he doesn't know what or who he's talking about. There are a lot of people like that. They talk just to hear themselves talk."

"I can agree with that," I said. "Especially since we don't even know his name. I'm also thinking that if he really had any information, he would have already turned it in. I think he would have at least mentioned it to someone other than Merle's friend."

"I think we're both at the point where we're grasping at straws. And believe me, there are people out there who will provide those straws for as long as they think we're gullible enough to believe them."

"I realize that. And that's why we've got to keep our wits about us and sort out the truth from fiction. However, I'm sure Merle believed what his friend said. And it may all be true. Merle said he would talk to him again."

"Well, I've been busy contacting everyone I can think of," Carol went on. "And I know my phone bill is going to be astronomical. But here goes: I finally got to talk to Bob Gordon. I called him at his home around ten o'clock last night. He said he knew Patricia. He is one of the deacons of the church that she attended, and he remembered her well. He spoke very highly of her. He said she had a real pretty voice and that she sometimes sang solo at the church services. He said she didn't always come to church on Sundays, but she was usually there on Wednesday nights. He said he was aware of her problems, and that he had seen her come to church with black eyes and bruises on her face. He also said that at the close of the church services, she would walk down the aisle to the altar and tell the congregation that she didn't want to live the kind of life she was living and she would ask them to pray for her.

"After Mr. Gordon told me that, I could tell by his voice that there were tears in his eyes. For he kept saying, over and over, that she was a good woman. I got the distinct impression that he thinks something has happened to her. It wasn't really anything he said. But it was just the way he said it. I don't know how to explain it. He never actually said that he thought Patricia was dead. But when he spoke of her, it was like he knew he wouldn't see her again."

"Did you ask him about the deer lease?"

"Yes, I did. But he said there were so many deer leases in that area, that it would be almost like looking for a needle in a haystack. However, he suggested that I talk to Jack Thompson. He gave me Thompson's phone number and I called him. We had an interesting conversation, and I think you should know about it."

"Who is Jack Thompson?"

"He's the ranch foreman on the Jim Pierce ranch."

"Did you ask him about the deer lease?"

"Yes, I did. He said there's a lot of deer in that area. They live in the woods and run wild. In fact there's a lot of them on the Jim Pierce ranch. He said he'd heard Lewis talk about deer hunting, but he didn't know of any special place that Lewis had leased."

"How well does Jack Thompson know Lewis?"

"I don't know. But since he is the ranch foreman, and Lewis worked on the ranch, I'd say he knew him well enough."

"Did you say Lewis 'works' there? Or he 'worked' there."

"Well, that was one of the things I wanted to tell you. Lewis was fired from the ranch, two days ago. Or rather he was laid off."

"I wonder why."

"Thompson didn't say what the reason was, nor did I ask. But after I tell you about the rest of the conversation, I think we can both read between the lines. So, hang on. Here it goes …

"I told him I was Patricia's sister, and I asked if he knew her. He said he did. He said she had come out to the ranch several times with

Lewis. Then I asked if he knew she was missing. He said he did. But he said she was gone a week before he heard about it. And that he first learned of it in town, at a Saturday night dance. He said several people at the dance asked him what he knew about it, and he told them that it was news to him. Because Lewis hadn't mentioned anything about his wife being gone. Thompson said, that on the way home from the dance, he didn't think much about it. Other than it had probably been just a domestic quarrel and that was why Lewis hadn't said anything about it. But the next day, he got to thinking about it some more. He said he didn't know why it stayed on his mind. But he got to thinking about how nervous Lewis had been during the past week. He said Lewis was late coming to work every day that week, but he knew that Lewis drank a lot, and his wife was gone, so he thought that was probably the reason for it.

"He said Lewis was an hour late to work again the next day, which was a Monday, so he decided to have a talk with him. And in the course of the conversation, he asked if it was true that Patricia had left him. Lewis told him it was, and that she had run off with another man. Thompson said there was something about the way Lewis answered that particular question, that bothered him. He said he had been around Lewis long enough to know that he was extremely jealous of her, and yet he didn't seem to be upset that she had left him for another man. But he said he figured it wasn't any of his business, so he just told Lewis to get his act together and start coming to work on time.

"However, when Thompson learned about the missing persons report, and knew the exact date of Patricia's disappearance, he started thinking again about Lewis' behavior the first two weeks she was gone.

"Thompson remembered that on the Friday before Patricia left, Lewis said he had a dental appointment the following Monday, and asked to have the day off from work. But as it turned out, he came to work on that Monday morning. And when he arrived for work, instead of parking in his usual place, he drove his car up to the big barn and parked behind it.

"Later that same day, he and Thompson drove over to another ranch to buy some hay. Thompson said that during the ride over there, Lewis seemed real nervous and that they didn't say a half dozen words to each other during the entire trip. But after they returned to the Pierce ranch, Lewis decided to wash his car at the barn. Thompson didn't explain how or why, but he said he just happened to walk upon Lewis as he was washing out the trunk of the car, and he noticed blood on the rear bumper. He asked Lewis how the blood got there, and Lewis replied that he had gone fishing over the weekend and that he had caught a lot of fish, and he had placed them in the trunk of his car. He cleaned the car thoroughly. Then every morning after that, when he came to work, he always parked his car beside the barn and locked it. Thompson knew that was unusual, and one day he asked Lewis why he had suddenly started locking his car. Lewis replied that there was something wrong with one of the door locks.

"Thompson said he had no reason not to believe Lewis, but still he wondered why Lewis insisted on locking the car every day. After all, the weather was over a hundred degrees and even hotter inside a locked car. Another thing was that, up until that week, Lewis had always parked his car down the lane, along with the other ranch employees' cars and trucks. And always before, the windows were left rolled down. Thompson said Lewis would have known that if his car doors automatically locked, he could have easily reached inside and unlocked them. And besides that, he carried his car keys in his pocket.

"Thompson said that, ordinarily he might have forgotten about Lewis' sudden interest in locking the car, but the more he thought about it the more he began to remember other things that happened during that first week Patricia was gone. He said that on Tuesday of that week, Lewis asked to go fishing in one of the creeks located a couple of miles back in the woods near the back part of the ranch. He gave Lewis permission to go, but later he started thinking about that, too. He said he remembered how Lewis had bragged about his new fishing boat. Thompson had never seen it, but Lewis said it was a fine boat. Lewis said he took it to the lake almost every weekend and he always caught a lot of fish. Thompson said he then wondered why

Lewis would want to fish in a small creek where, as far as he knew, there were no fish at all.

"Then Thompson said he got to thinking back to the days before Patricia left. He recalled that on several afternoons after work, he had drank a few beers in the barn with Lewis and some of the other ranch employees. He said Lewis liked to brag about his girlfriends.

"He said he had a couple of women that he could go to any time he wanted to. And that he had a special girlfriend who worked at the beer joint down in Singleton. During one of the conversations in the barn, someone mentioned that they had heard that Patricia had been arrested for DWI the month before. Lewis said it was true, and then he said, quote: 'them sonofabitching Laws knew they had better take her to jail before I killed her ass.' "

"Well, that was typical use of Lewis' vocabulary," I said. "But did you ask Jack Thompson if he knew about the fire at the dump?"

"Yes, I did. The dump where Lewis made the fire is on the Jim Pierce ranch. Thompson said that on or about the tenth of August, he told two employees to take a pickup load of cardboard boxes to the dump and burn them. When they got to the dump, they saw Lewis burning something. They said Lewis met them at the gate and told them to just leave the boxes and he would burn them. They said he acted nervous and told them to go on back to the barn."

"Did the two guys see what Lewis was burning?"

"No. They said they didn't get close enough to see what was burning, but that it was one heck of a fire."

"Well, Thompson was Lewis' boss. Wouldn't he have known what was burning?"

"No, not necessarily, because as I understand it, Lewis often worked back at the dump, cutting scrap metal and burning brush that the bulldozers left behind. Thompson said the bulldozers were used for clearing the land, and they also dug trenches at the dump, making it like a landfill for garbage. Then when the trenches were full, the bulldozers came back and covered them up.

"I wondered why Thompson was telling me about the bulldozers. But he recalled that it was on a Monday morning before the fire, that one of the operators complained that his bulldozer had been moved sometime during the weekend, and there was almost an hour's time on it that couldn't be accounted for."

"I think you should tell Detective Adams everything that Thompson told you," I said.

"Adams already knows about it," Carol replied. "Thompson reported it, and Adams has been out to the ranch looking around. He and Thompson went to the dump and while they were there, they found a pair of Lewis' sunglasses and a pair of pliers. I told Emil about it, and he said the pliers could have been used to start the bulldozer."

"I wonder what else they found."

"I don't know. Thompson only mentioned the pliers and the sunglasses."

"Well, I think your conversation with Thompson narrows things down to a lot more than pliers and sunglasses. And I'm now more convinced than ever that our suspicions are right on target. I'm going to call Adams and see what he says about it. But first I want to take a few minutes to think about what you've told me. I want to make sure I've got everything straight."

After the conversation with Carol was over, I spent the next hour or so thinking about it. Then I called Detective Adams.

I asked if there were any new developments on the case.

"No, ma'am, there's not," Adams answered. "Or perhaps I should say there's not any that I can talk about right now. However, we're still looking into it.

"Have you talked to your sister, Frances?"

"No, I haven't. But I know she hasn't seen or heard from Patricia. If she had, she would have told our mother about it."

"Well, I have reason to believe that your mother may know something she's not letting the rest of the family know about."

"Well, I don't know where you got that information, but I can assure you that it is not true."

"I can tell you where I got it," Adams went on. "I got it from Lewis and Patricia's daughters. They say that both Frances and your mother have covered up things before, and they're pretty upset about it."

"I think they should be upset. I think the time for them to be upset is long overdue. But I know my mother and Frances a lot better than Patricia's daughters, and to think that Mother and Frances are keeping secrets about this thing, is absolutely absurd."

"That may be true, but you have to understand my position," Adams said. "I'm down here with a missing persons report in my hand, and I have to gather and consider all information that comes in on it."

"I understand that. But there's too many things in this case that simply do not add up. Quite frankly, I think there are several people who are trying to play games with you. But I am not one of them. I told you, in our last conversation, that I think Lewis murdered Patricia, and I still think so."

"And I'm thinking the same thing, but I can't prove it. That's another reason why I want you to talk to Frances. I want you to find out what she knows."

"I thought Lewis was supposed to go to Frances' house this weekend," I said. "Maybe the daughters should go with him. Then maybe they could find out for themselves. But if they don't go, maybe one of the Law Enforcement officers in Navarro County could talk to Frances."

"I've already checked into that," Adams replied. "I've talked to them, and they're supposed to send an officer out there. But I haven't heard anything back yet. They're probably short on manpower like we are. But even if they do send someone out, Frances might not tell them everything that she would tell you."

"Well, I don't think she knows anything to tell. That's why I'm not really concerned about what she would say. But I am concerned about the missing carpet and mattress. Have you learned any more about that?"

"I know that there is a mattress missing, and part of the carpet in the house has been cut and removed."

"Have you been to the house?"

"Yes, I have. Deputy Siracusa and I went out there this week and we saw where the carpet had been removed from the hallway, and part of the living room. There was also a section removed from one of the bedrooms. However, Lewis has explained when and why the carpet was taken out. He said that he and Patricia removed the carpet the same day she disappeared. He said she wanted to make a walk-way through the house and put linoleum on it, instead of carpet. He said they worked on it together the afternoon she left. He showed me a piece of the cut out carpet and said the rest had been thrown into a garbage dumpster in Bedias. He also showed me the knives they used to cut the carpet."

"What about the missing mattress?"

"The mattress wasn't what you'd call 'missing,' " Adams replied. "It was thrown away several months ago. Lewis said he went to sleep one night smoking a cigarette, and it caught the mattress on fire. The next day, he took the mattress to the dumpster."

"So it wasn't the mattress that he was burning at the dump, on Pierce ranch."

"No, it wasn't. Not if he was telling the truth about it."

"Do you think he was lying?"

"I think that's very possible, because he's told me nine dozen different stories already. But if he's hiding anything, he'll slip up. They always do."

I wanted to tell Adams what Jack Thompson had said about the bulldozers, and about finding the pliers and sunglasses at the dump. But I chose not to, because, for all I knew, the pliers and sunglasses could be important evidence, and I didn't want Adams to think I was repeating something I wasn't suppose to know in the first place. I also knew that at that stage of the investigation, I couldn't afford to make him angry. He was my only legal connection to the case, and if he refused to talk to me, my line of legal communication would be over. And if that happened, Patricia might never be found.

"Detective Adams, have you learned any more about the fire at the dump?"

"Well, yes and no," he replied. "I went out to the dump and I found the spot where Lewis made the fire. And I searched all around it. But all I found was ashes. I also know who the two witnesses were and I talked to them. But they said they didn't get close enough to see what Lewis was burning."

As we talked on, another phone rang in his office, and he excused himself to answer it. Then I heard a rustling noise in the background which sounded like papers being shuffled from one place to another on his desk. He was obviously very busy. The thought crossed my mind that I should hang up and call back later. But then I knew that would be the worst thing I could do. So, I waited.

"Sorry to keep you waiting," he said, picking up the phone again. "I'm going to have to cut our conversation short for now. I have some other business I need to take care of."

"That's quite allright," I replied. "I understand. But before you go, can you tell me if Patricia's prescription for her diet pills has been refilled?"

"No, it has not."

"Has her paycheck been picked up?"

"No. It's still at the restaurant where she worked."

"And one last question. Have you located either Charles Lancaster or the guy named Bill?"

"No. We haven't been able to find out anything about the guy named Bill. But we believe old Charlie is still somewhere in the Wichita Falls area. We're still trying to locate him. And I think when we find him, we'll find Patricia."

As we ended the conversation, I thanked him for his time and said I hoped he was right in thinking Patricia had left with another man.

Oh, how I hoped he was right, I thought. Never mind the moral concept of it. I was tired of being wrought with worry. The most important thing now, was to know that she had really left on her own, and she was alive and well.

CHAPTER 11

I poured a cup of cold coffee and set it in the microwave to heat. Then I went to my desk and took out the folder which held the notes that I had jotted down pertaining to the investigation. I had always been somewhat of a pack rat, keeping notes about anything and everything I thought to be important.

I first began writing notes about Patricia's disappearance the day Tammie called to tell me she was missing. Since then, I had jotted down names, dates and places. Who I talked to, and what they said. Questions I had asked, and the answers I received. I spent hours reading the notes over and over, hoping to find something that would bring the pieces of the puzzle into focus. Something I could see. Something I could put my finger on. But regardless of my long late night endeavors in reading them, and no matter how many times I read them, my thoughts always went back to page one. Page one. Square one. The day she left. The key to the mystery had to be there.

I thought about my earlier conversation with Adams, and what he said about the missing carpet. The part that was most clear in my mind was the part where he said Lewis told him that both he and Patricia had removed the carpet, and that they removed it the same afternoon she left. He indicated that Patricia was with him when they took the cut carpet to the dumpster.

I remembered Patty Lynn had said that she came to the house that Sunday to visit Patricia. Patricia was not home, but Patty Lynn talked to Kimberly who was in the yard raking leaves. Kimberly said Patricia and Lewis had gone to Navasota to look at some hay for the ranch. Patty was not at the house when they returned. However, they did return, together. Then they took Kimberly to Tammie's house. They arrived there somewhere between one and three o'clock in the afternoon. They visited with Tammie, her husband Garvin, and their children. Before that, they had left Jennifer with Rhonda to spend the night with Rhonda's daughter. After they visited Tammie, they went to Fred's place for the turkey shoot that began around four o'clock.Shortly after they arrived there, Patricia became ill. Then, an hour or so later, Lewis drove them home. He said Patricia was sick and that she lay her head in his lap on the way home. Then after they arrived home, they argued and Patricia left.

I read those words over and over, studying the events of that Sunday, until they became imprinted in my memory. I had studied the time of day, hour by hour, that each of them supposedly had happened. Also, I was reasonably familiar with that part of Texas, and I knew the approximate distances between the towns in that area. I considered the time it would have taken to drive to and from Bedias and Tammie's house, and to Fred's place, and the time that was spent there. But it didn't add up. It couldn't. After all, there are just so many hours in an afternoon. And it was obvious that Lewis and Patricia had spent the afternoon driving to and from their daughters' homes, and at Fred's place. There had not been time to stay home and cut carpet for a walkway through the house. Lewis had said the carpet was cut in the afternoon and also hauled to the dumpster. Surely he had not meant to say the carpet had been cut in the morning. Kimberly was there and she knew it was not. So, the cold fact was that when Lewis said that he and Patricia cut the carpet on that Sunday afternoon, he was lying. Lying through his teeth, hoping everyone would believe him.

There was no getting around it, over it, or under it. I thought Lewis was lying when he said Patricia had helped him cut the carpet and haul it away the same afternoon she disappeared. How could she have helped him? By his own admission, he had said that she was sick when they arrived home, and that she had immediately gone to bed. Then they had had an argument and she left. All of which supposedly had taken place in less than two hours. So, how could there have been time to cut carpet and dispose of it?

I could understand why she may have wanted to make a walkway of tile or linoleum near the living room door and throughout the hallway. But what bothered me was the fact that part of her bedroom carpet had also been cut and removed. The bedroom was small, measuring approximately eleven by fourteen feet, and in it there were two beds, a dresser, a chest of drawers, and a closet. All of which made the room crowded. Therefore, part of the bedroom furniture would have had to have been removed before cutting the carpet. That alone would have taken time. Even if she had helped him. But he had said that she was ill, and in bed. So, how could she have helped him?

Besides all of that, going back to when the missing persons report was filed, why didn't Lewis mention the carpet in his first interview with Adams? When Adams asked him to recall the day of Patricia's disappearance, the places they went and what they did up until the time she left, Lewis was very cooperative. He had explained the events of that day, hour by hour, without hesitation. So, if he wasn't lying, why didn't he mention the hours he had spent moving furniture, cutting out carpet, and hauling it to the dumpster?

I gathered my notes, placed them inside the folder and put them back in the desk drawer. And while the drawer was open, I noticed a calendar mixed in with some other papers. It was a sportsman's calendar with pictures of fish and fishermen on it. Richard had ordered it through the mail, but evidently when it came, I had misplaced it and it had ended up in my desk drawer.

I took it out and leafed through it, turning it to the page that said August. Well, next week will be the beginning of September, I thought. At least he would have the use of it for four months. And that was better than nothing.

It was a nice calendar. Most of the pictures in it were of older men sitting in boats or on river banks with their fishing lines in the water. But one picture was that of an old gentleman baiting his line, getting ready for a big catch.

It reminded me of the time I had insisted upon going fishing with Daddy and Grandpa, back when I was around the age of seven. I knew they didn't want me to go, and Daddy said I wouldn't like it, but after I cried a while, Grandmother told them to take me anyway.

The ride down to the river was fine, but after we arrived there, and I watched Daddy and Grandpa bait their fishing lines, I decided very quickly that I would never be a fisherwoman. The can of bait smelled terrible and I refused to sit near it. I got up holding my nose and walked a short distance away. Then as I stood there watching, I reminded Grandpa of the time he baited a trap to catch the animal that had killed one of Grandmother's prize chickens. The bait he'd used then didn't smell that bad, I told him.

"That's because I don't use the same kind of bait for fishing that I use in the traps," he chuckled. "You see, there's all kinds of bait. And it's important to know the right kind to use. But first of all, you have to decide what it is that you're wanting to catch. And then you decide on what kind of bait to use."

Oh, Grandpa, how I wish you were with me now, I thought. You were probably the most intelligent man I ever knew. And you would know what to do now, too. I know you would.

I closed the desk drawer and turned off the lamp, and left the room. On my way to the kitchen to start dinner, I placed the calendar on the dining table so I wouldn't forget to give it to Richard.

However, as I cooked dinner, I continued thinking of Grandpa and our long ago memories. And as I thought of fishing bait, I developed another idea. One which Grandpa might have referred to as 'another kind of bait.'

Later that night, I called Mother. It had been a while since I talked to her and I was curious to know if she had heard from Patricia.

"No, I still haven't heard a word from her," said Mother. "I keep thinking she'll call, or at least write to me. She's got everybody just worried sick about her. I just don't know what to think about it anymore."

"Have you talked to Frances lately?" I asked.

"No, I have not," she replied. "And I'm tired of everybody thinking that Frances knows anything about it. I can't count the times Frances has cried and told me that if she knew where Patricia was, she would tell me. You know Frances has a heart condition, and her worrying about Patricia is not helping matters. Darlene has already had to take her back to the doctor again."

"Well, is Frances allright now?"

"I think so. But she doesn't need any more stress."

"I wonder if Lewis has been out to her house yet. I hope that didn't upset her."

"No, he hasn't gone out there yet. He says he's going this weekend."

"Mother, have you heard anything about any carpet missing from Patricia's house? Or anything about a mattress being gone?"

"Where did you hear that?" she asked.

" I can't remember exactly," I lied. "It could have been just a little rumor going around. You know how people talk. I thought you may have heard it."

"Yes, I've heard about it," she went on. "And I think it's just a story somebody's got going around. Now, I do know that there has been some carpet removed from the house, but from what I understand, Lewis and Patricia took it out before she left. In fact they did it the same day she left. As for the mattress, Lewis said there never was another mattress."

"Well, I wonder how the mattress got into the story," I said, calmly.

"I have no idea."

"Have you talked to the girls lately?"

"Oh, yes. We talk almost every day. And they are really getting put out with the Sheriff's Department in Grimes County."

"Really? Why would they be upset with the Sheriff's Department?"

"Tammie doesn't believe the Law over there is even looking for Patricia. She says all they're doing is asking a lot of questions. She said that Lewis has gone down to the Sheriff's office several times and given them leads as to where Patricia might be. But evidently they're not following up on them."

"Really? What kind of leads?"

"Well, someone said they saw Patricia working in a grocery store in Ennis, Texas. This person said that Patricia had dyed her hair, but she was recognized anyway."

"Mother, Ennis is not far from Corsicana. And if Patricia was that close to Frances, she would certainly have contacted her. Do you know who saw Patricia in the store? And did this person talk to her?"

"I don't know who saw her. I've told you all I know about it. However, I also heard that the Grimes County Law set up an appointment for Virginia to come in and talk to them. But Virginia didn't keep the appointment."

"Have you talked to Rhonda lately?"

"No, I haven't. In fact, I haven't talked to her since Patricia left."

"Well, I thought surely you would have heard from her. Didn't you once tell me that Rhonda was the most vocal one of the girls?"

"She is. And I thought she would have called. But I guess she's just busy."

"I can understand that," I went on. "And I can imagine the hurt and worry that all of the girls must be feeling."

"Well, they are all hurt and worried sick about this thing. I talked to Tammie yesterday, and she said that if the Sheriff's Department didn't hurry up and find Patricia, she's going to call the Texas State Troopers."

I thought Mother had meant to say 'Texas Rangers' rather than 'State Troopers,' and for an instant, I thought about telling her that the Texas Rangers probably already knew about the case. But instead, I chose not to comment about it, one way or the other. For I wanted her to think that I knew nothing at all about the case, other than what I learned from her. I had my reasons for feeling that way, and in the dark recesses of my mind, I knew they were good reasons, having to do with my own safety as well as with Carol's.

"Mother, this thing is very hard on the entire family," I said. "Most especially the girls. I'm sure it's rough on Lewis, too. He probably sits and grieves a lot, but at least his work keeps him busy during the day. By the way, does he still work at the Jim Pierce ranch?"

"Yes, I think so. But now there's talk that he may be leaving soon to take another job somewhere in northeast Texas. Or he may go to Louisiana. He's got relatives there."

"Oh, surely he wouldn't leave the girls to worry about him, too."

"Well, I don't know. He might, because he's really disgusted with the Grimes County Law. They've asked him a lot of questions and he says he has already told them everything he knows. But he thinks they're still watching him."

"But Mother, he could put an end to that. All he'd have to do is tell the Sheriff that he wanted to take a polygraph test."

"Isn't that the same thing as a lie detector test?"

"Well, yes, some people call it that. But it's nothing to be afraid of. It's really a very simple test, and people take them all the time. In fact, I used to take one every six months. It was one of my job requirements."

"I never knew that."

"Well sure I did. And polygraph tests are very painless. You just sit in a chair and answer questions. The questions are simple, too. The polygraph examiner will ask questions like, 'what day is it, and when is your birthday, and are you married, and how old you are.' Things like that."

"Then why are they called lie detector tests?"

"Because they can tell certain things about a person."

"You mean if Lewis lied about anything, they would know it."

"Well, maybe. But put it like this: They're not going to care if he stole an apple when he was ten years old. Or even if he stole a six pack of beer when he was older. The point is that he should take the test. He should take it not only for himself, but also for the girls, and for you and Daddy, as well as the rest of the family. And it could help the Sheriff's Office in their investigation."

"And if he took it, they might leave him alone and start looking elsewhere," Mother chimed. "You know, that sounds like a good idea. I think I'll call Tammie, in the morning, and talk to her about it."

"Oh, I definitely think you should. But Mother, just between you and me, please don't tell her that I mentioned it."

"Okay. But are you sure that taking a polygraph test is all that easy?"

"They're very easy. Now, I've got to go. I'll call you again in a few days." Then I hung up the phone, and remembered again what Grandpa said about bait.

After my conversation with Mother was over, I walked out to the patio and sat with Richard. He asked what Mother and I had talked about, and I told him.

"If Lewis is as innocent as he says he is, he should have already taken a polygraph test," I said.

"You must be joking," Richard replied.

"No, I'm not joking. I'm serious as I can be!"

"Well, I'll bet he doesn't take it!"

"Why shouldn't he take it?" I went on. "He says he's innocent, and he says he's told the Sheriff's Department everything he knows about Patricia's disappearance. He's even gone to the Sheriff's office and given them leads to follow up on. Of course I think he's lying. I just want him to make a legitimate effort to prove that he's not. That's why I'm hoping he'll take the test. Why are you so sure that he won't take it?"

"He's not going to take it because he's a liar. And he's a thief. He may be innocent in this thing about Patricia. Which I don't think he is. But even if he is, he's still a liar and a thief, and he's not about to get on some polygraph machine and admit it."

"Okay. But how do you know he's a thief?"

"Why hell, I've known that for years. I imagine all the men in your family knew it. But we knew it only because Lewis told us about it. Hell, we didn't even like to listen to him. And we'd get up and walk off because we didn't want to hear his crap. But every time he was around us, he'd start it. He liked to brag about it. Like he thought it made him tough."

"Was it any one certain thing that he stole?" I asked.

Richard paused for a moment and then continued.

"Look, he was married to your sister for, how long, twenty-six years? Well, during those years, I saw him probably twenty times, at the most. And each time was always like the one before. He and Patricia would come to your mother's. They would walk in and say hello to everybody, then Patricia would stay in the house and visit with the womenfolk, and Lewis would go out to his car and get a six pack of beer. Then he'd come around to the back yard and sit and talk with the men until dinner was ready. Then after dinner, the men would go back outside until it was time to leave. Now, it was during those times that Lewis did his bragging. And he bragged about other things, too. For instance, his love affairs."

"Love affairs? You never said anything to me about them!"

"Well if I had, you might have told Patricia, and then he would have given her another beating just for knowing about it. But believe me, he had his love affairs and he liked to brag about them. In fact, the last time I saw him, I think it was Thanksgiving 1985, he was bragging about another new girlfriend. He said she was an Oriental girl. He tried telling me and Emil about her. And I said, 'God damn Lewis, when are you going to stop that crap?' Then Emil and I turned around and walked off."

"Then I guess that's why you didn't act surprised when I told you that Jack Thompson said Lewis bragged about his girlfriends."

"If I had talked to Thompson, I'd have told him to check his ranch inventory."

Two days later, I called Mother again. I thought that by now she had had time to mention the polygraph test to the girls, and I was curious to know what they thought about it. And I was more curious to know what Lewis thought about it. And as things turned out, I quickly received an answer without even realizing it. It was an indirect answer, of sorts. But it was still an answer. And it hit me like a bombshell. The hell of it was that it hit my mother, too.

I could tell she was excited when she answered the phone. So, I immediately asked if she had heard from Patricia.

"Yes, I have," she said, excitedly. "And I've been trying to call you, so I could tell you about it."

"Tell me what, Mother?"

"Patricia has been found. She's in a hospital somewhere in Dallas."

"Slow down a minute, Mother. Now tell me what hospital she's in, so I'll know where to find it. I can be there in thirty minutes."

"I don't know the name of the hospital. All I know is that it's in Dallas."

"Do you know why she's in the hospital? Do you know what's

wrong with her?"

"Well, I was told she was found somewhere, and she was suffering from exposure. She was taken to a hospital and now she's in a coma. But she woke up once, just long enough to give the nurse a phone number to call."

"And whose phone number did she give?"

"It was Dottie's. Lewis' sister."

"Was Dottie the person who contacted you about it?"

"No, I haven't talked to Dottie yet. Elena was the one who told me about it."

"Who is Elena?" I asked.

"She works at a cafe in town, the old hamburger place," Mother replied. "One of Lewis' cousins just happened to eat there last night, and he told her about Patricia being in the hospital. Then she came by, on her way home from work, and told me about it."

"Have you talked to the girls?"

"Yes, I talked to Tammie, this morning."

"Do you know if they're coming up to be with Patricia? Tell them I said they're welcome to stay at my house as long as they like. And we can go back and forth to the hospital together."

"I'll tell them. But I don't know yet, whether they'll go or not."

"Of course they'll come up. Patricia is their mother. And Lewis will probably show up too. Now, I'm going to go, so I can start calling the hospitals. My guess is that she's in Parkland. I'll call you as soon as I find her."

And that was the beginning of two days of hell, as I stayed on the phone continually searching one hospital after another throughout the Dallas area, seeking information about Patricia. I sought information on anyone and everyone named Patricia, as well as information on any unidentified patients. And each time, I explained to the hospital receptionist, the date of Patricia's disappearance, where she had disappeared from, her age and physical description. But the replies were all the same: 'I'm sorry ma'am, we don't show that we have a patient by that name, or anyone fitting that description. No ma'am, we don't have any unidentified patients. Perhaps if you call one of the other hospitals.'

I was still checking the list of hospital phone numbers, crossing off those I had already called and putting check marks by the remaining numbers that I intended to call, when suddenly the phone rang. I answered it immediately, thinking it was one of the hospitals calling back, but instead, it was Carol.

"Have you heard that Patricia is supposed to be in a hospital, somewhere in Dallas?" she asked.

"Yes, and I've been calling some of the hospitals, trying to find her. I was just getting ready to call some more."

"Well, I think we should talk about it before we get our hopes up. I just got through talking to Mother. I don't know what all she told you, but I'm inclined to think that there's something fishy going on."

"What do you mean by that?"

"I just think it's kind of strange that neither Lewis nor the girls have left yet to go to Dallas. And knowing them as I do, I know that if they really thought Patricia was there in a hospital, they would have already gone. As soon as Mother told me about it, I was prepared to take off work and come up. But the more we talked about it, the more evasive Mother became. And that set me wondering just how much truth there is in it."

"Well, at Mother's age, she could very possibly have been confused," I said. "But I know she wouldn't have just made up the story. She said that a woman named Elena came to the house and told her about it."

"But did she tell you who told it to Elena?" Carol asked.

"Yes. She said it was one of Lewis' cousins."

"She told me that, too," Carol went on. "And I know the cousin she was talking about. His name is Lenny Compton, and I wouldn't trust that jerk as far as I could throw him."

"Well, anyone who would deliberately make up a story like that must have a hell of a sick mind," I replied.

"There's no telling what else they're capable of doing," Carol went on.

"Or covering up," I added. "Which leads me to think that if he made it up, he either suspects something or he knows something he's not telling. Maybe it was meant to distract our attention so we would forget about the polygraph test."

"That's possible. Who knows what goes on in the minds of people like that."

"But he could have been telling the truth. We don't know that he wasn't."

"Well, why don't you call Mother again," Carol went on. "It might save you some time making phone calls to the hospitals. Then let me know what you find out."

I called Mother again. However, keeping her age in mind and remembering her excitement during our last conversation, I wanted to avoid upsetting her any further. I calmly explained to her that I had called several hospitals, and that I had been unable to find Patricia. But that I would keep trying. Then suddenly, in the split second that I waited for Mother's response, I realized that Lewis and the girls surely must have known about Patricia being in a hospital before Elena and Lenny knew it. And if the story was true, they would have called Mother and told her, instead of letting her hear it from a woman she hardly knew. And at that point, I decided it was time for more questions.

"Mother, have you talked to Dottie yet?"

"No, not yet."

"Well, it seems to me that since she was the one the hospital called, she would have called you. She doesn't live very far from you, does she? And another thing, the person who called her would surely have told her which hospital Patricia is in. That would be the first thing they would say. And why would Patricia give Dottie's phone number to the hospital, instead of yours or Tammie's. Or if she knew she was in Dallas, she could have given mine."

"I don't know why she didn't," Mother said. "And I've told you all I know about it."

"Well, have you heard the name 'Parkland' mentioned? It's the Dallas County hospital. I've called there once, but I could call again."

"Patricia wouldn't need to go to a county hospital," Mother replied. "She has her own insurance. She has hospital insurance and life insurance."

"I know, Mother. That's not what I'm implying. It's just that you said she was found suffering from exposure and in a coma, and if that were true, she would have first been taken to Parkland. I've heard that it's a good hospital."

"Well, I think she probably checked herself into a hospital, to get away from everybody. Some people do that, you know."

"But Mother, if her condition was as it was described to you, there's no way she could have checked herself into a hospital. Think about this: if she had checked herself in, she would have had her insurance card with her, and her social security card. She would have had to have some identification."

"Well, I'm sure she did have identification," Mother went on. "She had her purse with her when she left. I think she's up there in a hospital trying to get some rest, and I think maybe she doesn't want Lewis to know where she is."

"Mother, Patricia was no fool. She would know that the quickest way for Lewis to learn her whereabouts would be to tell Dottie."

It was obvious that Mother did not appreciate my choice remarks on the matter, and she paused for a few seconds as though trying to decide whether to hang up on me or continue the conversation. But at the moment, I didn't care. I was tired of the games. I was tired of people playing sick games with my parents, then trying to play those same games with me at my parents' expense. I was tired of playing detective, trying to solve what was supposed to be a mystery. As far as I was concerned, there was no mystery. For everything that had happened and everything that had been said always went back to square one. Lewis Crocker was the answer to the whole damn thing, and he was still buying time. And playing games.

"Mother, how does Daddy feel about what's going on?" I said angrily.

"He doesn't talk much about it. He just sits in his chair and grieves. He says Lewis knows where Patricia is. And that she's right where he left her."

"Well, tell me exactly what you think has happened to her. Do you think she's in a hospital, or not?"

"I don't know. I've been thinking about it and I just don't know. But I think that wherever she is, she wants to be left alone."

"You may be right, Mother," I lied. I was too tired to say anything else.

I decided that in light of the fact that the girls were still at home and, as far as I knew, had made no attempt to contact anyone in Dallas, they evidently knew more about the story than Mother did. Therefore, my next call was to Tammie.

I asked if she knew the name of the hospital Patricia was in, and if she had heard any more from her.

"Oh, Aunt Jean, that was all a lie," she said. "Aunt Dottie never received any such call. It was just a stupid lie that one of my cousins made up."

"But why would anyone make up a story like that?"

"Because he's stupid, that's why. He's just plain stupid. You can't believe anything he says. He lies all the time."

I paused for a moment absorbing her words. I felt like screaming in red hot anger. I had never met Lenny Compton, but I thought that anyone who would fabricate such a heinous story and tell it for the truth, must surely suffer from a severe emotional disorder. And because of that, I vowed to refuse him the pathetic satisfaction of knowing the pain he had caused. I would not honor his lie by continuing to discuss it with Tammie.

"Oh, by the way, I talked to Aunt Carol today," I said, still trying to regain my composure. "And I also talked to Grandmother. They're doing fine. But of course they're still worried about your mother, and I am, too."

"I know," Tammie replied. "We are, too. But we still haven't heard from her."

"Has your dad gone out to Aunt Frances' yet?"

"No, he hasn't. But I think he's going to go tonight. He said he was."

"Will you be going with him?" I asked.

"No. He said he was going out there kind of late tonight. He said he wants to check out the bars in several little towns around there, and see if he can find Mama with her boyfriend."

"But he's definitely going to Frances' house, isn't he?"

"Oh, yes. But he probably won't stay long. He said he was coming back home tonight."

"Well, I hope you'll let me know what he finds out."

"Oh, I will. And you never know, he might even bring Mama home with him."

After that, our conversation ended and I sat down to think about it. I couldn't help wondering why Lenny Compton had made up such an atrocious lie. What could possibly have been going through his mind? Carol had known him from school, so evidently he was an adult. But what were his reasons for the lie, and did someone else help plant the idea in his mind? Did he know something about Patricia's disappearance? Could he have been one of the two boys at the gas station in Madisonville that Aunt Margaret talked about? She said the boys had suddenly started avoiding her when she drove in for gas, and she had been suspicious of them. And she had heard that they lived somewhere around Bedias. That would certainly put them in Lewis' 'territory,' as he liked to call it. And the fact that Lewis and Lenny were cousins, Lenny probably knew almost everything that happened the day Patricia disappeared. In fact, as devious as he was, he might know everything about it. And if he knew everything about it, and he was helping to cover it up, that could very well be his reason for the lie.

As for Elena, I thought she was as innocent as Mother. For her role had been only that of a friend trying to help another friend. I could imagine her anxiously waiting for the restaurant to close that night, and then hurrying across town to Mother's house, not knowing that the message she carried was a lie. But after all, it was not the kind of story one would have wanted to tell over the phone. Especially not to a friend who was of the age of seventy-seven.

But more than that, I wondered if someone else had come to the restaurant with Lenny, that night. Someone Elena had not recognized, but someone who was equally as devious as Lenny and, over plates of hamburgers and greasy French fries, had helped him fabricate the lie. Someone who, in my opinion, had a lot to hide, and Lenny knew it.

I wondered if Adams had heard Lenny's story, and I shuddered to think what would happen to the case if he heard it and believed it. Mother had previously mentioned that Lewis was keeping in touch with the Sheriff's Office. Now, it was easy to imagine Lewis walking into Adams' office, telling him that Patricia was in a hospital in Dallas. And Adams saying something like: 'Well, if you're sure she's in a hospital, I guess that means she's been found, and I guess it wraps up the missing persons report.'

But surely Adams wouldn't believe such a jumbled up story, I thought. He's an experienced investigator; he would see through it in a minute. And even if he half-way believed it, he'd check it out before closing the case. After all, he knew Lewis had lied to him before. And there were still the suspicions about the carpet, the missing mattress and the fire.

CHAPTER 12

Sleep had become more difficult for me, and again that night, my sleep was restless. Half awake, half asleep, my thoughts continued to ramble as I kept remembering all that I had learned about Patricia's disappearance. I thought of everyone I had talked to and the conversations that transpired with them. And then there was the dream that never seemed to leave me. It never changed. It was the same as when I had first dreamed it, thirteen years before. In the dream, once more I would walk across the manicured lawn at the J. M. Day Funeral Home in Madisonville. Then I would walk up the steps and across the gray painted porch, and enter into the foyer. From there, I saw a large room of empty chairs lined neatly close together, waiting to receive the crowd of mourners. But I was alone as I walked toward the casket and stood there crying, looking down upon it. The casket was closed and a large wreath of white and yellow flowers covered it. It was Patricia's casket, and my tears fell upon the flowers. They were angry tears. Bitter tears. And, once again, the unknown voice would tell me the name of her murderer, and say: "But the Law's have him now."

Oh, the dream. The horrible dream. How many times, I had recalled that dream. But tonight there was, later, another dream. One in which I was a child again. And, as the dream began, another little girl was with me and we were running in darkness along a dusty dirt road. There were long deep ruts in the road, but we held hands and skipped over them and ran on for miles until suddenly the dark night became even darker, and I tripped and fell. I called for the child to wait, but she didn't realize that I had fallen, and she kept running to wherever it was that we were going. I was trying to save her from the darkness. And in the distance, I could hear her calling back to me.

"Hurry before it's too late," she called. "Hurry before it's too late."

I called for her to wait for me, for I could no longer determine the direction her voice was coming from. Then I continued running for what seemed like miles, searching for her, answering her each time she called. And although the night was black, somehow I knew there were thick woods at the end of the road. As I ran, I called out to her again, telling her to stay away from the trees, and to wait on the road so I could find her. Then finally, I thought I saw her standing on the road waiting for me, and I ran toward her, telling her not to be afraid of the dark, that I was there with her and I would protect her. Then as I came closer to her, I noticed that she appeared to be about the age of seven, with long curly brown hair, and that she was wearing a pink organdy dress with white flowers on it. I recognized the dress as one I had given Patricia back when she was in second grade. The dress had been too delicate to wear except for church or on special occasions. And I wondered why the child whom I was now trying to reach would be wearing it. Then I realized that the child in the dream was Patricia, and that we were both young children again. I wondered why we had been running on the road after dark and why she was standing there near the trees, so lost and afraid, waiting for me. Then, for a fleeting moment, she turned toward me holding her left hand out to me. And I ran toward her, desperately trying to reach her. But as I reached out to touch her, the trees swirled angrily around us until we were both engulfed in total darkness and she was gone.

Still her words lingered with me. "Hurry before it's too late. Hurry before it's too late."

I awoke from the dream, then lay in bed a few moments longer wondering what it meant. Perhaps for all intents and purposes it had meant nothing at all, other than the fact that Patricia was lost and I was wanting so desperately to find her. Still I wondered about the trees in the dream and the darkness of the long deep rutted road. I lay there trying to remember the dream more clearly, trying to remember what the danger was that had been waiting for her in the trees, and whether the trees could have been on a deer lease at the end of the road. But as I got out of bed still thinking about it, the message behind the words frightened me most of all. "Hurry before it's too late. Hurry before it's too late."

I got up and made coffee, then went into the den and opened the blinds on the door leading to the patio. Then in the half light, half darkness of the morning, I stood there watching a soft rain sending leaves gently fluttering to the ground. It was the first hint of Autumn and I welcomed the change in seasons. But my depression deepened even further as I thought of Autumn coming and going, for then there would be Winter, and after that the seasons could go on forever without my knowing what had happened to Patricia.

"Hurry before it's too late. Hurry before it's too late." The words seemed more clear now than in the dream. I caught myself whispering them aloud, and for a fleeting moment I imagined Patricia's presence beside me. I thought she looked at me and smiled. I reached for her hand and we stood there together, warm and safe. I was completely absorbed by the tranquillity of those few seconds for they seemed so real. In my mind there was no doubt that we were together in spirit, whether we were as children at play or as adult sisters watching a morning rain. Then suddenly, as quickly as it came, the moment was gone and she was gone, and I was forced back into reality.

I walked back into the kitchen and made buttered toast to have with the coffee, then returned again to the den to sit and watch the rain. The rain was heavier now and I watched as it blew leaves and small tree limbs across the yard. It was a lonesome kind of morning. One that was made for curling up on a sofa with a good book, or maybe catching up on a year's worth of mending. A day for trying out new recipes in the kitchen or straightening clothes closets. Those were a few of the things I ordinarily did on days such as this. But now they seemed of no consequence whatever. For I could only think of Patricia and the words she had called to me in the dream.

"Hurry before it's too late. Hurry before it's too late." Oh how I prayed that somewhere, someone would find her before it was too late. I wondered if fate intended that I play a part in it, and if so, what part would it be. I had neither the strength nor the authority to set out roaming the woods, looking for a long deep rutted road. And besides that, I could not completely dismiss the thought that perhaps she was indeed with Charlie Lancaster, or Bill, or Benny, or someone else. Everyone has dreams, I reminded myself. Bad dreams, happy dreams, ridiculous dreams. I could not base my feelings on dreams.

I decided to call Detective Adams again that morning and see if there was any news on the case, and to ask if he had heard Lenny's lie.

"Yes ma'am, I have been informed that Patricia is supposed to be in a hospital somewhere around Dallas," he said. "And I am in the process of trying to verify it."

"May I ask who gave you that information?"

"It was Lewis. I believe one of his relatives received a phone call about it."

"Well I've heard the same story and I've spent the past two days calling the hospitals and clinics here in Dallas. Then when I called Tammie, trying to get more information on it, she said the whole thing was a lie. She said there never was a call to that effect, and that one of her cousins, Lenny Compton, had made the whole thing up."

"Well, I suspected it might be something like that, because Lewis acted real nervous when he told me about it and, as far as I know, none of her family ever left to go see about her. I thought that was rather strange. But still it's my job to check out any leads that come in, so that was what I was doing."

"Detective Adams, I want to ask your opinion about Lewis. Do you think he's really concerned about finding Patricia?"

"He seems to be. He's been down here several times wanting to know if we've come up with anything new."

"Okay. Now I'd like to ask you another question. Do you think he's coming to your office to ask you what you know, or to find out just how much you know?"

"That's a good question. In fact my boss and I were talking about that this morning."

"The way I see it, this thing could drag on forever with Lewis playing his little mind games," I said. "I'm telling you I think he has killed her and I think he's counting on his little games to keep you on any kind of wild goose chase that he can think of. And my family and I are damn tired of it. We want him to take a polygraph test because everything that has happened points to the direction of murder."

"And, I've told you before, I'm thinking the same thing you are about that," replied Adams. "But I don't have the evidence to prove it."

"What about the cut out carpet? And the missing mattress? How and when was there time enough on the Sunday of Patricia's disappearance for her and Lewis to cut carpet and dispose of it before she left? Remember they spent most of that day with family and friends before they went to Fred's place, and within two hours after they left Fred's, they engaged in a heated argument and Patricia supposedly just walked off into the night. Besides that, what about the blood in the house?"

"Ma'am, I am telling you that I think he killed her," Adams went on. "But I'm also thinking that when she left, he may have followed her and took her somewhere else to do it. Because I didn't notice any blood in the house when I first went out there to investigate. But I can't say that there wasn't any there when she left. You know she was gone over a week before the missing persons report was filed. That would have given him plenty of time to clean up the blood and paint the whole house if he had wanted to. In fact the back bedroom, which was Lewis and Patricia's bedroom, looked as though it had recently been repainted. But I don't know whether it was done before or after she left, and if I had asked Lewis, he probably wouldn't have told me the truth about it anyway."

"Is there any way that you can get him to take a polygraph test?"

"He has been given the opportunity to take a polygraph, and he has consented to do so. And I am hoping that he will. But if he refuses to take it, there's nothing I can do about it. Because the law says that he cannot be forced to take it if he doesn't want to."

"Do you know when he plans to take the polygraph test?"

"It will be just as soon as I can get it set up. I don't want just anybody giving it to him. The polygraph examiner that I have in mind is one of the best in the state of Texas, and I want him to give the test. His name is Hylton Kennedy, and his office is in Houston. I've already talked to him and we expect to meet with him in a few days."

"Well, I am relieved that Lewis has consented to take it. And I hope and pray for our family's sake as well as for his, that he passes the test with flying colors. At least, if he passes it, it will narrow the investigation and turn it to a different direction."

"That's precisely what I'm thinking," Adams went on. "By the way, have you talked to Frances yet?"

"No, I haven't," I replied. "But I promise you, I will talk to her next week. Regardless of the outcome of Lewis' polygraph test."

"I'd appreciate that," Adams said. "And I want you to let me know what you find out."

"I will. But I just remembered something. I forgot to tell you that Lewis was supposed to have gone to see Frances this weekend. You might ask him what he learned while he was there. However, I suspect that him going out there was just another of his schemes to throw suspicion in another direction."

"Do you really believe that?"

"Yes, I do. And I'm afraid that after he has used up all of his little schemes, or whatever you want to call them, he will then get up and leave the country. That's another reason why I feel that time is so important."

"Well, try not to worry any more than you have to," Adams went on. "I know it's tough on you and it's tough on everyone who is involved in it, but remember that I'm going to do everything I can to solve this case. And as for Lewis leaving the country, don't worry, we know everything he does, every day. Now you just try to take it easy. But don't forget to have that visit with Frances. And report back to me."

In looking back, the next few days seemed to blend in memory, each one disappearing almost as quickly as it began. But on one of those mornings, I awoke with the overwhelming feeling that the case would soon come down like a bombshell, and I lay there thinking of the sadness it would bring when it finally lay open for all the world to see. I suspected that the polygraph test would be the beginning of the end of it. And I shuddered as I thought of how we would cope with the reality of the evil of it all.

The following Thursday morning I received another phone call from Carol. One that would confirm my suspicions that the case would soon be coming down. However, I was unprepared for the direction it would take before it finally crumbled.

"Sis, I have some news for you," she said anxiously. "So, sit down and listen carefully."

"Are you all right?" You sound like you're out of breath."

"I'm okay," she replied. "I'm just nervous and very upset."

"It's something about Patricia, isn't it? Has someone found her?"

"No, not yet. But just a few moments ago, I had a call from Mother. Lewis is in a hospital in Bryan. Mother said he tried to commit suicide."

"When did it happen? Have you talked to the girls about it?"

"No, I haven't talked to the girls, but from what Mother said, it must have happened a couple of days ago. She said Lewis had had an appointment to meet with Detective Adams and a Texas Ranger at the Sheriff's office in Anderson, and they were to drive him to Houston to take a polygraph test. However, he failed to show up at the Sheriff's office and later that morning, one of the girls called Adams and asked him to come out to the house. She told Adams that she suspected that Lewis had taken some pills and he was refusing to leave his bedroom, and that he was nervous and acting very strange. She also said that Lewis had written several notes and had placed them in a dresser drawer."

"I'd like to know what he wrote in those notes," I replied. "I'll bet it was something about Patricia."

"Oh, he probably did write something about her," Carol went on. "But now I think I should tell you what I did after I got through talking to Mother."

"I thought you said you talked to her only a few moments ago," I replied.

"Well, actually it was closer to an hour. And I did it just to see what his reaction would be."

"What are you talking about?"

"I called the hospital in Bryan, and I talked to Lewis."

"Is he all right?"

"He's fine. But I want to tell you about my conversation with him."

"Okay, I'm listening."

"Well, when he answered the phone, I told him who I was, and I asked how he was feeling. And he said something about his knee, and that his lip was numb. Then before I could say anything else, he said, 'Now, Carol, I didn't hurt that girl,' meaning Patricia. Then I told him that we were all so worried about her. And he said, 'Well, she's changed a lot since you saw her. She got to where she wouldn't eat. She was all fucked up on them damn diet pills. I don't know what happened to her, or where she is. She could be dead for all I know. She's been gone for nearly a month, and she hasn't let anybody hear from her.' "

"Well, I can tell by his choice of words that his vocabulary hasn't changed. What else did he say?"

"That was all, because I couldn't stand to listen to anymore. I just said that I hoped he got well, and that was it. Then after I hung up and got to thinking about it, I was mad at myself for calling the bum in the first place."

"Are you sure you remembered everything Lewis said? Think carefully."

"That's all he said," Carol went on. "But I wonder why he was so quick to tell me that he hadn't hurt Patricia. I hadn't even mentioned her name before he blurted out that he didn't hurt her. His voice sounded so callous. Like he was trying real hard to lie. Just listening to him talk about her made cold chills run up and down my spine. That was why I cut our conversation so short. And after I hung up the phone, I felt I had betrayed her, and you, by talking to him."

"You shouldn't feel that way. I'm glad you called him. And I think he told you a lot more than he realized."

"What do you mean by that?"

"I think he's still trying to be the sly fox and he's trying hard to cover his tracks. He's looking for a place to hide. That's why he's in a hospital."

"It's odd that you should say that," Carol went on. "It fits perfectly with the conversation I had with Tammie."

"When was that?"

"Well, after I talked to Lewis, I couldn't resist calling Tammie, just to see what she would say about him being in the hospital. We only talked a few moments because she was in a hurry. You know she's always in a hurry. But anyway, I asked if she had heard from Patricia, and then I told her that Mother had called and told me that Lewis was in the hospital. And of course I asked if there was anything that I could do to help her and her sisters."

"What was her reaction to Lewis' so called suicide attempt?"

"She seemed very agitated by it. But first of all, Lewis didn't really try to commit suicide. He just pretended to. He was full of alcohol and he said he had taken some nerve pills. And he wrote out his will. And that scared the girls."

"And, for him, that was a convenient thing to do on the morning that he was to take the polygraph test," I said. "He probably faked the whole thing so he would have an excuse for not taking it. So what about the notes he wrote?"

"Well, as I understand it, Tammie called the Sheriff's office in Anderson, and told Adams that Lewis was at the house trying to commit suicide, and that he had written some notes. So, Adams and a Texas Ranger went to the house and found Lewis in his bedroom. They asked him if there was anything he would like to tell them, and he said no. He did tell them, however, that he had written his will and he got it out of the dresser drawer and showed it to them. It was several pages long, but it just rambled on about different items that the girls were to inherit in the event of his death. Then the officers asked if he would like to reschedule the polygraph test for a later date, and he said he would think about it. But he said that he knew he had been drinking too much, and he first wanted to go into a hospital and dry out. So, the girls took him to the hospital in Bryan, for a physical examination, with further plans to check him into another hospital for alcoholism."

"So, the sly fox found a hole to crawl into, after all," I said. "But he knows he can't hide there forever. And when he does come out, the hounds and the hunters are going to be on his trail again. Hotter and faster than ever."

"Oh, Lewis is probably already thinking of ways to buy more time," Carol went on. "And when he gets out of the hospital, I won't be surprised at all if he just suddenly leaves the country. And we never hear of him again."

"That's what I'm afraid of, too," I replied. "And if he does, Patricia may never be found. Something has to happen and very soon. We have worried and prayed for so long. I know God answers prayers. Why isn't He hearing us now?"

"He will. I know He will. And I think it will happen when we least expect it."

After Carol and I finished our conversation that day, I decided to go for a long walk, and think about everything she had told me. I loved to walk, especially during the early Autumn afternoons. The large old trees in the neighborhood had already begun to carpet the sidewalks with layers of red and yellow leaves, and in the quietness I listened to their crunching sounds as I walked in the brisk wind among them.

When would we know the answer, I wondered. When would we know what had happened to Patricia. When and where would she be found? Would it be before these age old trees became completely bare? Or would this beautiful Autumn pass into Winter, and then into Spring and Summer, and then into another Autumn with new red and yellow leaves for me to walk on. Would I know the answer by then? Or would it be too late? "Hurry before it's too late. Hurry before it's too late." The words in the dream kept haunting me. Where was the long deep rutted road in the dream, the road with the thick trees at the end of it? Was the wind blowing there? Was it blowing leaves to the ground, gently carpeting a grave?

CHAPTER 13

A few days later, I was still confident that the case would crumble under the pressure of a polygraph test. So I called Detective Adams again, hoping that Lewis had either taken the test or had at least rescheduled it for a later date.

"No, ma'am, he has not taken the test," Adams replied. "And as I've told you before, there's no way that we can force him to take it. He must, of his own free will, volunteer for it. And as it stands now, I don't think he's going to do that."

"Have you questioned him any more about Patricia?"

"Yes, we have talked to him. But we didn't learn anything new. He's still sticking by his story. And unless something else comes up, we may be in for a long run on this."

"Is he still in the hospital?"

"No, he's not. But while he was in there, his daughter Rhonda came to my office and threw a fit. She cussed me out. And I can guarantee you, that if she does that again, she'd better be prepared for the consequences."

"I'm sorry that she would do a thing like that. I'm sure she's just overwrought with worry about her mother."

"Well, she didn't cuss me out as much about Patricia, as she did about Lewis. She tried to blame the Sheriff's Office for Lewis being in the hospital. And I am not going to stand for that. I'm an experienced investigator and I'm trying to solve this case. I've tried to be nice to those girls, and to you and your sister, Carol. But I am not going to put up with any more temper fits, or anyone hampering my investigation. And that includes you."

"I was not aware that I was hampering your investigation," I said. "Surely you can't believe that that has been my intention."

"Well, I've asked you to talk to your sister Frances, and you haven't done that, have you?"

"No, not yet. Because I don't think there's anything that she can tell us that will be beneficial to the case."

"But you don't know that there's not. She may have the key to this whole case. And she doesn't live but about an hour's drive from Dallas, does she?"

"That's true. But I thought someone from the Law Enforcement in Navarro County was going out to talk to her. You told me that, remember?"

"Well, he hasn't gone out there yet, and even if he does, Frances probably won't tell him everything that she will tell you."

"Well, Lewis went out there this past weekend. Have you talked to him about that?"

"I saw Lewis yesterday, coming out of the beer joint in Roans Prairie. I was at the gas station there. He came over, belligerent as usual, and wanted to know if I was still checking out the leads he had given me, and if not, why not. I asked him if there was anything else that he wanted to tell me. He said no. Then he got sarcastic again. I told him to get out of my face or I would slap him. And I told him that the next time I saw him, I hoped to have a warrant for his arrest for murder."

"Have you learned anything more about Charlie Lancaster, or Bill, or Benny?"

"No, but I'm still working on it. The Sheriff in Wichita Falls has not located Charlie Lancaster yet. But old ex-cons like him don't usually stay in one place for very long. As for the guy named Bill, I can't find anyone who knows anything about him, not even his last name. But the other guy, the one named Benny, is supposed to live on a lake somewhere around Corsicana. I'd like to talk to him. And I think Frances may know him. That's why I've asked you, repeatedly, to go down there and try to find out what she knows. Now, if you really want to help this situation, you'll do that. And, until then, I'm not telling anything else to anyone, other than the family."

"Is that right? Well, in case you've forgotten, I'm part of the family."

"I'm talking about Lewis and Patricia's family."

It was evident, from the tone of his voice, that Lewis or the daughters had cursed him out, again. And they had probably branded Carol and me as troublemakers, and told him not to tell us anything else. But to me, it confirmed that we were on the right track, and getting closer.

"I'll get in touch with Frances tomorrow," I assured Adams.

"All right, you do that. And report what you find out to my office. If I'm not here, you can leave a message. Now, I've got work to do. I can't spend all of the taxpayers' money talking to you on the phone."

The nerve of that guy, I thought. How dare he talk to me in that tone of voice. Just who did he think he was? Furthermore, just who did he think he was talking to? I was not some backwoods girl who couldn't find her way out of a paper sack. And the day would certainly come when I would confront him in person and tell him exactly what I thought of his rudeness.

It was now the eleventh of September, a quiet autumn Sunday. I called Mother to see if she had a new phone number for Frances. She said she didn't. Then I asked how Lewis' recovery was coming along from his hospital stay.

"He's doing all right. But nothing is going to help him until he puts the bottle down. That was the trouble between him and Patricia. That and his jealousy. Tammie wants him to go to an alcoholic hospital and dry out, but he won't. Now he's mad at the Sheriff's Department again. And the Texas Rangers. He said he spent a whole day with the Rangers, telling them that Patricia was living at a lake somewhere in northeast Texas. And they told him that they were not going to bring her back. They said for him to go up there and get her."

"Oh, hell, Mother. You can't believe that. You know if Lewis thought she was up there, he would have already brought her back. I think he's fishing around, looking for an excuse to leave the country."

"That could be. But he thinks the Law is watching him."

I sincerely hoped they were. But I chose not to talk about it.

Later I called Darlene and explained that I must see Frances. I said I was worried sick, and I thought it would help us both if we could visit.

Frances and Darlene arrived at my home the next morning. It had been several years since we had seen each other. And, of course, our first topic of conversation was about our children and grandchildren. We showed photographs and talked about how many there were, how old they were and what they were doing in school. It was good to sit and relax over cups of hot coffee and share our families' achievements together. But still we both knew that we would also discuss Patricia's disappearance. And I felt the tenseness in Frances' voice as I approached the subject.

"So, tell me, what do you think really happened," I said. "Do you think Patricia just walked off into the night, or what?"

"I don't know," Frances replied. "But I can swear that I have not seen her or heard from her. And I wish people would stop thinking that I have. If I knew anything more than that, I'd tell you."

"Well, have you heard the rumor that she has a boyfriend named Benny, and that he lives in Malone?"

"That's a lie. That's a damn lie. I know who Benny is. He worked with Howard for years. But he wasn't Patricia's boyfriend. In fact she only saw him once."

"When was that?"

"It was a couple of years ago. One Friday night, she took her baby and left Lewis and came to my house. She got there just as we were going out for dinner and she went with us. And while we were at the restaurant, Benny came in and walked over to say hello to us. I introduced him to Patricia and he sat with us for a few minutes. Then the music started playing and he looked over to her and said, 'I'd ask you to dance, but I'm wearing my tennis shoes.' And that was all there was to it. He got up and left, and when we finished eating, we left and went home. And when we got home, Lewis was parked in the driveway waiting for us. He spent the night and Patricia went back home with him the next day."

"Okay. But tell me how Lewis knew about Benny?"

"Howard may have mentioned Benny's name and Lewis jumped to conclusions."

"Did Lewis ask about Benny when he visited you after Patricia left?"

"No, he never mentioned Benny's name."

"What did he talk about?"

"He just came out late one afternoon, a couple of weeks ago, and he asked if we had seen or heard from Patricia. Of course I told him no. But we invited him in anyway. And he sat at the dining table for a couple of hours talking about her. He said that she had left him and run off with a boyfriend, and that he was looking for her. He said he just couldn't understand why she would leave like that. Especially since they had been getting along so well. But then he said that she had really changed in the past several months. He said she got, pardon my language, 'fucked up' on diet pills. And he was mad at her doctor because he had refilled her prescription and had given her a new three month supply."

"Wait a minute. When was the new prescription refilled?"

"He talked like it was right before she left."

"Okay. Now one of her best friends saw her the afternoon she disappeared, and she said Patricia told her that she only had three pills left. And that she didn't want any more because she had lost enough weight already. Another thing, has Mother told you what Patricia said the last time she saw her?"

"I don't know. I've only talked to Mother a couple of times lately."

"Well, believe me, all was not well with Patricia's and Lewis' marriage at that time. In fact she was planning to leave him, once and for all. From what I gather, she planned to do it as soon as her retirement check came. And it was already being processed to be sent to her. And ironically, it arrived several days after she left. But she has not returned to pick it up. Also, her last paycheck from the restaurant hasn't been picked up. Doesn't that sound a little strange to you? It does to me."

"Maybe she's planning to come back later for the money."

"Or maybe Lewis planned to try to cash the checks himself. I think if she had planned to leave when she did, she would have made arrangements for someone else to pick up her checks and mail them to her. Or she could have stayed with friends for a few days and picked up the checks herself. Another thing, I don't think she would have left Jennifer. And Kimberly's birthday was several weeks ago and Patricia didn't call or write to her. That just doesn't sound like Patricia. You know how devoted she was to her girls."

"Well, all I know is that Lewis sat in my kitchen and talked about her for two solid hours. He said he loved her, but she ran off with a boyfriend."

"I've heard that garbage and I don't believe a word of it. First, Lewis said she had a boyfriend named Bill. Then it was Charlie Lancaster. Then it was Benny. And next week he'll think up another name, and it will go on and on. It makes me mad as hell that he's smearing her name all over the country. And the hell of it is, there's people in Grimes County who will believe anything. But tell me which boyfriend did he tell you that she left with?"

"Somebody named Charlie Lancaster."

"How does he know that's who she left with?"

"I don't know, but he seemed worried about her. He said he hoped that she hadn't left with Charlie Lancaster, because he's an ex-convict and he's already killed two people."

"Sounds like Lewis is not sure that she left with Charlie. But what else does he know about him?"

"That's all he said, other than he thought Charlie had family in Fort Worth."

"Okay. Knowing how jealous Lewis is, don't you think he would have gone out there and tried to find Charlie, hoping to catch Patricia with him?"

"I thought about that. But Lewis said he was just going to let her stay, if that was what she wanted."

"Well, did he tell you what happened the afternoon she disappeared?"

"He said they cut some carpet out of the house and threw it away. Then later, they went to a turkey shoot with some friends and after that, they came home."

"Did he say anything about Patricia being sick that afternoon?"

"No, he didn't."

"Okay, did he say what happened after they got home, or whether anyone else saw her leave. Perhaps a neighbor?"

"Yes. He said they went home and Patricia took a nap. Then she got up and changed clothes and slung her purse over her shoulder, and left."

"Did he say whether anyone else saw her leave?"

"Yes, he did. He said that both Kimberly and Virginia were in the house when Patricia left. And that they asked her not to go, but she did anyway. I asked if he and Patricia had had a fight, and he said no. He said they used to fight, a long time ago when they were kids, but that they hadn't fought in years."

"But you knew he was lying when he said they hadn't fought in years."

"Sure, I knew it," Frances replied, defensively. "I was just repeating what he said. And I can tell by the look on your face, what you're thinking. But I think you're wrong. I don't believe for a moment that he has done anything to hurt Patricia. He said he loved her."

Darlene and I glanced at each other. And by her expression, I knew immediately that she did not share Frances' thoughts that Lewis was innocent.

"I think I'd like to go for lunch," said Darlene, glancing at her watch. "We passed by a cafeteria not far from here. Why don't we try that, this time?"

"Sounds like a good idea," I replied. "That's just the place I had in mind. We go there a couple times a week. And if we hurry now, we'll miss the rush."

I decided to temporarily drop the subject of Patricia and Lewis, hoping Frances would think about it during lunch, and perhaps remember something else that Lewis had told her.

As we were walking out to my car to go the cafeteria, I complimented Darlene's dress and long dark curly hair.

"Darlene, you're still so pretty. You should go back to modeling again."

"I've thought about it," she laughed. "But I'm too busy enjoying my children these days. And too, Nathan works out of town sometimes and the kids and I go with him. So I really don't have a lot of time to concentrate on other things. But maybe I will someday."

During the drive to the cafeteria, Darlene and I continued our conversation about her former modeling career. I noticed, however, that Frances seemed very quiet. As though she was trying to remember something and wasn't sure what it was. But I decided not to press the issue, at least not for now. I wanted to give her time to remember everything that Lewis had told her.

However, as we sat down to lunch, Darlene brought up the subject of Patricia and Lewis again.

"You know, I just can't help thinking of the last time I saw Aunt Pat," she said. "It was during the first week in July. I stopped by to see her on my way home from Houston. She was so glad to see me. And I don't care what Lewis says. She had not changed. Oh, she had lost weight and she looked real pretty, but her personality had not changed. She was very cheerful, and she said that she and Lewis were planning to buy some property at Lake Fairfield, and build a house on it. She said that was if she could get him to do it. She seemed to be in such good spirits. I just don't see how she could have changed so much before she left. At least not the way Lewis said she did. But if she changed at all, I know she must have had a good reason. Of course I loved her very much."

"We all loved her," said Frances. "And Lewis said he loved her. That's why I can't believe that he has done anything to hurt her."

"But Frances, you of all people know how mean he was to her," I said.

"I know that. But he said they didn't fight any more. He said they hadn't fought in years."

"Well, you must not have heard about him chasing her down the highway with a loaded gun just three weeks before she left. He was trying to kill her then."

"No. I didn't know that."

"I know he was mean to her," said Frances. "And it breaks my heart to think about it. But surely, he wouldn't kill her."

166

"Why wouldn't he? God knows he beat on her enough," I said.

"But he said he loved her."

"Oh hell, Frances. If he had loved her, he wouldn't have beat her all those years. That's not love. Love does not hit, slap and bruise. That's hate."

"My gosh, look what time it is," said Darlene, glancing at her watch. "We need to hurry. I've got to get home in time to pick up my daughter from school."

And so it was that we returned back to my home and, shortly thereafter, as Darlene and Frances prepared to leave, I walked with them to their car. When I hugged Frances good-bye, I asked her to pray for Patricia.

"Frances if you can think of anything else Lewis told you, I wish you'd tell me now."

"But I've already told you everything he said," she answered. "Why don't you talk to Kimberly and Virginia. They know more about it than I do. They were both there at the house when Patricia left, and they talked to her."

"Are you sure they were there?"

"Yes. Lewis said they were."

I knew instantly that Frances had just given me a valuable piece of information by saying that Kimberly and Virginia were at the house when Patricia left. For I knew beyond a doubt that Lewis had lied when he told her that. And at last, in my mind, the pieces of the puzzle were beginning to fall into place. All except one. However, I said nothing more about it.

As I started around to the other side of the car, Darlene met me halfway, and motioned to me not to say anything. Then she put her arms around me and whispered so Frances could not hear.

"Aunt Jean, this has something to do with the investigation, doesn't it? I mean, that's why it was so important for us to meet today."

I didn't want to lie to her. So I hugged her again and said nothing.

"But you don't have to tell me if you don't want to," she said. "I understand. Believe me, I do. And you can trust me. Just promise to call me immediately, when the time comes, so I can be the one to tell

Mother before anyone else does."

"I will. I promise you."

Later that afternoon, I sat in the den and made written notes of everything Frances had told me. Then I prepared myself, mentally, for what I hoped would be my last conversation with Detective Adams. Damned law man, I thought. If it wasn't for the fact that he was working on Patricia's case, I'd tell him where to get off so quick. Well, if I'm lucky, I won't have to talk to him at all. And as things turned out, I didn't talk to him. When I called the Sheriff's Department, his secretary said that he was not in his office. And it was she who wrote down the information I had learned on my long awaited visit with Frances.

"Just please be sure that he gets the information," I said. "Every last word."

"Oh, yes ma'am, I will," she answered. "I've got it all written down and I'll give it to him as soon as he comes in."

Well, so much for Adams, I thought. Now, I'll wait a couple of days and see what he does with the newfound information from Frances. But suppose for some unforeseen reason he doesn't receive it? Suppose it gets lost in the shuffle of paperwork? Or worse yet, suppose he thinks it's insignificant to the case?

I could feel my anger slowly rising, and I decided that if Adams failed to contact me within a week, I would pay him a visit, face to face. And I would tell him that everything Frances had said further proved that Lewis was lying through his teeth. And that he was still playing the "sly fox" trying to cover his tracks by whatever means possible. In the first place, if Kimberly and Virginia had been at the house when Patricia left, why hadn't Lewis told Adams about it? It would have been an easy way to relieve the suspicion from him and cast it elsewhere. But the fact was that Kimberly and Virginia were not there, and they knew nothing of Patricia's disappearance until Lewis told them. And also, there was the never ending suspicion about the missing carpet and mattress, as well as the bloody hand print and the fire. And besides that, there was the more recent fact that Lewis had faked a suicide attempt as an excuse not to take the polygraph

168

test. He was guilty. He was guilty as hell, and I intended to make enough noise in Grimes County to prove it.

I sat on the den sofa crying in hurt and anger at the nightmare my life had become. I was no longer the ordinary woman, busy with life's ordinary problems. Instead, due to worry and frustration, I had recently acquired a very different personality. One which left me short on patience, long on anger, and further to my dismay, a vocabulary of curse words that would make a seasoned sailor blush.

CHAPTER 14

Early the next morning, I received another phone call from Merle.

"Hey, Sis, are you awake yet? I'm getting ready to leave for work, but I wanted to check and see if you've heard anything more about Patricia. Remember my friend in Navasota? I talked to him again last week. He said he talked to that gas station guy again. The one who said he saw Patricia the morning after she left. And the guy said he still thinks he saw her."

"Well, tell him not to bet his paycheck on it. Because Frances and Darlene came to visit me, and I know that Lewis went to see Frances and told her a bunch of lies. And I think he's guilty. And I can't prove it. And I'm mad as hell."

"Whoa. Slow down a minute. Hang tight, Sis. Tell me what happened."

"That's just it. Nothing new has happened. Lewis is still playing his stupid fox game, lying through his teeth. And the Grimes County law, and Carol and I are still trying to find enough evidence to bring him in."

"I don't know. In a way, I've got my doubts that anything bad has happened to Patricia. I think things could turn out to be the way Lewis said they were. I know he's sorry as hell and all that, but surely he knows that if he killed her, he'll be caught."

"Merle, I've listened to almost those same words from Frances, and my answer to you is the same as it was to her. Quote, I don't care what anyone says, Lewis is guilty. Unquote."

"Well, if he is, he'd better not let me get my hands on him. Because hell won't be hot enough to hold him. I saved his life once, many years ago, just before he and Patricia married. He came by the house one day and said he'd bought an old race car. And he asked me and my wife to go with him and Patricia out to the old salt mine road to try it out. My wife and I followed them about ten miles, all the way to the end of it. And when we got there, Patricia decided to wait with us instead of going on with Lewis. Thank God, she did. Anyway, Lewis got back in his race car and revved up the engine as fast as it would go, and took off. He went about three hundred yards before he lost control of it and flew through a barbed wire fence. He and the car went in separate directions, and I found him lying on the ground bleeding like a stuck hog. He was all bruised and cut up, his face was a bloody mass, and if I hadn't rushed him to the hospital, he would have bled to death. You know, I kind of hate to say this, but something told me when I picked him up off the ground that day, that I was making a mistake. And every once in a while, in years to come, I'd think about that. I guess it was just something that stayed with me."

"I think everybody in our family has memories of him that they would like to forget."

"I can't dispute that," he laughed. "So, I'm going to say bye for now and get to work. Be sure to call me if you hear anything new about Patricia."

After that, I got up and made coffee, then sat in the den looking out into another gray rainy morning. And once again I asked myself the same questions as I did every morning. Will this be the day that Patricia is found? And if she is found today, will she be alive?

It was becoming increasingly harder each day to deal with my anxiety. Grief was the proper word to describe it. I had almost forgotten how to smile or converse with anyone about anything except about Patricia. I became secluded in my home, listening for the phone to ring and watching for the mail. Noticing unfamiliar cars hoping to see her. Always watching. Always waiting.

I went to my desk and took out the old letters I had received from her, so many years ago. All twenty-eight of them. The first letter I opened was dated October 20, 1968, and it read in part: "Jean, I think it is very sweet and lovable of you to think of me. About the necklace, I will keep it and cherish it as long as I live, and when I die, Tammie can wear it. But I won't talk about that because you're going to outlive me, and I'm going to live to be a hundred. Hope you like the new pictures of the girls. Love you always ... Your little sister, Pat." "Oh, Patricia," I whispered. "If only we had known then what we know now. How different our lives might have been."

I decided to call Carol and see if, within the past few days, she had talked to Adams.

"No, I haven't talked to Adams," she replied. "But Mother called this morning. She said a Texas Ranger came to visit her and Daddy yesterday. His name is Brian Taylor. His office is in Brenham, and he's working on the case with Adams. She said the Ranger seemed very interested in the case. He asked for names, addresses and phone numbers. And he asked about Patricia's marriage relationship. Mother told him that she believed Patricia would come back when she got ready. Daddy called her down about saying that. Then as the Ranger was leaving, Daddy walked outside with him and they talked for a while. But when Daddy came back in, he refused to tell her what they talked about. But I'll bet I know what Daddy told him."

"I do, too. He's probably thinking the same thing we are. But he's not going to tell Mother because he knows it could get back to Lewis."

"I wonder if we should try to contact the Ranger?"

"No, let's wait a few days. Give him time to gather some new information. He has our phone numbers. We'll be hearing from him. Now that the Ranger and Adams are both working on it, I expect the case to come down any day. And when it does, I think it's going to explode, and it's going to split our family."

"Well, I have a week's vacation the end of September," Carol said. "And if Patricia is not found by then, I'm going to Grimes County and find her."

"I'll go with you, but where will we find her? We could tell Lewis to his face that we think he killed her, but we have no proof. Don't you see? That has been his game all along. He knows the Law can't prove murder without a body."

Later that day, my son, William called. When I told him of the plan to go to Grimes County, he strongly advised against it. But he knew I would probably go anyway. So, as an ex-Marine who saw combat in Vietnam, he gave me a brief education in "scouting."

"Be careful who you talk to and how you phrase your questions. Don't trust anybody. They could be your enemies. By the time the sun sets the first day, people will know you're in town and the questions you asked. So, if you go, go in quick, learn what you can and get out. And don't let them see you leave."

I finished a second cup of coffee, thinking about the conversation with William, and of the danger I could possibly find in Grimes County. However, within the next hour, I would have second thoughts that the case would be solved in Grimes County. Instead, my thoughts quickly turned in an entirely different direction. A direction less than five miles from my home.

Richard had come home from work early to edge and mow the yard, while I cooked dinner. I could see the television from the kitchen, but when the six o'clock evening news came on, I walked into the den and turned the volume up in order to hear it over the noise of the lawnmower. Then I stood there in a sudden chill as I listened to the newscaster's words.

He first caught my attention when he mentioned Lake Ray Hubbard. For the lake was nearby and I was reasonably familiar with its surroundings. I quickly turned the volume up even more, and listened closer, as he reported that the Dallas Police and other crime scene personnel had recovered two bodies from the lake, early that morning. The bodies were that of a man and a woman, both shot and bound together with rope. The man had been identified as being a forty-seven year old man from the Wichita Falls area. However, the woman had not yet been identified. The newscaster gave her description as being a white female approximately forty years old with shoulder length brown hair. Then a phone number flashed on the screen and the public was asked for help in identifying her body.

I stood there numb, as though I were frozen. Oh dear God, I thought. It can't be Patricia. It can't be. Bodies are found in lakes every day. And more than a few have been found in Lake Ray Hubbard. I could remember back when the lake had been expanded, and of later reading of boating accidents caused by tree stumps underneath the water. Yet, on quiet summer days, the lake was a picture of beauty as colorful sailboats and fishing boats dotted its tranquil waters from morning until sunset. But still, from time to time, we were jerked back into reality as the local newscasters reported another murder. Another body found in or near Lake Ray Hubbard.

I began switching the television channels, frantically hoping to find the same report on another station. Surely it was there somewhere. Surely one of the stations would tell the man's name who had been shot and tied to the unidentified woman. They said he was forty-seven years old and from the Wichita Falls area. Surely they knew his name. Could it be Charles Lancaster? But as I searched through the channels, I heard nothing more about it. Then I decided to call the TV station and ask for the name.

"I'm sorry, I can't give out that information," was the answer.

"But can you give me the phone number that flashed on the TV screen during the report? The one to call to help identify the woman's body?"

"Yes. Just a minute. I'll get it for you. But I'm sorry I can't be of more assistance to you, other than to give you the phone number."

I wrote the number on a note pad and thanked her. However, I could not bring myself to tell her why I wanted it. For I needed time to think about it, and brace myself for what my first reaction would be if I dialed the number and learned that my worst fears were true.

My sleep was more restless than ever that night. It seemed as though I awoke every hour upon the hour thinking of what I would say when I called the number of the Dallas County Morgue the next morning. I knew it was important to give an accurate physical description of Patricia, and each time I woke up, I rehearsed it over and over in my mind until I fell asleep again. I would say that she was forty-two years old, five feet three inches tall, her weight approximately one hundred-twenty. And that she had dark brown hair and brown eyes. For distinguishing marks, I would tell them about the scar on her thumb, and that she had received a broken right arm, left leg and ankle in a car accident, back when she was thirteen. And about the plastic pin in her ankle.

Oh, God, how could I stand it if it's really Patricia's body lying there in the Dallas County Morgue? And if it is, who was the murdered man found with her? Was it Charles Lancaster? Was the gas station attendant in Shiro correct when he said he saw them on the morning after she disappeared? That had been forty-three days ago. Had they spent those forty-three days in the Dallas area? Surely not, because Patricia would have called me. But could it be that Lewis tracked them down, found them together, and killed them somewhere else? Perhaps the night he visited Frances? But no, that would not have been his style. He could not have handled both of them. But if it was Patricia and Charlie, and Lewis didn't murder them, who did? Detective Adams had said that "old Charlie is an ex-convict who served time for murder." So, Charlie must have had his share of enemies. So, was it a murder for revenge by his enemies? Or was it a murder of passion stemming from insane jealousy?

As I lay there in bed, unable to sleep, my thoughts continued to ramble, each one more bizarre than before. Finally, at four-thirty, I got up and made coffee. The house seemed unusually cold, even though Dallas was known for its cold September mornings and warm afternoons. And although the central heat thermometer read seventy degrees, that morning, the chill throughout the house remained.

Wearing my warmest robe, I walked out to the patio and gathered several pieces of wood, and made a fire in the den fireplace. Then I poured a cup of coffee and sat on the sofa, waiting for the room to get warm. As I sat there, I watched the clock, nervously waiting for the television morning news. And when it began, I listened carefully as the story was repeated about the bodies found the day before in Lake Ray Hubbard.

I told Richard of my plan to call the Dallas County Morgue that morning. "It could be anyone," he replied. "They're always finding bodies somewhere. But I think the chances are very remote that Patricia's body would be found in Ray Hubbard."

"You may be right," I replied. "But surely you understand why I have to make the call, don't you? I have to know that it's not her."

"I understand that. And you should call. But are you going to be able to stand it if it is her? Why don't you wait until I get home this evening. I'll be home around four o'clock. I'll call the morgue when I get home."

But even as he spoke, he knew I wouldn't wait until then. I couldn't. I couldn't stand the fear of not knowing.

By nine o'clock that morning, I was searching for the piece of paper upon which I had written the number, but evidently Richard had taken it with him. I then got the phone directory and searched through its pages until I found the number of the Dallas County Morgue. But as I dialed it, I knew I was wasting my time. *'Don't be foolish,'* my thoughts conveyed. *'What about all the blood in Patricia's house? What about the fire? Concentrate on that. Go to Grimes County and see what you find before you grasp at any more straws.'*

Nevertheless, I completed the call to the morgue and spoke with one of the doctors there, telling him that I had called in reference to the news story about the unidentified body of a woman found in Lake Ray Hubbard.

"A positive identification has been made on that," he answered. "It was made this morning."

"Could you tell me if the woman was from Grimes County?" I asked.

"No. She was not from Grimes County. She was from New Orleans, visiting relatives in Dallas."

I thanked him and hung up the phone, once again relieved that I had heard the word, 'no,' to another fearful inquiry. It had been the same as when I had checked the hospitals in Dallas. It served as a glimmer of hope. The desperate hope that Patricia was still out there, somewhere, alive and well.

I spent the rest of the morning and most of the afternoon working in the yard, staking tall flowers that had seen their best days of summer, and discarding faded blooms from others. It had been a good year for roses, though. For they still bloomed in abundance. Some years were like that.

As I watered the roses, pangs of loneliness and worry tugged inside me to the point that I found myself unable to control the tears that flowed freely down my face. I was tired of the nightmare my life had become. Even though Richard and the children and Carol were supportive of my feelings, I felt that I no longer resembled the woman I had been two months before. For, since then, I had developed a raw hatred for the person or persons who knew what had happened to Patricia, and who chose to hide behind a web of lies. It was a hatred that, at times, I felt would totally consume me. I wanted an answer! I was tired of playing games! It was now the twentieth day of September, she had been missing forty-four days! Someone knew exactly where she was! And, in my heart, I knew who that someone was. Damn him! Damn his hideous games! He was determined to be the winner by lying his way out of it! And if enough time passed by, he may indeed win, after all.

I turned the water hose off, then went into the house and took a shower. And when Richard came home, I was at the stove cooking spaghetti sauce.

I told him of the call to the Dallas County Morgue.

"Well, I knew you would, and I'm glad you did," he said. "At least we don't have that worry any more."

After that, he puttered around the yard a while, then settled in the den to watch a sports program on TV, while I finished cooking dinner.

Suddenly the phone rang, and I answered it. It was Carol. But her voice was almost a whisper, and I knew immediately that something was wrong.

"Jean, is Richard there?"

"Yes, he is," I answered. "He's in the den watching television."

"Tell him I want to talk to him," she went on.

"Okay, but don't you want to talk to me, too?" I said lightly.

"Yes, I want to talk to you. But first, I want to talk to Richard."

I paused briefly, then began shaking, completely consumed with uncontrollable fear. I knew what she would tell Richard. She didn't have to tell me, first. It was already there in the pretended calmness and soft whispering of her voice.

"You want to tell him something about Patricia, don't you?"

"Yes," her voice whispered.

"What are you going to tell him?"

"I'll tell him first, then he can tell you."

"No, you won't," I said, hearing my voice grow louder. "I don't want to hear it from Richard. I want to hear it from you. Just answer my question: Has Patricia been found?"

"Yes. They found her body this morning."

"Don't you tell me that!" I screamed. "I won't hear it. Do you understand me? I won't hear it!"

Then, suddenly, Richard was beside me trying to take the phone receiver from my hand.

"Don't touch me," I told him, shakingly. "Leave me alone! She's my sister!"

"Carol, I want you to tell me, again."

"But honey, your voice is shaking so bad. Can you hear me?"

"I can hear you. Now, tell me where Patricia's body was found."

"Her body was found buried at the dump on the Jim Pierce Ranch. And Lewis did it. But the Laws have him now."

My mind was reeling as I stumbled toward the floor. Those words, those exact words I had heard thirteen years ago in the dream. Now, within seconds, the dream flashed back into my mind as clearly as the night I had first dreamed it. And once again, I relived the horror of walking up the steps of the funeral home and through its doors until I came to the room where Patricia's body lay in a closed casket. And again, I saw myself looking down upon it, dripping tears on the flowers while listening to an unknown voice say: "You know who did it. But the Laws have him now."

"Jean, are you going to be all right?" Carol went on.

"No, I'm not going to be all right!" I screamed. "That sonofabitch! That low-life sonofabitch! That low-life scum of the earth! How could he do such a thing to her? She was his wife for twenty-six years, the mother of his children and grandmother of his grandchildren. And he murdered her! And buried her like a damn dog in a garbage dump! No, I'm not all right! And believe me, he's going to pay dearly for what he's done, if I'm allowed to have anything to say about it. But first tell me who told you that her body was found?"

"Mother called and said she had learned of it from Uncle Marvin."

Uncle Marvin was the Honorable Judge A. M. McCaig, County Judge of Waller County. He was also a dear and trusted member of our family. And we knew that what he had told our parents was true.

"What else did Uncle Marvin tell Mother and Daddy?"

"He said that Patricia's body had been found about eleven o'clock this morning at a dump on the Jim Pierce ranch. I don't know whether he knew who found it or how it was found. If he did, he didn't tell Mother. However, Emil and I just finished talking to Detective Adams a few minutes ago. Adams confirmed that the body was found this morning, and that Patricia had been shot with a 308 deer rifle. Adams also confirmed that Lewis was arrested and placed in the Grimes County Jail, and that Lewis has confessed. Emil told Adams to make sure Lewis stays locked up, otherwise, Adams could have another murder case on his hands. Adams said: 'Don't worry, Lewis Crocker is not going anywhere. He's in my jail now. And he's going to stay there.' We also learned from Adams that Patricia's body was taken to Houston for an autopsy, and it will be several days before it can be released for the funeral."

"Do you know how it was found?"

"No, not yet. But I expect to learn more about it tomorrow."

Carol and I then closed the conversation, both knowing that it would be forever imprinted in our memory. But for now, there were the immediate tasks to attend to. Notifying Frances and Merle, and other members of our family. Contacting Patricia's daughters and trying to comfort them. Funeral arrangements must be made, hoping the daughters would consent for Patricia to be buried in Oak Glen Cemetery. And throughout it all, we had to try to live with our own heartbreaking grief. But in the deep recesses of our minds, we also knew that the time would come when we would set out to learn the rest of the story behind the murder. And that we would cry loudly for justice.

CHAPTER 15

At one o'clock the next afternoon, I parked my car in front of the J. M. Day Funeral Home in Madisonville, got out and walked across the street toward it. Its large white building, ancient trees and manicured lawn looked the same as it had for more years than I cared to remember. And it seemed always to be waiting. In years passed, it had waited for my grandparents, several aunts, uncles and cousins. Now, it stood waiting for my sister, Patricia.

As Richard and I walked across the street, I began to tremble, remembering the old dream again. But this time the horror was painfully real. The brutal murder, the body buried in a garbage dump. The web of lies and deceit. But the murderer would pay for his evil deeds, I vowed. And his lies wouldn't save him.

Patricia's children: Tammie with her husband Garvin, Rhonda with her husband Donald, and Kimberly and Virginia stood near the front steps with Carol and Emil. We greeted each other and then went inside, Garvin and Donald to the business office, the girls, Carol and I to the casket room. And it was there that I detected a touch of hostility between Carol and Rhonda. They were discussing pallbearers for the funeral. Rhonda wanted Lewis' brothers as pallbearers. Carol angrily refused.

"No," said Carol. "I won't have it. It was a Crocker who took my sister out of this world, and I'll be damned if I'll see a Crocker carry her casket."

"It's not your choice," replied Rhonda. "We have the legal rights. Not you."

"Well, you can have them if you want to, but I think you should realize that our entire family is very upset, and if Lewis' brothers are pallbearers, there could be trouble at the funeral. Suppose there is a fight? We surely don't want that to happen."

"By the way, has Patricia's purse been found?" Carol went on.

"Yes, it was found in the septic tank behind the house," Rhonda answered.

I didn't say anything, but I cringed as I remembered the lie Lewis had told about Patricia slinging her purse over her shoulder just before she supposedly disappeared into the night. Now, I was listening as Rhonda described how the purse had been wrapped in plastic, and the articles that were found inside it.

Rhonda had brought Patricia's Bible to be placed in the casket. Carol had brought a rosary that Patricia had once admired. I had forgotten to bring anything, so I stepped aside and watched as they handed the items to Mrs. Day.

But it was then that I silently vowed to write about Patricia's life and murder. I would not let her be forgotten with the last shovel of dirt thrown upon her grave. Somehow, I would make her live not only in my heart, but in the hearts of those who read about her. I wanted her to be remembered as something more than 'a poor country girl who loved her family, but who was murdered and thrown into a hole in a garbage dump.' Her life deserved to count for more than that. And I wanted others to learn from it, both women and men. I wanted to try in some way to make them realize the consequences of a love too soon, lack of education, alcohol and violence. But, as we walked out of the casket room, I knew it would be years before I could bring myself to write about her. For the hurt was still too new, the unbearable pain was much too great. And there were many things yet to be learned.

We were out on the lawn still discussing who to choose for pallbearers. Neither Rhonda or Carol had changed their minds. Rhonda still insisted on Lewis' brothers, While Carol refused. I had never met the brothers, therefore, I had nothing against them personally, but I felt that out of respect for our family, they should politely refuse. However, I did not object to them being at the funeral.

"Well, I could be one of the pallbearers," said Garvin.

"I could, too," said Donald.

"And I think Patricia would like that," I replied. "I know she always thought a lot of you both."

"Yes, and we loved her, too," said Garvin.

Garvin was tall, dark-haired and lanky. I liked him, and it was easy to see that behind his quiet nature, he was a fine young man. I could still remember Patricia's proud smile as she introduced him to me, several years ago. Back when he and Tammie were at Mother's on Thanksgiving Day. Patricia pretended to be reluctant to see Tammie engaged, but we knew she was secretly pleased as punch when Garvin and Tammie married. It had been the same way with Donald and Rhonda. Donald was also a dark-haired young man, a few inches shorter than Garvin. And a bit more shy. But he was a hard worker and likable, and Patricia was equally as proud of him.

We stood near the steps of the funeral home, talking about the forty-four days Patricia had been missing before her body was found.

"Somehow, I felt all along that she was dead," I said.

"We knew within a week after she was gone, that she was dead," said Garvin.

"You what!" I asked.

"Of course, we didn't know for certain, but we suspected it," he went on. "I've seen Lewis pull that gun on her more times than I can count."

"He sure did," said Donald. "And not only did he pull the gun on Pat, he also pulled it on me. I've had to look down the barrel of that gun several times."

I looked at them in disbelief, even though I knew I was hearing the truth.

"Yeah, he did," said Garvin. "And when Lewis would get the gun after Pat, somebody would call the Law, and the Law would come out after him. But when they started to take him away, he would look back at her and give her that threatening look, and then she would tell them to let him stay."

"You are serious, aren't you?" I asked.

"Yes, I'm serious," Garvin went on. "And I can tell you something else. Donald and Rhonda just happened to drive up to the house within thirty seconds after Pat was killed. Lewis said, after he was arrested, that he thought they had heard the shot."

"Did they hear the shot? Did he tell them he had shot her?"

"No. But I wish I had known," replied Donald. "Maybe I could have got some help for her."

"What did Lewis say when you drove up?" I asked.

"Well, we were in a hurry, so I stayed in the car with the kids. Rhonda ran up on the porch and tried to open the door, but it was locked. She banged on the door, and Lewis called out to her. He told her to wait a minute.

"Rhonda waited a few minutes, then Lewis came out on the porch, closing the door behind him. He asked her if she had seen her mother. And she said no. Then he said that he and Pat had had an argument, and she had gotten mad and left him. He said she just walked off down the road, and he thought Rhonda may have seen her. Rhonda assured him that she had not seen Pat, and that she had come by to get a nightgown for Jennifer. Lewis let her come in the house for the nightgown, but he stayed right behind her, rushing her out of the house. He followed her outside and then stood by the car and talked about twenty minutes."

"And during that time, Patricia was in the house dying!" I exclaimed.

"I don't know if she was dying, or already dead, but she was in the house at that time."

As I listened to those words, my anger quickly reached its boiling point. And I turned my head away to keep from screaming. I must be standing here in another horrible dream, I thought. One beyond my wildest imagination. This couldn't be real. It was like a grotesque movie unfolding before my eyes. Or a fiction book too gory to read.

I glanced at Rhonda, and she walked over to where we were standing.

"Rhonda, is it true that you were in the house just after it happened?" I asked.

"Yes. But it was an accident."

"What do you mean, it was an accident?"

"The whole thing was an accident," she replied. "Daddy said they got in an argument, struggled for the gun, and it went off accidentally."

I paused for a moment, glancing across the wide green lawn of the funeral home, remembering Patricia's trust and respect for me. And I vowed to keep it by refusing to engage in further controversy with her daughters. For they were part of her, all we had left of her. But as I walked to my car that afternoon, and drove to Oak Glen to mark her grave site, I knew the time would come when I would stand in court against Lewis, seeking justice for Patricia's murder. And in turn, at least one of the daughters would stand against me.

On September 24, 1988, the day of Patricia's funeral, the hostility among family members was higher than I could possibly have imagined. Our family was quite large in number, and I suppose, considered by standards, it was an ordinary family. Among them were cattle ranchers, retired oil men, postal workers, school teachers, a county judge, military career men, accountants, farmers, sales clerks, and housewives. And they were all hardworking people who obeyed the law, paid their taxes and attended church regularly. But Patricia's death had affected them all much more than I had expected. I could see the hurt and anger in their eyes. And as we greeted each other and began to assemble for the funeral, I was acutely aware that any one of the men, young or old, was capable of standing up if Lewis' brothers touched Patricia's casket.

Uncle Marvin would be the answer, I thought. And I phoned him out of fear.

"Jean, I know the family is mighty torn up right now," he said. "And I agree there could be trouble. And we don't want that. Now I don't have any jurisdiction in that county, but I have a home there and I've got friends. Tell you what, since I'm on my way there now, I'll see what I can do."

As I parked my car in the back driveway of the funeral home, Uncle Marvin parked behind me. Tall and lean, and still brown-haired at sixty, he got out and walked hurriedly toward me. He hugged me briefly, then glanced at his watch.

"Jean, I'm in a hurry," he said. "There's people waiting for me. That's my truck, behind you and the keys are in it, in case it has to be moved."

I knew by his facial expression that he was concerned about the possibility of trouble, and I was confident that he would try to prevent it. And as the mourners began filing inside the funeral home, I soon learned what Uncle Marvin's prevention would be. For there among the hundreds of mourners stood several policemen and Sheriff's deputies quietly watching. Then I saw Sheriff Ed Fannin walk through the doorway, and when I glanced into the family room, I noticed a policeman at the back door.

When the service began, Aunt Margaret, Carol and I sat in the second row of seats reserved for immediate family members, behind Mother and Daddy and Patricia's daughters. Frances and her family sat in the third row, Merle and his family sat on the back row. The small room we were in was crowded, and the larger room was even more crowded. I glanced through the doorway, and saw mourners standing against the wall, trying to make room for others.

Then I noticed Richard and Emil, and Merle's sons, Andy, Darrell and Johnny, and two of our cousins, Kenneth and Lee, sitting with Garvin and Donald on a long front row near Patricia's casket.

"Don't worry about it," said Carol. "How do you think Patricia would feel if it was you or me lying there in that casket? I can guarantee that she wouldn't want any trouble, and she'd do her best to prevent it. But watch what I tell you, somebody will pull a fast one before it's over."

"Well, I certainly hope not."

But Carol's suspicion that 'somebody would pull a fast one' was right on target. And it happened within minutes after we were seated.

The two ministers had walked upon the podium and opened their Bibles to begin the service. Then we heard whispering among the mourners.

"See, what did I tell you?" said Carol.

"What are you talking about?" I replied.

"Look who's coming in the back door," she said. "I knew it would happen. I guess we haven't suffered enough, already."

"Oh my God, it's Lewis, " I said. "How in hell did he get out of jail?"

"No, that's not Lewis. That's his brother," Carol went on. "And he's not alone."

"What is that supposed to mean?"

"Watch and see."

Then as I turned back around to listen to the ministers, Lewis' brother walked in front of me and stopped. His breath reeked of liquor as he bent over to talk to Kimberly, who was sitting in front of me. Then he walked around us and stood near the back row where Merle and his family were seated.

Suddenly, I heard the loud scraping of a chair against the floor behind me. And I looked around as Merle stood up. Merle, my big easy going, even tempered brother, who had probably never hit anyone in his life now stood there, his face beet red.

The policeman walked toward him.

"Get that guy out of here, or I'm going to bust him," said Merle.

"Now, sir, sir, just calm down," the policeman replied. "The man hasn't done anything to you."

"The heck he hasn't," Merle went on. "But I won't argue with you about it. I'll just wait outside."

Then Carol noticed two other men, one of whom she knew, standing in the back corner near Lewis' brother.

"Get them out of here," she screamed.

"They don't have to leave," Tammie yelled. "They're our family, and they don't have to leave."

The next thing I saw was a blur of men's boots running past me on their way out the door. Carol, Aunt Margaret, Rhonda and several other women also went outside. And so did I.

However, instead of engaging in the argument between Aunt Margaret and Rhonda, I talked to the policeman. Suddenly, the arguments were over and everyone went back inside, except the policeman and me. I waited and explained why our family had reacted the way it did. The policeman talked to someone on his radio, then placed his hand on my shoulder.

"I understand, and it's okay now," he said. "Let's go back inside, the funeral is starting again."

And as we walked through the door, I noticed that the intruders were gone.

As the funeral began, the minister talked about how good and kind Patricia had been, and how she loved her family. He said she had been saved in church, and was now in the loving arms of God. Then he talked about how her days had been numbered, and that it had been her time to die.

I felt like standing up and screaming: *'No, you're wrong. God did not choose her time to die. Lewis Crocker chose her time to die.'* But of course I said nothing. I only bowed my head and cried harder.

When I glanced up again, I noticed a young man with long dark hair, whom I did not recognize, standing in the hallway. His glare at me and the smirk on his face was unmistakable. Then suddenly, the policeman came and sat beside me placing his arm around my shoulder.

"It's all right," the policeman said. "I'm going to stay with you."

For a moment, the tone of his voice caused me to wonder if perhaps my life was in danger, and if someone had asked him to watch out for me. I knew within reason, I had made my share of enemies during the investigation, and it was because I had stood firm in my belief that Lewis had murdered Patricia. But who was the man in the hallway? Why did he continue to stare at me?

The policeman handed his handkerchief to me and spoke softly, trying to console me as the funeral went on. But he continued to glance toward the hallway. Then suddenly, he stood up glaring and pointing at the young man. After that, the hallway was empty.

As he sat back down beside me, he handed a card to me, which read: Detective Joseph Piazza. "I have to go now," he said softly. "But when you get home and start thinking about today, I want you to remember the things I've told you. And if you need me, I'll be there."

I joined the long line of family mourners as they walked beside Patricia's casket, paying their last respects to her. And once again, as though I were reliving the dream again, I stared with flowing tears at the closed casket adorned with roses. But this time I knew the dream had ended. This was real. As real and as cold as the grave which lay waiting.

Merle's three sons and Garvin and Donald and another man were pallbearers. And outside, I saw Uncle Marvin and Joe Piazza in a serious conversation.

Then we followed the hearse out of town and along the winding country roads to Oak Glen Cemetery. And as I followed, never had there been more vengeance in my heart.

Carol, Emil and Richard asked me to let them drive, but I refused.

"No. I've come this far. I'll go the rest of the way. And if my enemies think that I'm going to go home and forget about this, they're in for a rude awakening. By the way, Carol, did you see the guy in the hallway? I don't know who he was, but he kept staring at me."

"Yes, I saw him. I hadn't seen him since he was a kid, but I recognized him. He's Lenny Compton. Better known as Lying Lenny."

"So he's the one who supposedly sent the message to Mother that Patricia was found in a coma and was in the hospital in Dallas. How cruel can a person get."

"He's the one," Carol replied. "And if he shows his face at the cemetery, he may get his jaws slapped for it. But he probably suspects that, and he won't be there. At least not where we can see him."

However, as we drove through the gates of Oak Glen, and as Patricia's casket was carried to her grave, I found myself glancing at the mourners, looking for Lenny. But he was not among them. And I secretly wondered if his absence had been the topic of conversation between Uncle Marvin and Detective Piazza. I also noticed that the intruders who had invaded the corner in the family room at the funeral home were not among the mourners at the cemetery.

"Of course they're not here," Carol said. "There's sheriff cars all along the road. Sheriff Ed Fannin arranged it. And we'll have escorts when we leave, too."

The cool September wind rustled gently through the tall ancient trees as the crowd of mourners gathered together at the grave site, and the minister gave the last service for Patricia. As he spoke, Carol and Emil, and Richard and I stood together, our hands clasped tightly, but I heard nothing except the wind whispering memories back to me.

I had been, and would forever be, Patricia's oldest sister. I first saw her the day after she was born. I was with her the day she cut her first tooth, and the day she took her first step. I had combed her hair and dressed her for play. We had laughed and picked wildflowers together, and there were summer vacations she had spent with me. In later years, I had left Denver, in a snowstorm, bound for Houston to attend her wedding. We had shared visits and many letters. Then later, as our families grew, there were years when the time seemed lost. But she had always known that I loved her and she loved me.

Now, I stood beside her for the last time, listening to the lonesome rustle of the wind, watching as it fluttered the ribbons on the flowered wreaths.

Until today, I hadn't given much thought about the *Hands of Fate* or the *Powers of Destiny.* Except for my dreams. But now I was convinced beyond a doubt, that a Power much greater than life had been with me from the day I first learned of Patricia's disappearance. It was a form of Guidance I had been unable to explain. A Strength I could not see. But it was there. It was with me the day I insisted upon the missing persons report. It had been with me during the arguments giving me the determination to find her. Then on the twentieth of August, one month from the day before Patricia's body was found, I had come to Oak Glen to purchase burial plots, including one for her.

Some may say that it was the second part of the dream, and that indeed it was Destiny. Others will say that of course it was God. I believe, and will always believe, it was all of that.

As the graveside services ended, Darlene and Patty Lynn came to hug Carol and me. I glanced behind them, hoping to see Frances.

"Aunt Jean, Mama is so torn up, she just couldn't stand to come inside the cemetery," said Patty. "She waited in the car. You know about her heart condition. She hasn't been feeling well lately."

"I understand. And tell her we love her."

"Oh, Aunt Jean," cried Darlene. "The minute I left your house that day, I started praying for Aunt Pat. I loved her so much. I just can't believe she's dead."

"I know, honey. It's hard for any of us to believe."

"I just don't understand how Lewis could come to Mama's house and sit at her table drinking coffee for two hours, telling her how hard he was trying to find Aunt Pat, when he knew he had killed her and buried her."

"He was trying to gain sympathy. He was trying to cover his tracks."

"But he told Rhonda it was an accident," Darlene went on.

"I've heard that, too."

"Well, we'd better go now," she said, hugging me. "Mama is waiting for us."

Afterwards, one by one, Patricia's neighbors and friends were among the sea of faces who came to offer their condolences to Carol and me. I particularly noticed the tall blonde-haired lady now walking toward us. She wore a gray suit and white bow tie blouse, and was obviously a businesswoman.

"Hello, I'm Pauline Nicholson," she said, extending her hand to us. "Someone told me, you were Pat's sisters. And I wanted to express my condolences to you."

"Thank you," said Carol. "I remember you now, We talked on the phone during the time Patricia was missing. You have the dress shop."

"Yes," Pauline replied. I first met Pat there, one evening about three years ago. She came in looking for a dress to wear to a wedding, and we started talking and right away we became friends. Actually, more like sisters. Later, I learned of the torment she was going through, and I tried to help her."

Pauline talked a few moments more, then removed her glasses and blotted mascara beneath her eyes. "It's all so sad. I miss her. I will always miss her."

"Well I suppose I should be going," she said, glancing at her watch. "I just wanted to meet you, and tell you that I will miss Pat very much. She was a good person. And I think it's sad that the last year of her life was in such shambles. Especially the last six months."

I looked at her curiously, wanting to hear more. Wondering how much she really knew about Patricia. But this was not the place to ask her, so I made no further comment.

"I really have to go now," she said. "But I'm glad I met you. The next time you're in Navasota, come by the shop. I'll be there."

As Pauline walked away, I turned around and came face to face with another woman. A tall thin woman with faded brown hair streaked with gray. She wore a blue flowered dress, and I guessed her to be around the age of sixty.

She hesitated a moment, as though wondering whether she should say anything at all. But she extended her hand to Carol.

"You don't know me, do you?" she said.

"Yes, I remember you," Carol replied.

"Well you might not want to talk to me, but I want to tell you that I'm very sorry for what Lewis done to Pat. I think it was a low down dirty shame. And I think he should have turned that gun on himself. He'd have been better off. And that's all I have to say."

Then she immediately turned and walked away.

"Who was that?" I asked Carol.

"That was Lewis' Aunt Clara."

After that, there were others who came by extending their hands, expressing their sympathy, saying kind words about Patricia. And as we made our way to the car to leave, I saw a dark-haired pretty young woman, wearing a beige dress, walking hurriedly toward us. I recognized her as Monica Stevens. The waitress I had met in the restaurant in Madisonville. The girl who had grown up with Patricia's daughters.

"Oh, ma'am," she called. "Could you wait a minute, please? My parents would like to talk to you."

"Sure," I replied. "We can wait a few more minutes. How are

you, Monica?"

"Oh, I guess I'm doing okay. I'm working every day, trying to make a living."

Then she turned and motioned to her parents as they walked toward us.

"I'm so sorry about Pat," Monica went on. "You know, I'll bet Lewis came in the restaurant a dozen times while she was missing, and never once did he let on like he was worried. Every time I'd ask about her, he'd say, 'oh, she'll come back when she gets ready.' That damn liar. Oh, excuse me. I know I shouldn't cuss in a cemetery."

"Don't worry about it," I replied. "I've said worse than that before."

"Oh, here they are," she went on. "Mama and Daddy, this is Carol and Jean, Pat's sisters. And Carol and Jean, this is my mother, Carmen Mitchell and my daddy, Walter Mitchell."

"Pleased to meet you both," said Walter. "You had a fine sister, and we thought a lot of her. She was a good woman. A hard working woman."

"Thank you," I replied. "We appreciate your thoughts."

Walter Mitchell was rather short in height and I guessed him to be about the age of fifty. He wore the typical western wear for men of that age. Brown pants, white striped shirt and a white Stetson hat. And I gathered that he was a farmer.

Carmen Mitchell was tall and heavy-set with short curly red hair. I guessed her to be in her late forties. Her blue dress and hat matched the color of her eyes. And when we said hello, I sensed the sincerity of her smile.

"It's nice to meet you, Mrs. Mitchell," I said.

"Just call me Carmen," she said. "That's what Pat always called me. And I knew her for nearly twenty years. Her girls practically grew up with my two daughters. They all went to school together and played together. And there were times when their report cards come in, that Pat and I accused them of playing in school."

"Now, Mama," Monica said.

"Well, you know it's true," Carmen went on. "Why you girls used

THE DARK SIDE OF TWILIGHT:

to always be together, either at my house or Pat's. And it got worse as you all got older."

"Mama, please," Monica said.

"Well, I guess I am getting a little carried away with myself, talking about that. And the Lord knows that's not what I came here to talk about. What I really want to say is that I'm terribly sorry about what happened to Pat. She was like a sister to me, and I loved her just as much as if she had been my own sister. God knows she didn't deserve to die the way she did. But may she rest in peace. Heaven knows she does deserve that."

"Yes, we were aware that there were problems in the marriage."

"Humph! Problems is not the word for it," Carmen continued. "Why for the past several months, every time he turned around, he was blacking her eyes, beating her and choking her. And pulling that gun on her."

Carmen then paused, crying hard and wiping her eyes with a pink flowered handkerchief. I placed my arm around her shoulder, and for a moment, I thought she'd break down completely. But she didn't. She was a strong woman. One who expressed her feelings regardless of where she was or who might be listening."

"I don't know how much you know about guns, but it was a big old thing," she continued. "It was a real mean looking gun."

"Yeah, I seen it once," said Walter. "If it was the one I'm thinking about, it was a 308 deer rifle with a scope on it. Lewis brought it by my house to show it to me, not long after he bought it. He said it could drop a deer clear across my pasture."

"And now I hear that the sorry bum is saying he killed Pat accidentally," Carmen went on. "Well nobody is going to convince me that it was an accident. I don't care what they say, I'm telling you it was no accident. And I'll stand in a courtroom and tell the judge that it was no accident. It was murder. Pure cold blooded murder. What's more, I think he'd planned it for a long time."

As Carmen talked on, Carol and I glanced at each other, trying to appear surprised at everything Carmen was saying.

"And there's more that I could tell you," Carmen said. "There's

194

things that went on while Pat was missing. But it would take too long to tell you here. I understand you live in Dallas. But the next time you come through Bedias, come to my house and I'll tell you about it. We live nearly seven miles out in the country, but I'm usually at home and I'll be glad to see you."

Walter then wrote a phone number on the back of a rumpled business card and handed it to me.

"You keep that," said Carmen, as I placed it in my pocket. "And remember, I'll be looking for you."

Carol and I then said good-bye to Carmen and Walter. But we knew we would talk with them again. And I wondered how many other secret-keepers we would find before it was all over.

As Carol and I walked across the cemetery toward the car, the wind suddenly felt colder. But the leaves were falling as gently as before. Quiet and Peaceful. And I walked on, pulling my jacket closer around my shoulders, wondering whether it was the coldness of the wind or my imagination.

CHAPTER 16

The next morning, Carol and I drove to the Sheriff's office in Anderson. It was time to meet Detective Larry Adams, in person. Adams was forty-five years old, six-foot-five in height, with gray hair, blue eyes and a friendly smile.

"It's nice to meet you after all this time," he said. "I know we talked on the phone a lot, but I didn't know whether or not we'd ever meet each other."

"That's one of the reasons we came by," I said. "We wanted you to see that we are real people, not just a couple of screaming voices on the phone. But we also want to ask a few questions about your new prisoner."

"He's pretty quiet," Adams said. "He hasn't said much since he was arrested."

"I've heard that he's saying Patricia's murder was an accident," I said.

"Yes, Lewis said it was an accident," Adams replied. "And he also said it was self-defense."

"If it was an accident, why didn't he try to get help for her? I understand that one of the daughters was at the house immediately after it happened. And that he stood out in his yard for twenty minutes talking to her. Why didn't he tell her that her mother was in the house dying?"

"That's a good question," said Adams.

"And did he say why he took Patricia's body to a garbage dump and buried her like an animal? And why he left her there for forty-four days while he went around lying about her, trying to make her look like a tramp?"

"He said he was scared."

"I'll just bet he was scared," I said. "He was scared of getting caught."

"I can't argue with that," said Adams.

"And why is he saying it was self-defense?" I went on.

"He said they got into an argument, they struggled over the gun, and the gun went off."

"Did he mention the fact that Patricia was sick when they drove home from Fred's place that afternoon. And that she was so sick she lay her head on his lap all the way home."

"No, he didn't tell me that. But I know about it."

"Well, how could a woman five feet two inches tall, and sick, have the strength to struggle with a gun?"

"That's a good question," Adams replied. "And I think we both know the answer."

"I want to ask you just one more: Did Lewis say whose idea it was to get the gun, in the first place?"

"It was Lewis," replied Adams. "He said he got up and took the gun out of the bedroom closet."

"That's what I thought," I said. "Lewis Crocker has been around guns all of his life. Carol and I both know that. And we don't believe he, or Patricia would have allowed a loaded gun in the house because of their youngest daughter and grandchildren. There were three children age five and under living in the house. And other children were in and out daily. So, common sense would tell us that when he took the gun out of the closet, he intended to use it. I think picking up the gun and loading it, showed his intent to kill her. And that makes it murder. Not self-defense."

"If the gun was 'bolt-action,' Lewis also had to cock it to shoot it," Carol said. "My husband has hunting rifles and I know that much about them."

"Well, I'm sure the District Attorney will have a long list of questions to ask him at the trial," Adams replied.

"Who is the District Attorney?"

"He's Latham Boone. You can find him at the courthouse, across the street. But he won't be the one to try Lewis' case, because Boone is going out of office at the end of the year. We'll have a new district attorney in January."

"Do you know who the new district attorney will be?"

"His name is David Barron. I can assure you, now, that he is already familiar with the case. He's been our assistant district attorney for the past four years. And he's a good man. He's tough and he's hard to beat. And he's a good friend."

"What about Brian Taylor, the Texas Ranger on the case?"

"He's one of the best in the state," Adams went on. "He's a good man. It was thanks to him that we finally found your sister. But I'd prefer to tell you about that at a later time. Are you coming down for the trial?"

"Yes. Both Carol and I will be there. Will you be there?"

"I wouldn't miss it. I'm sure I'll be called as a witness."

"Well, it's getting late and we have a long way to go. Thanks for your help."

"Thank you," he said. "I'm glad I got to meet you. You know, in a case like your sister's, inside information can be very important. And I want to thank both of you for your help. You know, a detective's work can be difficult at times. A case comes in and, most of the time, we'll know little or nothing about the personal lives of the people involved. We have to start from scratch gathering leads until we can make the picture come into focus. But one of the problems with this case was that I didn't count on Lewis being such a liar. I'm sorry it turned out like it did, and I'm sorry it took so long to find her."

"Well, I hope he won't be able to lie his way out of it."

"I sincerely doubt it," Adams went on. "Of course, his bond has been set at one hundred thousand dollars. And it's possible that someone could go his bail and get him released until trial. But I hope that won't happen."

It was late that night when Richard and I arrived back home in Dallas. And by the next morning, I knew I was ill. I spent the next two days in and out of doctor's offices, hearing the same diagnoses, – severe depression and I had developed a skip in my heartbeat. One doctor suggested a long vacation and a visit with my son in Alaska. Another suggested that I go home and rest, and try to forget about what happened to Patricia. The following week I took the medication the doctor prescribed and slept long hours to regain my strength. Then I awoke one morning, ready to go back to Grimes County. I had promises to keep, and miles to go seeking justice and the truth about Patricia's murder.

I decided to call Mother, and let her know that I was up and about again.

"I'm glad you called," Mother said. "I'm worried about you. I wanted to call you but I didn't want to upset you."

I assured her that she couldn't upset me more than I was already, and that I had called about her and Daddy.

"Well, Daddy just sits in his chair and stares out the window. He won't talk to anyone. And I try not to cry in front of him. Frances had another spell with her heart. And Merle has learned that he has high blood pressure. And I'm afraid Carol will have a nervous breakdown."

"Well, that's something else Lewis Crocker has done for our family," I said. "He has damned near killed all of us."

"I think I'm going to lose all of my children over this," Mother cried.

"No, Mother. You won't lose us all. It's the toughest thing we've ever had to face. But you won't lose us all."

Mother was still crying. "I'm going to cut down the pink rose bush," she said. "Every time I look at it I think of the last time I saw Patricia. She always came to see me on a Sunday, and I find myself staring at the roses and still looking for her every Sunday."

"Mother, I know it's hard for you, and I wish we could bring her back, but we can't. Have you heard from her daughters?"

"Yes. They visited Lewis," she went on. "And he told them that the case may not come to trial."

"Well, tell him not to be in a hurry to get rid of his jail uniform."

"He told one of the girls, quote: 'When I stand before the judge and tell him why I had to kill your mama, I'm going to walk out of that courtroom a free man,' unquote."

"Mother, you're going to hear a lot of garbage, so get used to it. But I don't want you to believe anything he says, because he's a liar.

Just believe me when I tell you that he's on his way to prison."

After the conversation with Mother was over, I called Carol. "I can't help it," Carol cried. "It's more than I can handle. I'm driving Emil up the wall, and I'm even afraid for my children to go to school. I'm afraid something will happen to them. And yesterday, I told my best friend to leave my house because she advised me to forget about Patricia. I feel like my world has crashed at my feet and I'm looking down at it, unable to pick up the pieces."

"Carol, we're both hurting. But I think Lewis is planning to lie his way out of a murder trial. And I think it's time for us to go back to Grimes County."

"I'd like to find out what's going on with the Sheriff's department that would make Lewis think that he may not go to trial. The sonofabitch murdered our sister. Why wouldn't there be a trial?"

"I'd like to know what he had in mind when he told his daughters that 'when he stands before the judge and tells him why he had to kill their mother, that he would walk out of the courtroom a free man.' What the hell is he going to say? Is he going to tell the judge that he beat his wife and cheated on her for twenty-six years and how many times he threatened to kill her? And that one day she made him kill her and bury her body in a garbage dump, and then she made him go all over the county telling lies about her? And now that his ass is in jail, he doesn't deserve it? Does he think everybody is going to believe his lies?"

"I want to go to Grimes County as soon as we can. I want to find people who knew Patricia. I want to find out what they know about her, and her marriage problems. And I want to know who found her body and how it was found. And everything else they care to tell us."

"I can meet you in Madisonville, Wednesday afternoon," Carol said. "But I forgot to tell you that I received an anonymous phone call, a couple of days after the funeral. The caller was a woman and she said it would be best if you and I stay out of Madisonville. That's all she said."

"Well, all I have to say to that is, 'it's a free country, and at my age, I'll go where I please. Unless the law tells me different.' "

"Okay, Sherlock. I'll see you in Madisonville, Wednesday afternoon at three."

I tried to remember how many times I had driven the Interstate from Dallas to Madisonville. The countryside never changed, except for the grass and trees that changed with the seasons. In springtime, colorful dogwood, redbud and plum trees brightened the creeks and roadside parks. In autumn, the rolling hills wore colors of red, orange and gold. In years gone by, I always enjoyed the three hour drive, thinking of happy places and being with my family. But this time I thought only of the heartache of losing Patricia, and the fear of what I would learn before I came this way again. But regardless of what I learned, I could face it with Carol. She was my best friend, my sister and my confidante. And as I turned off the interstate in Madisonville, she was waiting.

"You're fifteen minutes late," she said, as I parked beside her. "I told Priscilla if you didn't show up soon, we were going to go meet you."

"You know who that reminds me of, don't you?" I laughed.

"Yes, and we need to call her as soon as we check in at the motel."

"So you're back in town," Aunt Margaret said when I called her. "Well, why aren't you at my house? I've got an extra bedroom and soap and water. You don't have to stay at a motel."

"We appreciate that, but we have some business to take care of."

"Well, I want to know where you're going and when you get back. And if you're not back on time, I'll send Bill after you. I'm serious. You girls could get in trouble snooping around. Promise me you'll be careful."

I said I'd call her every day. But Carol and I had already decided that our first call would be to Jack Thompson, foreman of the Jim Pierce ranch.

Later that afternoon, Carol called Jack Thompson and set up an appointment to talk with him the following day.

I phoned the office of Latham Boone, District Attorney of Grimes County. I wanted to know whether there would be a trial or not. And if not, why not.

"I'm sorry, Mr. Boone has left for the day," a man's voice answered. "This is David Barron. Can I help you?"

I first introduced myself by name, then as Patricia's sister.

"Oh, yes ma'am. I'm glad you called. I'd like to extend my sympathy to you and your family. I didn't know Mrs. Crocker, but it was a very sad thing that happened. I have the file on my desk now."

I thanked him, and then asked if it was true that the case may not come to trial.

"I don't know where you heard that. But I can assure you that it will go to trial. The date hasn't been set on it yet, but we intend to take it all the way. It will be sometime after the first of the year, probably in February. Mr. Boone is retiring the end of December, and I'll take office as district attorney in January. But I intend to prosecute the case to the best of my ability."

"Mr. Barron, I am so happy to hear you say that. And if there's anything I can do, please let me know. In fact, my sister and I are in Madisonville now. We plan to talk to some of Patricia's friends."

"Could you give me a phone number where you can be reached?" he asked. "I think Brian Taylor would like to meet with you."

"That would be fine. My sister and I will be here for several days."

THE DARK SIDE OF TWILIGHT:

CHAPTER 17

The next morning as we turned onto the highway that would take us through Bedias and to the Jim Pierce ranch, I noticed tears in Carol's eyes.

"I can't help it," she said, tearfully. "Every time I go through Bedias, I keep thinking if I go to her house, she'll be there, and the nightmare will be over."

"Carol, I know how you feel, but we've got to get through this thing. We can't let it destroy us. If we do, then Lewis will win. Think about that."

"I'll be okay," she said. "But I want to go to Patricia's house. It's something I've got to do. I want to see where that bastard killed her."

When we came to the stop light in Bedias, I turned and drove slowly down the narrow gravel street, again remembering the hot summer afternoon of my last visit with Patricia. The visit now seemed so long ago, but for a moment, it seemed like yesterday. As I came to the end of the street I saw her car in the driveway. And the flowers she had carefully tended were still in bloom. The baskets of fern hanging on the front porch appeared green and crisp. Even the leaves from the tree in the driveway had been raked and placed into barrels near the old camping bus. And as I glanced toward the porch, I half expected to see Patricia running down the steps to meet us. For a moment I stared at it all, imagining the nightmare had never happened. But the stark reality was that the house now stood in cold silence. Its walls reeking with dark memories of horror and murder.

I walked to the front window and looked inside, noticing the rose colored drapes now torn and left partially hanging. I glanced at the chairs where Patricia and I had sat during my last visit, and then toward the kitchen where the girls had laughed and cooked on that day. And through the hallway, I saw the door which led to Patricia's and Lewis' bedroom. Then I glanced at the long narrow path of bare flooring where Lewis had removed the carpet. The bare pathway was approximately five feet wide and ran the length of the living room and hallway and ended at Patricia's bedroom door. And as I glanced at its bareness, I knew the reason it had been scrubbed so thoroughly.

Carol and I walked to the back of the house and looked through Patricia's bedroom windows. The carpet and curtains were gone. The room had been freshly painted and was empty, except for Patricia's clothes and shoes in the closet. But as we looked further, we saw a mattress partially covered with black plastic leaning against a wall in a dark corner. I wondered if Patricia had been lying or had fallen on the mattress when she was shot.

I couldn't look in the house any more. But as I stepped away from the window I felt loose dirt beneath my shoes. And when I looked down, I was standing on the septic tank where Lewis had hidden Patricia's purse.

"Did you see the mattress?" said Carol. "I'll bet that's where the sonofabitch killed her. And there's spots here on the windows that look like dried blood."

"It could be. That's probably why there are no curtains on the windows. Look at the size of the bedroom. As small as it is the whole room was probably splattered with blood, including the curtains. He could have wrapped her body in the curtains and buried them with her."

"But when the girls came home, wouldn't they have seen a lot of blood?"

"They probably did. But Lewis explained that he had cut his finger."

"Jean, I have a feeling that we're being watched, even as we speak."

"I don't doubt that a bit. Let's leave now, before we get into trouble."

The feeling of being watched and not knowing who was watching stayed with me, and as I drove back down the street toward the highway, I glanced frequently through my rearview mirror.

We were about five miles south of Bedias when I first suspected that we were being followed by an older model white pickup with a dirty windshield. But thinking perhaps it could be a farmer, or just someone in a hurry, I slowed down to give it room to pass. However, it didn't. Instead it continued to stay close behind me, tailgating my rear bumper, regardless of my speed.

"Well, as they say in the movies, 'it looks like we've got company.' See that gray house ahead of us? Let's stop and see if we have any relatives there."

"You know we never had relatives who lived there. And it would be our luck that that fool following us lives there."

"That's a chance we've got to take. If we don't, we may end up in a pasture."

A moment later I skidded across the driveway at the gray house, and the pickup passed on by. But there would be other days when it would find us again.

Finally, we drove through the black wrought-iron gates of the Jim Pierce ranch. Jack Thompson was sitting on his porch waiting for us. As he walked toward us, he turned away briefly, spitting tobacco juice onto the ground. Then he looked at us inquisitively.

"We're Patricia Crocker's sisters," Carol said.

"Glad to meet you. Come on in and sit a spell. I'll be glad to talk with you."

Jack Thompson was of medium height with reddish hair streaked with gray, and had a red handlebar mustache that I suspected many old-time cowboys would have envied. He was wearing blue faded jeans and shirt, and brown boots, and from looking at his tan leathery face, I guessed him to be in his mid-forties.

"Ya'll come on in," he said, and then motioned for the black dog lying on the porch to leave. "You may have to excuse the housekeeping. My wife is down in Houston, again. We've got a new grandson and she thinks she's got to be there to help take care of him. Course she always was the motherly type."

"We understand," I said, as we walked inside. "And we won't stay long."

"Oh, don't get me wrong," he replied, walking toward the living room sofa. "You're welcome to stay the rest of the afternoon. I'd enjoy the company. I'll just move the newspapers and both of you can sit right here. Would you care for coffee or iced tea?"

"No, we're fine," said Carol. "We just wanted to ask a few questions."

"Well, it was sure a tragic thing that happened to your sister," he said. "I still shake when I think about it. But I think I've already told you almost everything I know about it, the day we talked on the phone."

"Did you know Patricia?" I asked.

"No, I didn't know her well. But I talked to her several times when she came to the ranch with Lewis. If he forgot something at work, they'd come back by, usually late in the evenings."

"But of course you knew Lewis quite well, didn't you?"

"Oh, yes. I knew him. I was his foreman during the time he worked here."

"How long did Lewis work here at the ranch?" I asked.

"He was hired on the twenty-second day of June, and I fired him on the twenty-sixth day of August," Thompson replied.

"So, he worked on the ranch property nineteen days after he killed and buried Patricia," I said, shuddering. "What kind of work did he do?"

"Well, he was hired as a general laborer which meant that he had access to the whole ranch," Thompson went on. "And I think he also had the combination to the lock on the main gate. During working hours he had access to one of the company trucks. At one point, around the time his wife went missing, I remember that I sent him to repair some hinges on some of the gates back in the woods, near the dump. But later, when I went to look at them, none of them were fixed. He said the truck broke down. I don't know if he spent that time working on the truck, or what. But he later hauled trash to the dump."

"So he was familiar with the area where the dump is located," I said.

"Sure, he was," Thompson went on. "He worked back there, for about a week or so, cutting pipe and scrap metal."

208

Patricia Crocker

Jean Lasell

Carol Gully

Patricia, age 3

**Patricia and
Lewis, 1962**

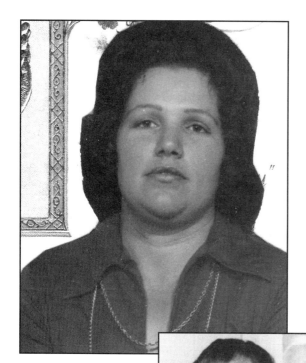

Patricia Crocker

Lewis Crocker

◀ **Texas Ranger Brian Taylor**

▼ **Detective Larry Adams**

◀
**Investigator
Tracy
Wright**

District Attorney David Barron

Deputy Jackie Siracusa

Brenda Williams

Judge Erwin G. Ernst

Grimes County Courthouse – Anderson, Texas

"Did anyone work back there with him?"

"No. He was the only one cutting scrap metal."

"Did he work at the dump after he buried Patricia there?"

"Yes, he did. He worked several days back there after he buried her."

"Did you notice anything about his behavior?"

"Well, he acted nervous and he was always late for work, but I thought he was just upset because his wife had left him."

"I believe you told Carol that you saw Lewis washing out the trunk of his car, and you noticed blood on the rear bumper. When did that happen?"

"It was the next day after his wife went missing," Thompson replied. "But at that time, I didn't know she was missing. In fact, I didn't hear about it until a week later. And even then I didn't think anything about it. I just assumed that they had had a lover's quarrel and she had left for a few days. But later, after I heard there was a missing persons report out for her, I got to thinking back and I remembered seeing the blood on the bumper of the car. But still, Lewis had said that he had gone fishing and caught a lot of fish and put them in the trunk of his car, and I had no reason to think otherwise. However, during the week after that, I started noticing that he would park his car in a different place every morning, instead of parking it where he was supposed to. And he'd roll up the windows and lock it, which was something he never did before. One day I asked him why he locked his car when the weather was so hot, and he said there was something wrong with one of the door locks and it locked itself automatically. I told him he ought to at least leave the windows down."

"But you know now why he was locking it, don't you?" queried Carol.

"Yeah, I know now," Thompson replied. "But I just wish I had known it then."

"He talked about his girlfriends, too, didn't he?" said Carol.

"Yeah, he did. But I don't know if I want to talk about that in front of you."

"I think we're all adults and we can handle it," Carol went on.

"Well, I wasn't around him much after working hours, but sometimes in the barn on Friday evenings I'd drink a beer with him and the other men. And we'd go over the work schedule, things we'd accomplished that week and what we needed to do the next week. And we talked about other things. Like parties and barbecues, and fishing and hunting. Lewis liked to talk about women. Now, I don't want you to think that we were all a bunch of married men talking about women. Several of the men were single and it was natural for them to talk about their girlfriends, and women that they wished were their girlfriends. And Lewis was the type of man that, whenever somebody said something, he'd always say something else to top it. So, he talked about his girlfriend in Madisonville and he said he had one in Roans Prairie, and another one in Anderson. He called them his 'screws,' and he said he could go to them any time he wanted. Now, I hope you'll pardon my language. But you asked me, and I told you."

"Do you know their names?" I asked.

"The only one I remember, off hand, is the one who works out at Claude and Betty's. That's a restaurant and lounge down near Roans Prairie. The girlfriend's name is Helen. And the only reason I remember her name is because my wife's name is Helen."

"Do you know her last name?"

"No," replied Thompson. "But you can imagine the look I gave him when he said Helen. Now, ladies, how about that cup of coffee? And I have orange juice or milk for the little one."

"That will be fine. Thank you."

A few moments later, Jack Thompson returned from his kitchen, carrying a yellow tray with three cups of coffee for us, and a glass of orange juice for Priscilla.

"I also have chocolate chip cookies if you'd care for some," he said. "Helen makes a fresh batch every week."

"No, thanks, we'll be going to dinner soon," Carol answered.

"Now, let me think a minute and see if I've told you everything," said Thompson, as he poured the coffee and sat down in his chair again.

"You said you fired Lewis on the twenty-sixth of August," I said. "That was almost three weeks after he buried Patricia's body at the dump. May I ask why you decided at that point in time to fire him?"

"Well, it was a number of things," Thompson replied. "He was acting nervous, and I think he suspected that I was watching him a little too close, like maybe I knew something when I really didn't. And, too, after the missing persons report was out, Larry Adams came out and talked to me, and we looked around the ranch property, including the dump. I didn't know exactly what we were supposed to be looking for, but when we got to the dump, we found a pair of Lewis' sunglasses and a pair of pliers. But since Lewis had worked at the dump, cutting scrap metal, I just thought he had lost his sunglasses there."

"How do you know they were his?" Carol asked.

"They were prescription sunglasses."

"What about the pliers?"

"Well, the pliers sort of rang a bell with me. I remembered that one of the bulldozers had been moved and there was nearly an hour's time on it that we couldn't account for. And I suspected that the pliers had been used to start it. And I still think so. You see, we had had bulldozers on the ranch clearing land and they also dug trenches at the dump. The trenches were used to bury garbage and junk that we needed to get rid of. And when one of the trenches got full, a bulldozer would make another one. In other words, the dump was like a landfill."

"But wasn't that the place where Lewis was seen burning something?" I asked.

"Yes, it was. We sometimes burn brush there," Thompson continued. "But Lewis wasn't burning brush that day. You know, you can tell the difference between a brush fire and any other kind of fire. But Lewis wasn't supposed to burn anything that day. Well, I saw some cardboard boxes in a pickup parked over by the barn, so I told two of the ranch hands to take them to the dump, and while they were back there, to see what Lewis was burning. Well, they got in the pickup and took off. Then about ten minutes later they came back to the barn, and I asked if they burned the boxes. They said they didn't actually get to the dump with them. They said Lewis saw them when they opened the gate going into the dump, and he hollered at them to wait. Then he told them to just leave the boxes and he would burn them later."

"Did the men see what he was burning?"

"No, they said they couldn't get close enough. But later, I asked Lewis what he burned, and he said it was just some trash. I never thought any more about it until Larry Adams and I went back there, looking around. That was when we found the sunglasses and pliers. And we found the place where Lewis had made the fire, but all that was left from it was a pile of ashes."

Thompson then paused briefly, and Carol and I bowed our heads in silence.

"Now, to answer your question of why I fired Lewis when I did, I just got to thinking about him and the more I thought about him, the more suspicious I became. I knew I couldn't prove anything on him, but I just didn't want him around here anymore. So I told him I had to let him go because we had to cut back the payroll."

"Will you tell us what happened the day Patricia's body was found?" I asked.

"You don't want to know that because it will only hurt you more," he said.

"Well, I want to know it," Carol said. "And I think we have the right to know it. I don't mean any disrespect, but how would you feel if she had been your sister?"

Thompson glanced down at his boots and then he looked at Carol and me.

"Allright, I'll tell you about it," he said, leaning back in his chair. "Now, evidently, it was first thought her body had been placed in water. Because, about a week before she was found, Sgt. Tommy Wright from the Montgomery County Sheriff's Department, brought a team of divers to the ranch and searched all the stock ponds. But of course they didn't find her because she wasn't there."

"But what happened on September the twentieth, the day her body was found? How did they find her?"

"Well, it started about daylight that morning. Texas Ranger Brian Taylor and investigator Tracy Wright from the Grimes County Sheriff's Office, and Sgt. Bill Smith who works for T.D.C., contacted me and asked my permission to come to the ranch. And they asked my approval for Sgt. Smith to bring a cadaver dog that was trained to find bodies underground and underwater. I gave my approval and met them at the main gate. Then I went with them to help them search. Sgt. Smith and the cadaver dog began checking places where a lot of brush had been buried by the bulldozers. The brush clearing had taken place during the time Lewis worked here. After the dog didn't find anything in the brush, we walked to the back part of the ranch, and to the dump. And when we got to the dump, the dog ran around it, and then stopped on the far side of it. The place where the dog stopped was an old trench that had been covered over and the dirt had already settled on it. But there was an area about six feet long and three feet wide in the dirt that didn't have the same conformity as the rest of the dirt around it. And it looked like it had recently been dug out and covered over again. In other words, that particular area just didn't look like the rest of the dirt on top of the trench. However, anyone just walking around out there might never have noticed the conformity of the dirt because there were two old rusty barrels and a water heater, and some other junk thrown on top of it, including an old piece of metal fence. Anyway, when the cadaver dog stopped there, Sgt. Smith knew it had found something."

"But how did the dog know it was Patricia's body?"

"The dog had sniffed one of her purses, and the purse had her scent in it. That was how the dog knew what it was looking for. Then when it was determined that there was a grave there, one of the ranch employees, Donald Ashmore, got into the trench and removed the rusty barrels and water heater. Then Sgt. Smith dug down in the dirt a few inches with a shovel and detected bone structure.

Then when Sgt. Smith was certain that it was human bone structure, he stopped, and the area was placed under tight security, and the Technical Service Team in Conroe was called to come to the ranch and exhume the body. You know, you have to be real careful about things like that. Then while we waited for the team to come from Conroe, District Attorney Latham Boone and Assistant District Attorney David Barron arrived at the scene."

"Wasn't Detective Adams there?"

"Yes, he was also at the scene. However, he had had a doctor's appointment in Bryan, early that morning, and that caused him to be a little late getting here."

"Were you there when the body was exhumed?" Carol asked.

"Yes."

"Do you know who arrested Lewis?"

"Yes. It was Adams and Taylor."

As Thompson finished telling us about what happened that day, Carol's face turned beet red and her tears flowed freely. But it had hit me in a different manner. For I had already, for the past two months, cried all the tears I thought I had left to cry. And now, I was tired of crying. I wanted vengeance. No matter what it cost, no matter whose toes I stepped on, I didn't care. I wanted Lewis to be punished, severely punished, for every dirty rotten thing he had ever done to Patricia.

"And just think how Lewis lied about her," Carol said to Thompson. "That sorry no good bastard. First he beats the hell out of her all during their marriage, then he shoots her like she was no more than a damn animal, then he buries her body in a damn garbage dump, and during the forty-four days her body was there rotting away, he's going to the damn beer joints telling everyone that she ran off somewhere with another man. And I'll bet you heard it, too, didn't you?"

"Yes, I heard it," replied Thompson.

"Well, did you ever really meet Charlie Lancaster or Bill, whoever they are?"

"Yeah. I seen old Charlie a few times. We were not friends but I knew who he was. He had a reputation for being a smooth talker and for dating women who had money."

"What about the guy named Bill?"

"I don't know who he was. I never heard of him."

214

"Well, getting back to Charlie Lancaster, do you know if Patricia knew him?"

"I don't know whether she did or not. But the last time I saw him, he was with a tall blonde-haired woman. She wasn't from this part of the country, though. Seems like I heard that she was from up around Amarillo."

"I wonder if Patricia knew her?"

"I doubt it. However, they could have all been casual acquaintances. They could have seen each other at barbecues or dances or somewhere like that. You know how small towns are. There's people who just sort of drift in. And they stay a while, and then suddenly they're gone. That's the way it was with old Charlie Lancaster. He drifted in, dated a few women with money, and a couple of months later, he was gone."

"Do you know where he went?"

"No. But I've got my suspicions," said Thompson.

"Detective Adams thinks that Charlie is in Wichita Falls," I said.

"Well, just between you and me, I don't think Charlie made it that far," Thompson replied.

"Why do you think that?"

Thompson paused for a moment, as though trying to decide whether he wanted to answer my questions or not. And as he thought about it, he reached for the coffee pot and poured more coffee into the three cups. Then he leaned back in his chair again.

"Mr. Thompson, if you know where Charlie is, I think you should tell Detective Adams. He has had the sheriff in Wichita Falls looking for Charlie."

"Now, I didn't say that I know where Charlie is. But I know where I think he is."

"Okay. Where do you think he is?"

"I think he's at the same place they found your sister. He's at the dump."

"What! Are you serious? Surely you're not!"

"I'll bet you my right arm that he's buried there," said Thompson.

"Why do you think that?"

"I don't know. It's just an eerie feeling I get every time I go back there. It's the same feeling I had when your sister was buried there."

"But why haven't you told this to Adams or Taylor?"

"Because I can't prove it."

"Well, do you know if Charlie has any relatives in this area? Maybe you could ask them if Charlie is missing."

"I think he has some cousins over in Bryan," Thompson went on. "But I'd feel awful dumb going up to one of them and asking if Charlie was missing. And even if he was missing, what would I say? I think he's buried at a garbage dump?"

"But how would he have gotten on the ranch? Did he ever work here?"

"No. But there are other ways."

"Are you insinuating that there could have been a connection between him and Patricia?"

"No, not at all. Not between him and Patricia."

"Then what are you saying?"

"I'd rather not talk about it, any more. Let's just leave it at that."

"You mentioned earlier that Lewis had the combination to the lock on the main gate," said Carol. "And it's our understanding that he killed Patricia around seven-thirty on the Sunday evening of August seventh. Do you remember if you were home that night?"

"No, I wasn't," Thompson replied. "As a matter of fact, I was out of town buying cows, and didn't get home until after midnight."

"Well, the reason I asked that question was because we were told that Lewis didn't bury the body until the next morning. And I wondered if perhaps you saw him drive through the gate at an odd time that day."

"No. He came to work that morning, about an hour late, as usual. And he asked if he could go fishing in the creek back in the woods. I wondered why he wanted to fish there, because the creek was half dry and there weren't any fish in it. I also wondered why he would want to fish in a creek when he had a big nice fishing boat at home. But then, I thought maybe he just wanted to be by himself a while, so

I gave permission for him to use the creek, thinking he'd go that afternoon after work."

"Did he?"

"I don't know," Thompson replied. "I was gone part of the day, and he never mentioned whether he went fishing or not. But now as I look back, I don't think he had any intentions of going fishing. Instead, I think he used that time to cover the grave with those old barrels and water heater and junk. And also looking back, there's something else that has bothered me about it. I can't figure out how he managed to carry the body by himself."

"What do you mean?"

Thompson paused for a moment, reaching for a note pad and pencil which lay on an end table by his chair.

"Well, I'll draw a map for you, as I tell you. Maybe that will help explain it better. You see, it was like this: the bulldozers had dug a long trench, about three to four feet deep, on the far side of the dump, leaving the dirt from the trench piled high in a slope along the side of it. And Lewis buried her in the trench up against the slope. But, in order to get to the far side of the dump, and to that slope, he had to either carry her, or drag her across the dump, or around it. Because there was no way that he could have driven his car around to it. See, he would have had to park his car way out here. Now, the thing that bothers me, and what I'd like to know, is how he was able to carry her body, dead weight, to that slope, by himself. To me, that is a mystery in itself."

"Do you think someone helped him?" Carol asked.

"I don't know," Thompson answered. "But just keep in mind that Lewis only weighed about one-fifty, and Patricia weighed about one-twenty-five."

"How soon after he killed her do you think he buried her?"

"I don't know. But if he buried her the next day, like he said he did, I don't see how he got her across the dump, by himself. Quite frankly, I don't think he would have chanced burying her in broad open daylight, because there were always ranch employees working, and he could have easily been seen."

"Well, I know he made a phone call to one of his daughters around midnight, on the night of the murder," I said. "He asked if she had seen Patricia, and if Patricia's black car was still at the daughter's house. I also know that the call was made from a pay phone in Roans Prairie. So, that would place him in this area at that time. That's why I asked if you were here at the ranch that night. I thought you may have seen him drive through the main gate."

"Well, I wish I had been here but, unfortunately, I wasn't. However, that's not to say that he didn't bury her that night."

"Do you remember whether the moon was full that night?" Carol asked. "If it was, it would have provided enough light."

"No. I don't remember if it was or not," Thompson went on. "But even if it had been pitch dark, the gravel on the road to the dump is white, and he could have driven through the gate with his car lights off, and still had enough light to see until he got back into the woods, out of sight."

"Assuming that Charlie Lancaster's body is also buried at the dump, how do you think it got there?" I asked.

"I'd rather not say," replied Thompson. "But I definitely think it's there."

"Well, have you ever heard anything that would connect him with Patricia?"

"As far as the two of them actually having an affair, the answer is no."

"Mr. Thompson, your choice of words leads me to believe that you know something about them. And since we're all adults, I'd like to hear it."

"Well, there's nothing I can tell you, except that you can rest assured that they were not lovers. If they had been, everyone would have known about it. For in a small community like this, there are very few secret keepers."

"So, you've never heard their names connected, is that true?"

"I heard some bar talk once. But I didn't believe it."

"Would you tell us about it?" I asked.

"Yeah, I'll tell you, but like I said, I don't believe it. It supposedly happened out at Claude and Betty's place. Now, keep in mind that old Claude is a strange character anyway, and he was the one that told it. He said it happened about a month before the murder. Anyway, to get on with the story, he said that Lewis and Patricia were in his place one night, they ate there and had a few drinks, and then sat around talking until closing time. And as they were getting ready to leave, Patricia went to the bathroom, and Lewis waited for her at the bar. And Charlie was also sitting at the bar. Claude said he was putting beer in the cooler, and when Patricia returned, she walked by Charlie, and asked if he was going to her house tonight, or somebody else's."

"Well, I really have to laugh at that," I said. "And I'll tell you why. In the first place, it doesn't even sound like something she would say. She wouldn't have dared say it, even if she'd wanted to. Just think for a moment: Everyone who ever met Lewis knew that he was crazy jealous. And Patricia knew it better than anyone. Now, picture this: Lewis is standing there waiting for her to come out of the bathroom. Charlie is sitting at the bar. Claude is putting beer in the cooler behind the bar. And it's reasonable to assume that all three men were talking to each other. Then, here comes Patricia out of the bathroom. She's walking toward Lewis, but on the way, she suddenly stops and flirts with Charlie. Give me a break! There's no way she would have done that. As jealous as Lewis was, he would have knocked her down and stomped her before she got to the door."

"I thought the same thing," Thompson replied. "That's why I didn't think it was worth mentioning. However, speaking of Claude, I'm going to tell you something serious. All the time you've been here, I've been wondering whether or not I should tell you. Now, I've decided I'm going to. You'll probably hear it sooner or later anyway. But before I do, would you care for more coffee?"

"Oh, no thank you," I replied. "We have to leave in a few minutes."

"Well, the other thing I want to tell you, about Claude, happened just three weeks before the murder. Lewis and Patricia had an argument and he got the gun after her. She ran to her car and left, heading toward Roans Prairie. Lewis took the gun and jumped into their other car and chased her down the highway."

"Yes, we heard about that," I said.

"But I don't think you've heard all of it," replied Thompson. "At least, not the part where Claude came in. Now, as I was saying, while Lewis chased Patricia down the highway, one of the daughters called the Sheriff and reported it. And the Sheriff came looking for both Patricia and Lewis. In the meantime, when she got to Roans Prairie, she saw a DPS highway patrol car and she pulled into a gas station. Whereupon the DPS officer arrested her. Lewis saw her being arrested, so he drove on out to Claude and Betty's place. And there, a customer came in and informed Lewis of Patricia's arrest, and that the Sheriff was also looking for him. Then, Claude asked Lewis if he was carrying a gun. Lewis said he had a rifle and a pistol in his car, and that both guns were loaded. Claude offered to keep the guns for Lewis to keep him from being arrested for the guns as well as for being drunk. Claude and Lewis went to the car for the guns, and Lewis handed a rifle to Claude to keep for him. But Claude never saw the pistol. Anyway, Claude took the rifle into his office and took Lewis home. Then, later that week, Lewis asked Claude to return the rifle to him. He said he wanted to go hog hunting. But Claude refused to give the rifle back, pretending that he had left it at home. After that, Lewis continued for a couple of weeks, asking for the gun back. Until finally, Claude gave it to him. And, about a week after that, Lewis shot Patricia with the same rifle."

"Well, Mr. Thompson, we thank you for sharing your information. It has been quite an experience for all of us. And thanks for the coffee, too. However, we have to leave now. Thanks again. We appreciate your help."

"Well, all I did was cooperate with the Law," replied Thompson. "I'm just sorry about what happened to your sister. And I wish we could have found her sooner. I know your family has suffered a great loss. But I think everyone who knew her will remember her with sadness. I know I will. And, to my dying day, I'll always wonder what was going through Lewis' mind on the days he worked at the dump, after he buried her there. I just wonder how he felt knowing his wife's body was buried just a few feet from where he was working. He had to have been a cold-hearted bastard to stand that."

"I think we all agree with that. But our goal now is to learn as much as we can about her last days and hours, before the murder. For instance, I'd like to talk to Claude and Betty."

"Well, as you go back through the main gate, turn right and take the highway to Roans Prairie, then turn right again and go about three miles west until you see an old red building trimmed in white. There'll be a sign out front that reads: 'C and B's Barbecue.' There's one more thing I want to tell you. There's a strange breed of people who live in this area. And while you may not know them, they could know you. So, be careful."

"Thanks, we will. By the way, do you know anyone who drives a dirty white pickup?"

"There's several of those around here. But just remember to be careful."

I walked to the car and waited while Carol pulled grass burrs from Priscilla's socks and shoes. And as I waited, I glanced at the tall trees which followed the gravel road from the main gate to the back of the ranch and then into a larger mass of trees that stretched as far as the eye could see. I thought of the drawings on Thompson's map, showing the trees surrounding the dump. Now, the trees looked so still. So gentle and peaceful. But they knew. They knew all along that Patricia's body was buried there, among them.

Later, as I drove back through the main gate, I glanced at the trees again, through my rearview mirror.

"Is something wrong?" Carol asked.

"I was just thinking that if trees could talk, what stories they could tell."

"That's for sure," said Carol. "You know, Jack Thompson scared me when he said a strange breed of people lived around here, and told us to be careful."

"Me, too. I think it was good advice. And a good place to start is with Claude and Betty. I don't think we should let them know that we're Patricia's sisters. Let's just pretend that we're passing through and stopped there to eat."

CHAPTER 18

Finding "C and B's Barbecue" was as easy as Jack Thompson had said it would be. But as we drove into the empty parking lot, I felt uneasy about being there.

We opened the screened door and walked inside, glanced around for a moment, and then sat at a table near the back door. A man, whom I assumed was Claude, was removing cans of beer from boxes at the bar. He appeared to be about the age of sixty, medium height with thin gray hair, and heavy to the point that his stomach hung over his trousers. A tall woman with dark hair stood by the cash register near the front door. She was wearing a red western shirt, blue scarf and faded jeans, and appeared to be around the age of fifty.

A few moments later, she brought menus and glasses of water to our table.

"How nice to see you again," she said, placing the menus and water on the table. "You're Patricia's sisters, aren't you?"

"Yes, we are. How did you know?"

"I was at her funeral, and I remember you. My name is Betty. Could I get something for you? Iced tea or coffee? We also have barbecue and cheeseburgers. And I make good french fries. I do most of the cooking myself, except on weekends when we're busy."

We ordered cheeseburgers, French fries and iced tea. Then she brought the tea to our table, smiled at us, and walked back to the kitchen behind the bar.

A few moments later, I heard the sizzling sounds of meat frying, and as I glanced toward the kitchen window, she looked at me. I turned around, pretending I hadn't noticed her, and began talking to Carol.

"Don't look toward the kitchen, we're being watched," I said. "You know, I've had an uneasy feeling about this place ever since we drove into the parking lot. I don't know why, but there's something about it that's spooking me."

"Maybe it's because we know that Patricia and Lewis spent a lot of time here," Carol said. "And we've heard about Claude taking the rifle to protect Lewis' hide and what he said about Patricia flirting with old Charlie. But let's just stay calm and pretend that we're only passing through."

It wasn't long before Betty returned to the table, carrying plates of cheeseburgers and a basket of French fries.

"I hope you won't mind if I sit here with you," she said.

"No, we don't mind at all. Please be our guest," I replied. "Perhaps you could tell us something about Patricia. How well you knew her, that sort of thing."

"Well, I knew her for ten years," Betty replied. "And of course I knew Lewis and their daughters. The daughters worked for me, from time to time, waiting tables. And Patricia and Lewis were in here a lot."

"Were they usually together?"

"Oh, yes. They nearly always came here on Friday nights to eat barbecue. And they loved to dance. Of course, we never had a band to dance to, but we have a good juke box with all the old favorites on it. And as you can see, we have a big dance floor. You should see it on weekends. It's always crowded."

"Yes, I know Patricia loved to dance," said Carol. "After Jean and our other sister married, Patricia and I were the last girls at home. And we used to go to sock hops on Friday nights, and dance to rock and roll. Then later, we learned to dance the Texas two-step to country music."

"Yes, I think Patricia mentioned that," said Betty. "I know she was a real good dancer. But Lewis didn't like for her to dance with anyone except him. He was a pretty good dancer, too."

"Did you see Patricia very often during the few weeks before she died?"

"Yes, I saw both Patricia and Lewis, several times during that time. In fact, they were here late on the Friday night before she was killed on Sunday. They came in and ate, and visited until almost closing time. Then the next night, Saturday night, they were supposed to meet their friends, Mack and Rosa, here. Lewis met them that night, and stayed a while. Then he left, saying he was going to pick up Patricia from her work. But they didn't come back. And I never saw her again."

"Did Lewis come back that night?" I asked.

"No, he didn't. But he came in on Monday morning, about eight-thirty, and he was already drunk."

"Was that the next morning after he killed her?"

"Yes, it was," replied Betty. "And I scolded him for being drunk that early in the morning. But he said that he and Patricia had had an argument, and she had left him again."

"From what I've heard, Lewis was seen in several places, between eight and eight-thirty on that particular morning. And I'm wondering just how he managed to do that."

"Oh? Where else was he?" Betty asked.

"Well, according to one of the daughters, he was in Navasota, specifically at that time. And he was at his work at that time. And he was here at that time. And you say he was drunk when he was here. It's all a little confusing to me. Because I fail to see how he could have sobered up so quickly between here and the ten miles to his work. And surely you have heard, as we have, that that was also the approximate time that he said he buried Patricia's body."

"Oh, excuse me, please," said Betty, getting up from her chair. "I think I hear the phone ringing in my office. I'll be back with you in a few minutes."

"I'd like to know what the hell is going on, or should I say, 'what went on,' " said Carol, as Betty walked away.

"I don't know," I said. "But I think we've just met one of those 'strange breed of people' that Jack Thompson warned us about. And I think she's lying to protect someone. So, let's hurry and leave. And whatever I say, don't question me in front of her."

A short time later, Betty returned to the table and sat down again. "Sometimes that phone has a mind of its own," she said, smiling. "I'll think I hear it ringing, and when I answer it, no one is there. But getting back to Patricia, I think I should explain to you that I was her friend, and I still am. But Claude and I also thought a lot of Lewis and their children. And I consider myself to be Rhonda's second mother."

"I understand," I replied. "I'm sure that both of them, as well as the daughters, had many friends. And we are not attempting to try to change that. It's just that we are interested in learning about Patricia's last days of life."

"Well, I wish I could help you more," Betty went on. "But she was working at Sallonger's and I didn't see her much that last week. Oh, by the way, do you plan to attend Lewis' trial? That is, if it comes to trial. Personally, I doubt that it will ever get that far."

"Why do you say that?" I asked.

"Well, I don't think a trial would accomplish anything, other than to stir up bad feelings. I think if he hadn't been arrested, and if the Law had just left him alone long enough, he would have killed himself."

"Do you really think so? Well, I wonder why he didn't do it during the six weeks Patricia's body lay buried at the dump. From what I hear, he was in the beer joints every night lying about her, trying to make people think she was no more than a whore."

"Well, people who knew her would never believe that," Betty went on.

"I'm sure they wouldn't, but I wonder if any of them ever told him to shut his mouth. Or were they scared of him, too?"

"There may have been a few who were scared of him. But we never took him seriously. We just laughed it off as being bar talk."

"Yes, I know he liked to drink and lie," said Carol. "I was his sister-in-law for twenty-six years. And believe me, you don't want to hear the stories I could tell you about that. But, he was not suicidal."

"I think he was, and still is," Betty inserted.

"Look, if he wanted to commit suicide, why the hell hasn't he

226

already done it?" I asked. "Everyone knows he's perfectly capable of using a gun. Why didn't he shoot himself with the same gun he shot Patricia with? Frankly, I wish he had. Because I don't like to think of my tax dollars being used to pay for his trial. And there will be a trial. Because he owes our family, he owes the State of Texas, and he owes society. And you can bet I'll be there when it happens."

"Well, I apologize if I've upset you," said Betty.

"That's okay. I have no hard feelings against you. It's just that we've been through so much, I can't help but get angry if I talk about it for very long."

"Here, let me take your tea glasses and refill them," said Betty.

She then picked up the plates and glasses from the table and walked quietly toward the kitchen while Carol and Priscilla made their way to the bathroom.

I sat there alone at the table and glanced around the huge barn-like room. The walls were covered with replicas of fish and fish nets, alternated with deer antlers and other trophies. And three pool tables stood along the west side wall. Then in the east corner of the dance floor, there was a juke box for dancing.

Suddenly, I heard a popping noise behind me and I turned toward the bar. But it was only Claude stacking beer boxes, clearing the way for the night customers to arrive. I quickly turned around again, pretending not to notice. I felt tears welling in my eyes. Oh damn. Damn it all to hell, I thought. I won't let them see me cry. Then I looked around the room some more. I looked at the tables, wondering how many times Patricia and Lewis had been here. And I wondered how the place looked on Saturday nights when the dance floor was crowded, and if Patricia had ever sat in the same chair that I was now sitting in.

For a moment I closed my eyes and imagined how it might have been on a night, a year ago. In my mind, I saw the place as loud and noisy. Waitresses carrying drinks to the tables. Claude serving beer from behind the bar. Betty sitting at the cash register by the front door. The dance floor was crowded and people were dancing to a slow country music song. And there among them, I saw Patricia and

Lewis dancing close together. Lewis trying to steady his feet enough to keep time with the music. And Patricia trying to help him. They both laughed for a moment, then pulled each other closer. She lay her head on his shoulder and he held her gently. They were in love. And oh, how they danced.

In my mind, I watched them dance to one country music song after another, holding each other close, happy and in love. Life was good for them, and for me. I would visit their home again on another hot summer day and find it alive with love and laughter. The nightmare was only a bad dream. It had never happened. It would not happen. For I was here with them in this noisy, smoke-filled room, listening to the music, watching as they danced.

"Jean, are you all right?" Carol asked, putting her hand on my shoulder.

"Yes, I'm okay. I was just concentrating a little too deeply, I guess. Wondering about the times Patricia and Lewis were here."

"Sorry to be late with your tea," Betty said, setting the refilled glasses on the table. "But as I say, that blasted phone has a mind of its own. And I know if I fail to answer it, someone will surely be on the line."

"Oh, that happens to me sometimes, too," I laughed.

"Well, I see it's getting about time for that evening crowd to start," she went on, glancing at her watch. "So, I'd better get busy. Ya'll go ahead and enjoy your tea. And if you see a bunch of bowlegged sweaty cowboys coming through the door, think nothing of it. It happens every day."

"Thanks, but we'll be leaving in a few minutes," I said. "However, there's something else I want to ask you, and I'll be brief. I know you're busy. I wanted to ask you about Claude keeping the rifle for Lewis."

"Who told you about that?"

"I'd rather not say who told me. But I'd like to know if it's true."

"Yes, it's true. Claude kept Lewis' rifle for about three weeks. And he didn't really want to give it back. Not that he wanted it for himself, or anything."

"Why did Claude keep it?"

"He was hoping to prevent anything bad from happening. We tried to make excuses for keeping the rifle, but Lewis began insisting that Claude give it back, and he gave it back because he had to. Then, about a week later, what we had hoped to prevent happened."

"You mean the murder."

"Yes."

Suddenly, I was conscious of the screeching sounds of pickup trucks driving into the dusty parking lot, slamming their doors. Then, one by one, eight or ten noisy cowboys walked through the screen door and headed for the bar.

"Carol, I've got an eerie feeling about this place. Let's leave now."

"Well, for heaven's sake, wait for me," she replied, taking Priscilla's hand.

As we stood at the cash register, paying our bill, Betty smiled.

"Well, I'm glad I got to see you again," she said. "Where are you staying? Will you be around for a few days? Maybe you can stop in again."

"Perhaps we will, some other time," I answered. "But for now, we're just passing through. We're on our way to Houston today to visit an aunt."

"Really? I thought you'd be staying in Madisonville," she went on.

"Oh, no. We rarely ever stay there," I lied. "Could you tell us the shortest way to get to Houston, from here?"

"Sure. Just take the highway out front. It will take you to Interstate 45."

As we walked outside to the car, several more pickups drove into the parking lot, carrying "bowlegged cowboys," as Betty called them. And I found myself looking for a dirty white pickup among them.

"What are you looking for? The white pickup?" Carol asked.

"Yes. As many times as Betty answered the phone, I was wondering if someone was calling to find out if we were there."

"Well, I hope not," Carol replied. "By the way, why did you tell her we were going to Houston?"

"Because I don't trust her," I answered. "Now, you tell me why she thought we were staying in Madisonville."

"A lucky guess?"

"I wonder. But just in case, I'm going to drive out of here heading west, the opposite direction from Houston. Then we'll circle back toward Madisonville."

"If we're going to go that way, we may as well stop at Sallonger's Restaurant. That's where Patricia was working that last week, remember?"

"Do you know where it is?"

"Not exactly. But Mother said it was on the highway near Carlos. So, it shouldn't be hard to find. We can always stop for coffee and dessert."

The drive toward Carlos was hilly and relaxing. And as I glanced at the large trees and thick underbrush along both sides of the highway, I thought how much the scenery had changed in such a short distance. I particularly noticed the thick underbrush and thought of the animals who lived inside it. Then the gruesome thought that dead bodies had been thrown into it. And I wondered if they had been found. Oh, God, I was becoming paranoid, I thought. First the white pickup, now the underbrush. It had to stop.

"I'll bet there's a lot of deer out there in that underbrush," said Carol.

"You're probably right," I replied. "But I'm not worried about the four legged animals in there. What bothers me is the two-legged animals. I think I must be getting paranoid. I'm just so damn suspicious of everyone, any more."

"Well, in our situation, I think we should be suspicious. For our own sake."

CHAPTER 19

Sallonger's Restaurant was a large red brick building adorned with dark gray window shutters and colorful flowers along its walkway. As we walked inside, I noticed a large fireplace, its fire softly burning, and there were intricately designed red lamps hanging slightly above round polished tables.

A tall lady with soft blonde hair, worn with jeweled combs, walked toward us. She wore a blue dress with an elaborate silver necklace, dark hose and black shoes. She greeted us warmly, escorting us to a table by a front window.

We sat there a few moments, glancing at the atmosphere, both Carol and I remembering that Patricia had worked here the day before she died. We wondered how that day had been for her. Was she happy? Was she sad? Who did she talk to? What did she say? Did she suspect that her life was in danger?

A few moments later, a waitress brought glasses of water to our table, and we ordered two coffees and a glass of juice.

"Could you tell us if Mrs. Sallonger is here?" Carol asked.

"Yes, she is. She escorted you to your table," the waitress replied.

"Would you like to speak to her?" the waitress went on. "I can tell her."

"Yes, please. Would you tell her that we're Patricia Crocker's sisters?"

A few moments later, when the waitress returned with our coffee and juice, the blonde haired lady returned with her and stood beside the table.

"Hello. I'm Mary Sallonger," she said, extending her hand to both of us. "I'm pleased to meet you. Lonie tells me that you're Patricia's sisters."

"Yes, we are," Carol replied. "And we were wondering if perhaps you would tell us something about her. We understand that this was her last place of employment."

"Yes, that's true," Mary replied. "Excuse me a moment, while I pour a cup of coffee for myself. Then I'll be glad to tell you all I can."

She then turned and walked toward the far end of the room, to a table upon which coffee pots and tea pitchers were kept. As she did so, I caught the aroma of expensive perfume. She was indeed a lady. A lady of means. A lady of beauty. She then poured a cup of coffee, placed it on a napkin in a saucer, and returned to our table, and sat in a chair between Carol and me.

"First of all, I'm very happy to meet both of you," Mary said. "I've often wondered about Patricia's family, and how sad they must feel. Really, I only knew her for three years, but she was a wonderful person. She was pretty, and she had a good personality. She was warm and caring. And such a hard worker. I was so pleased when she asked to work here. I knew she had worked for the school district for many years, and I asked her why she chose to leave there. But she was rather vague about her answer. So, I assumed that she didn't want to discuss it. It didn't matter to me anyway, because I knew she could do anything around here that needed to be done. However, I didn't want to hire her for just any job. So, I hired her as a hostess/cashier. That's what I do when I'm here."

"How long did she work here?" Carol asked.

"She was here only a week," Mary went on. "Her first day of work was on August first, and her last day was August sixth."

"That was the day before she was killed," said Carol. "Would you tell us what you remember about that day? Did you notice anything unusual about her?"

"Well, I wasn't here all day, but after we learned that she was missing, my employees had a lot of things to tell me. And I knew a few things myself. For instance, during her first couple of days here, I noticed that Lewis would come every night to pick her up from work, even though she had her own car, a yellow Buick. She seemed a little embarrassed about him being here, and one night she made the comment that he came to follow her home because her tires were bad. A couple of days later, she bought new tires, but Lewis kept coming in every night, anyway. I had heard that he had an alcohol problem, but I decided not to comment on it, as long as he behaved himself. Then, on the night of August sixth, her last night here, Lewis came in several times. He always sat at the table near the front door."

"What did he do while he waited?"

"Well, on that night, he sat at the same table. He appeared to be very aggravated and he smoked one cigarette after another. And he left several times, and would be gone about thirty minutes, then he would return. While he was gone, the waitress would clean the table and empty the ashtray. He started complaining about that. At one point he went to the bathroom and when he came back, the ashtray had been emptied, and he said, 'a man can't even go to the bathroom in this damn place, without having his ashtray emptied!' In the meantime, Patricia was becoming more nervous. She tried to calm him down, but they argued. I learned later, that they were to meet some friends at Claude and Betty's place, so that could have been part of his reason for being so angry. However, let me point out that Patricia was not working overtime. Lewis should have been aware of that, and I'm sure he was. After he confronted the waitress again for cleaning the ashtray, Patricia came to the office and asked if she could leave early. Of course, she was assured that it was all right. She left the office and went to where the employees' time cards are kept. Lewis met her there and jerked her time card away from her. He shoved her, trying to look at her time card. I guess he wanted to see whether she had worked as many hours as she was supposed to. Patricia started crying, and they left. That was the last time we saw her."

"When did you learn that she was missing?" I asked.

"Her last night here was on a Saturday, and she had the day off on Sunday. When she failed to show up for work on Monday, I called her daughter, Tammie. Tammie said she had run away again, and that she often did that. I was so shocked, I never called back. Nor did I hear anything more about her until Detective Adams came to question me about her paycheck."

"Well, thanks for talking with us. We appreciate it. But it's getting late and we have to go. I don't like to drive on country roads after dark."

"Neither do I," Mary said. "Especially on nights like this when there's no moonlight."

Her eyes welled with tears and she dabbed at them daintily as we walked across the room and stood by the front entrance saying goodbye.

"It was a pleasure meeting you both. I hope we meet again," she said. "I wish the circumstances were different, and Patricia had been with us."

"But, Mrs. Sallonger, for all we know, perhaps she was."

The thick trees along the hilly country road back to Roans Prairie, caused the moonless night to appear darker and more foreboding than I could have imagined. And as we came closer to Claude and Betty's barn, I found myself thinking again about the dirty white pickup. Wondering if we would see it on their parking lot as we drove by.

"Carol, when we pass Claude and Betty's place, I want you to look closely for the white pickup."

"Don't worry, I've been watching for it ever since we left Sallonger's. And if its driver is who I think it might be, his ears will ring for a month when I get through with him. Even when he was a kid, he was just a little wimp, and I slapped him then and I'm not afraid to do it again."

"Whoa, there, Watson," I laughed. "Stop and start over. First, tell me who you think was driving that old beat up dirty piece of junk with double bumpers."

"Okay, Sherlock, I think it could have been Lenny Compton. And if it was, he's going to have jaws to match his double bumpers. I won't stand for being chased all over the country."

"But suppose it's not him? Remember, you couldn't see who was driving?"

"Well, maybe it wasn't him, but as far as I'm concerned, he's a strong suspect because it's just the kind of stunt that would be right up his alley."

Fortunately, however, we didn't see the pickup at Claude and Betty's, nor did anyone follow us during the long dark drive back to Madisonville.

When we arrived at our motel, we stopped at the office for any messages we may have had while we were gone.

"Yes, ma'am, there were three calls," replied Allen, the desk clerk. "Mr. Gully called about fifteen minutes after you left. He asked if you said where you were going. I told him you didn't. A lady made the last two calls but she didn't leave her name. She said she'd call back later."

"About the last two calls, did you notice whether the lady's voice was that of an older lady? It was probably our aunt."

"No, ma'am, I was so busy at the time, I didn't notice," he went on. "But when she calls back, I'll put her through to your room right away."

"If anyone calls tomorrow, find out who they are and get their phone number. If they won't give their names, just tell them we've checked out and gone home."

Back in our room, I made coffee while Carol bathed and dressed Priscilla for bed. It had been a tiring day for all of us. However, Carol and I sat up late. As we talked, I remembered what William said: 'Mom, by the time the sun goes down the first day you're there, everybody will know you're in town.' "

The next morning, Carol and I decided to drive to the school where Patricia had worked, and see if her co-workers would talk to us. Our motive for wanting to talk to them was part of our strategy to build a case against Lewis. We knew that as long as she had worked there, her co-workers had seen her with black eyes and bruises. We wanted to know who saw her that way, when and how often.

Autumn leaves swirled in the cool wind as we crossed the residential streets on the south side of town. It was football season, and time for hayrides and rodeos. Bull riding and bronco busting, performed by young cowboys and cowgirls wearing shirts and faded jeans, worn-out boots, and dusty Stetsons. But few would deny that a good education was important.

"Turn in the first driveway," Carol said, as we came to the school. "I know which building she worked in. It's on the other side of where the buses are parked. The one on the left."

We stopped at the main building and walked to the office of Arthur Johnson. A sign on the door read: Arthur Johnson, Assistant Superintendent.

"Can I help you?" he asked.

"Yes, I hope so. We're Patricia Crocker's sisters, and we were wondering if we might speak to someone who worked with her."

Obviously irritated, Mr. Johnson stood up and walked to the door where we were standing. He was around the age of fifty, short in height, with dark hair and sharp facial features.

"I'm sorry there won't be anyone, other than myself, available to talk to you," he said curtly. "But if you wish to step into the next room, I'll try to help you."

He then ushered us into a small room with tables and chairs, and sat down.

"Now, what would you like to know?" he asked.

"We'd be interested in anything you can tell us about Patricia," I replied.

"Well, whatever I tell you, you're going straight to the District Attorney, and tell him about it. You're working for him, aren't you?"

"No, sir. I am not working for the District Attorney," I replied.

"Oh, come now. Don't tell me that," he went on. "You've been all over town asking questions. Do you expect me to believe that this is a social call?"

"No, sir, I do not," I replied. "My sister and I are here only to inquire about Patricia. I know that she worked here for many years."

"She did. And, at one time, her husband also worked here," he went on.

"Yes, I know that. Would you tell us something about him?"

"I can say that both he and his wife were good employees. You can tell that to the district attorney. And I'm sure you will."

"Mr. Johnson, I am not now, nor have I ever been employed by the district attorney's office. I have never met the district attorney. I live in Dallas."

"What difference does that make?"

"If I worked for your district attorney, I'd have a four hundred mile round trip to work each day. Don't you think that would be a little bit much?"

"I don't have time to argue," he said, opening the door for us to leave.

"Mr. Johnson, before we leave, would you answer just one question for me?"

"All right, what is it?"

"Did you ever see Patricia come to work with black eyes and bruises?"

"Yes. I did. A number of times," he answered, coldly.

"Thank you, Mr. Johnson," I replied. "That's all I wanted to know in the first place. Now, have a nice day."

As I backed my car out and headed toward the highway, Carol was smiling.

"Do you realize what you did to that guy?" she asked.

"What do you mean?"

"Well, he didn't want to tell you anything, and before he knew what was happening, he told you everything. And I'll bet he doesn't know he did it."

"Well, that's his problem. But he didn't tell us anything we hadn't already guessed. All he did was confirm it. And he told us something else."

"What was that?"

"We have an enemy in town. When Mr. Johnson said we'd been all over town asking questions and accused me of working for the district attorney, he had to have heard that from someone. But how did he know we would go to the school?"

"He acted like he was expecting us," Carol went on. "I think someone called him, told him a lot of B.S. and asked him not to talk to us. But I doubt that it was Lenny Compton. He wouldn't have the brains to do anything like that. It sounds more like something a woman would do."

"Well, remember the phone call telling you that we should stay out of Madisonville? Maybe it was the same woman. If it was, she must have an interest in the case. That's why she wants us to butt out. I think we should have lunch at the restaurant today, and see if Monica still remembers us."

As we drove by the restaurant, the parking lot was full and a line of customers was waiting outside. We decided to wait at the motel. And by the time we left for the restaurant again, the streets were wet with rain.

Monica recognized us immediately, and motioned to a table in a far corner.

"Monica didn't seem surprised to see us," Carol said. "I wonder why."

"Well, this is our second day in town, remember?"

A few moments later, Monica brought menus and took our lunch orders. Then when she returned with the food, I asked about Carmen.

"Oh, Mama's fine. If you have time, why don't you drive down and see her?"

"I'd like that," I replied. "But I wouldn't want to drop in unannounced."

"Oh, she wouldn't mind. She'd be glad for the company. If you'd like to go down there this afternoon, I could call and let her know."

"That's a good idea. Tell her we'll be there after we've finished lunch."

Monica then went on to other tables, waiting on customers, smiling shyly at the handsome young cowboys, and acting the perfect lady to old time truckers. But soon she returned to our table again, carrying a tea pitcher and note pad.

"Mama said she would be delighted to see you, and for ya'll to come on down. But she said to tell you that it's raining in Bedias, and the roads might be a little muddy. Now when you get to Bedias, turn left at the red light, and go about four miles until you see a long green trailer with a fence around it. Since it's raining there, my dad may be home. He's a heavy equipment operator, and sometimes he can't work when it's raining. But, if he's home, you'll see a red pickup parked by the trailer. Oh, I almost forgot. Watch out for our dogs."

CHAPTER 20

To say that it was raining in Bedias was putting it mildly, for what we found there had the earmarkings of a Texas tornado. Gusty wind, rain, and hail pelted my windshield as I turned left at the red light and followed the muddy road looking for a green trailer with a fence around it.

"Maybe we should turn back," Carol said. "Remember what Mother used to say about us 'having enough sense to come in out of the rain.' "

"I remember. But Mother never drove this road before. If she had, she'd know that I couldn't turn back if I wanted to. There's no place to turn around on it."

"Well, I think I'd better say my rosary," Carol went on. "We may need it."

When we finally arrived at the trailer, we were first greeted by four soaking wet dogs which came out one by one from beneath it, barking as though they were angry that we would have the nerve to disturb them. Then the front door of the trailer opened, and Carmen yelled fiercely at them.

"Buster, Jett, Rose, and Spike, shut up out there," she called. "Do you hear me? Get yourselves back under the house where you belong."

Then as the dogs disappeared back under the trailer, Carmen waved at us and held the door open as we hurried out of the car.

"Lordy mercy, look at that rain," she said, as we entered her doorway. "Ya'll come on in. I'm so glad to see you. Have a seat over there on the sofa. I'll get some towels for you, so you can dry your hair. And if you drink coffee, I've got a fresh pot made. Walter called a little while ago and I told him you were on your way down here. I expect he'll be here any minute now. He works for the County, but I know they won't be working in this much rain."

While Carmen was getting towels for our hair, Carol and I took our shoes off and left them on a rug near the doorway. Then we walked across the room to a brown sofa, and sat down.

When Carmen returned with the towels, I noticed two little dark haired boys, dressed in tee shirts and jeans, standing behind her.

"These are Monica's sons," she said, proudly. "This is Mike, He's four. And this is Kevin. He's two. They're both our pride and joy."

"Hello," they chimed, and Mike said, "Grandma, Priscilla is a girl."

"Of course she is. But I'll bet she'd like to watch cartoons with you. I'll make some sandwiches and ya'll can eat in your room."

Carmen then invited Carol and me to her kitchen, and we sat at her dining table as she made peanut butter sandwiches and Kool Aid. Then after she had taken the food to the children, she returned and poured coffee for us.

"I hope this rain stops," she said. "I'll be worried sick about Monica coming home tonight. Poor kid, she works so hard. But we help her all we can. Which is more than I can say for the boys' father. I told her before she married him that he would break her heart. But she was in love and wouldn't listen to me. She was a senior in high school that year, and she was so pretty, she was voted the Homecoming Queen. She could have gone on to college, and she could have had any boy she wanted. But he came along and swept her off her feet. I tried to tell her that he was a man with East Texas culture."

"East Texas culture? I don't think I've heard of that before," I said.

"Well, there's more than a few women in this part of the country who have experienced it," she went on. "When I say, East Texas culture, I'm talking about the kind of man who will chase after a woman, wine her and dine her. And he'll promise her the moon and the stars, trying his best to get in her drawers. Now that may sound poetic, but for an East Texas cultured man, stars and drawers go together. Then after he gets her, he'll dump her like a dog."

"However, most East Texas cultured men eventually do marry," Carmen continued. "But they have a tendency to think that for the price of the marriage license, they own their wives. Lock, stock and barrel. And when the new wears off, they're out kicking up their heels, chasing another skirt, getting drunk, going home and knocking their wives around. And, another thing, they mostly leave the raising of the children to the mother, because they don't dwell much on responsibility. And they don't know the meaning of the word, respect. In other words, pardon my language, they do their thinking with their peckers. Maybe their brains are in their peckers. Who knows? You could probably stick a flashlight in one of their ears and see light coming out of the other one.

"Monica married an East Texas cultured man. And he was really a horse's you know what. But the second time he hit her, Walter went after her and brought her home. She's been with us ever since. And if she lives here the rest of her life, that's all right with us. Because there's one thing for certain, we're not going to stand by and let a man abuse her. I don't care who he is."

"Well, we've had enough East Texas culture in our family," Carol said.

"Yes, you have," replied Carmen. "Indeed, you have."

Then the front door opened, and Walter called to Carmen.

"Honey, I'm home and I'm wet. Would you bring me something to dry off with?"

"Yes. But take your boots off, first. I don't want you tracking mud."

"Bless his heart, I don't know what he'd do without me," she smiled.

Then after she had taken a towel and dry shirt to Walter, she returned to sit with us. Walter left the room to change clothes, then returned and kissed her lightly on her cheek.

"I see you're wearing your new dress today," he said to her. "It looks nice."

"Well, thank you," she replied. "You've always said blue is my color."

"Redheads are supposed to wear blue," he replied, reaching for the coffee pot.

Carmen then explained that the day before had been her forty-sixth birthday, and that the dress had been his gift to her.

"The dress is very pretty," I said. "And the dress you wore to Patricia's funeral was pretty, too. By the way, at the cemetery, you mentioned that you knew Patricia's daughters. Have you seen them lately?"

"Yes, I've seen them several times, but not as much as I used to. But I guess that's to be expected, considering everything that's happened. Those poor, poor girls. They've been through so much, what with Lewis killing their mother, and lying to them the way he did. And from what I hear, he's still lying about it. He's now saying that it was self-defense and that he accidentally killed her."

"He's full of prunes if he thinks we believe it was accidental or self-defense," said Walter. "Why, when Patricia was missing, we learned enough from the girls to figure out what happened. I thought about telling the Sheriff some of the things we were hearing, but since he already had an investigation going on, I figured he knew everything we did."

"But would they have told the Sheriff the same things they told you?" I asked. "You know people sometimes talk about things with family members and friends that they would never discuss with an investigator. Would it bother you to talk about it with us?"

"No. Because other people know about it, too. And besides that, there's no reason why I shouldn't tell you. Patricia was your sister. And I think you should know. It might help you to understand everything a little better.

"Now, I guess you've heard that Rhonda and Donald drove up to the house just after Patricia was shot," Walter went on. "Well, let me back up to what happened earlier that day. That morning, Lewis and Patricia went down to Navasota to see about buying some hay. I don't know whether they bought it or not, but they came back home later that morning. Then they took the little girl over to Rhonda's to spend the night. And, around noon, they took Kimberly to Tammie's house to spend the night. Tammie said Patricia's eyes were swollen, and she asked her what was wrong. Patricia said she had been up all night crying. She played with Tammie's baby a while and then she and Lewis left to go to Fred's place for the turkey shoot that was to be at three o'clock that afternoon. But shortly after they got to Fred's, Patricia got sick and waited outside in the car, about an hour, until Lewis drove them home. Later that evening, he shot her. And just as he shot her, Rhonda and Donald drove up to the house. Rhonda went up on the porch and knocked on the door. The door was usually open, but that time it was locked. Lewis heard her knock and hollered at her to wait a minute. A few minutes later he came out and pulled the door shut behind him. They talked for a minute or two, and Lewis asked her if she had seen her mother. He said they had had an argument, and that she became angry and just walked off. Then when Rhonda told him that she had come to get a nightgown for the little girl, he opened the door and they both went inside. But he followed her as she went to get the nightgown. And when she came back outside to her car, he followed her again."

"Did Rhonda mention what kind of clothes Lewis was wearing at that time? He's saying they struggled over the gun and in self-defense he accidentally shot her. I think if it happened that way, he would have had blood on his clothes."

"She said he was wearing black pants. No shirt and no shoes."

"How long was Rhonda in the house?" Carol asked.

"Just a few minutes, I think," replied Carmen. "And when she went back outside, Lewis went outside with her and they talked there for about half an hour. Lewis kept saying he sure wished Patricia hadn't left walking."

"And all the time they were outside talking, Patricia was in her bedroom, either dying or already dead. Damn that lying bastard. If it had been an accident or self-defense, why the hell didn't he come outside screaming and yelling for Rhonda to call an ambulance? Why didn't he try to save her?"

"You can draw your own conclusions to that. We all know how mean he was. Anyway, Virginia and Kimberly were gone that weekend, but when they came home a few days later, they noticed that part of the carpet was missing, and they asked Lewis what happened to it. Lewis said that he and Patricia had cut it out and hauled it to the dumpster, the day she disappeared. And Lewis also told Virginia that he and Patricia had argued, and she had left him.

As Virginia walked through the house looking around, she saw what she believed to be Patricia's purse. And she noticed several blood stains. Then she and Kimberly looked through the house together. Kimberly found the blouse Patricia had been wearing when she last saw her, and it had blood on it. And she and Virginia found bloody rags and what they believed to be a bloody print on the front door. They also discovered a mattress missing from Patricia's bed. Lewis said he had burned a hole in the mattress and that it was also in the dumpster. So, the girls searched the dumpsters. But of course, they found neither the carpet or the mattress.

They returned home, and later when Lewis came in, Kimberly confronted him again about the mattress and carpet. They argued, and Kimberly stood up and told him that she was not going to let him treat her the way he had treated her mother. Then she moved out."

"Do you think they suspected murder, at that time?" Carol asked.

"I think they were horrified at what they had found in the house, and I think they knew Lewis was lying. But the whole thing was so horrifying, they didn't want to believe it."

Suddenly the phone rang, and Carmen answered it.

"It's Monica," she said to Walter. "She wants to know how muddy the roads are out here."

"They're too bad for her to be driving on," replied Walter. "Tell her I'll leave in about fifteen minutes and I'll meet her at the highway in Bedias."

"If you don't mind, I think we'll follow you when you leave," I said. "The road is probably worse now and I'd feel safer driving behind someone."

"I'll do what I can," replied Walter. "And if you get stuck, I can always pull you out."

He walked over to the hall closet, took out a pair of dry boots, and sat back in his chair to put them on.

"You know, as sad as it was, we were lucky they found Patricia's body when they did," he said. "Otherwise, I don't think she would have ever been found."

"Why do you say that?"

"Well, it looked to me like old Lewis was planning to leave the country. He tried to sell his school bus to Clarence Hudson for three thousand dollars. He told Clarence he needed the money to go to a lake in East Texas. He said Patricia was at the lake, and he wanted to go get her. He said the Sheriff knew she was there and he'd tried to get them to go get her, but they refused."

As we stood up to leave, I asked Carmen if she could think of anyone who might be watching us or calling around about us while we were in Madisonville.

"Yes, I can think of one, maybe two," she replied, seriously.

"Who are they? Would you tell us their names?"

"No, I'd rather not call any names. I might be mistaken," Carmen replied. "But remember, they may be closer to home than you think."

"Thanks for the tip," I said. "We'll remember that."

We then followed Walter across the rain soaked yard to the car and the pickup.

"Just follow me," he said, getting into his truck. "Stay behind me and try not to hit your brakes if you start sliding. But if you do slide off, I've got my chain with me and I'll pull you out."

Fortunately, except for a few anxious moments, we made it safely back to the highway in Bedias. Then, Walter parked near the red light to wait for Monica, and we waved good-bye.

"Ya'll be careful now," he called.

"Yes, sir. We will. Thanks again."

It was still raining when we arrived back at the motel in Madisonville. And as we walked into the office to check for messages, our hair was once again straight, limp and wet.

"I feel like a drowned rat," Carol said.

"Well, the storm brought us a lot of rain and gusty wind, but I hope it didn't leave any rats," Allen, the desk clerk, teased. "But I have two messages for you. One was from a woman who refused to give her name. I told her you had already checked out. The other call was from the district attorney's office. On that call, the lady left a message. She said to tell you Mr. Barron's secretary called.

"Thanks a lot, Allen," I said. "And thank you for being our friend."

Later, after warm baths, hair dryers, and dinner at a fast food restaurant, we returned again to our motel room. And as Priscilla slept, Carol and I sat in our beds listening to the rain and talking across the nightstand, discussing our visit with Carmen and Walter. Then we slept soundly through the night.

The next morning, I called the district attorney's office. His secretary answered the phone.

"Yes ma'am, this is Mr. Barron's secretary. Mr. Barron is in court this morning. But he'd like to know if you and your sister could meet with Ranger Taylor at the sheriff's office in Anderson this afternoon at four-thirty."

"Yes, we can. Please tell him we'll be there."

The storm that had blown so viciously the night before had at long last moved on. The skies were now, once again, clear and cool, typical autumn for South Texas. However, not knowing how the weather would be fifty miles south in Anderson, we decided to leave early for the appointment with Ranger Taylor.

As we drove toward Anderson, Carol and I glanced at the rain-filled ditches alongside the highway, the fallen trees in pastures, and scattered pieces of roofing. And as we passed through Bedias, I wondered whether Patricia's home had been damaged. But with the thought of the white pickup still in mind, I decided not to drive by her house.

"It's too bad we're not in another car. If we were, I'll bet we could drive around Bedias and find the white pickup. I'd like to meet its owner."

"I'm beginning to think it may have a connection with the woman who kept calling the motel," replied Carol. "Remember, Carmen told us that, 'it may be closer to home than we think.' "

But fortunately, during the long stretch of highway between Bedias and Anderson, the pickup was nowhere in sight. And when I stopped at the traffic light in Anderson, my thoughts were only of the appointment with Ranger Taylor.

The main street in Anderson looked like most other streets in small farming towns in the rural areas of Texas. There were feed and grain stores, a barber shop, a western clothing store, a boot repair shop, a library, and a small cafe next door to the sheriff's office. But it was the towering old courthouse in the center of the street that gave beauty to the town. The three-storied structure cast its shadows long and wide, as though constituting a symbol for justice.

THE DARK SIDE OF TWILIGHT:

CHAPTER 21

Texas Ranger Brian Taylor was over six feet tall, lean and hand-some, with dark hair and a friendly smile. He was born in Freeport, Texas. His father was in law enforcement for thirty years, and he hoped to follow his father's footsteps. Brian Taylor graduated from college in Lufkin and also the DPS Academy in Austin. After that, he worked several years as a highway patrolman in Belleville, before becoming a Texas Ranger.

"Just have a seat and make yourselves comfortable," he said, motioning to the chairs around a table in a back office. "I'm glad you're here. I've met your parents, and I've been wanting to meet both of you. But I've been so busy, I just hadn't got around to con-tacting you. I'll try not to take up too much of your time. I just need to ask a few questions."

"We'll be glad to help any way we can," I said. "I'm sure the Crocker case has been very exasperating for everyone who worked on it."

"Yes ma'am. From my point of view, it's been a rough case," Taylor replied. "And I'm sorry it turned out the way it did. But I'm relieved that we finally found her. I kept hoping we'd find her alive, but everything we came up with pointed to the fact that we wouldn't. It just got wilder every day."

"Would you tell us when you first suspected it was murder?" I asked.

"The minute I walked into her house and saw the way the carpet had been cut out," he replied. "But the carpet wasn't the only clue. The whole place smelled of blood and murder, inside and out. Then when I saw the bloody handprint on the front door, I knew he had hauled her body to another location. But finding her was another story. And Lewis knew it. He knew we wouldn't have a murder case without the body. So, he set out to try to make me and Larry Adams,

THE DARK SIDE OF TWILIGHT:

Tracy Wright and Jackie Siracusa, all look like a bunch of fools. And for a time, he thought he had a three ring circus going. But what he didn't know was that we were on to him, all the way."

"Well, he was doing the same thing to our family," I said. "He had everyone in the family believing Patricia had run off. All except Carol and me. It's true that during Patricia's adult life, we didn't visit as often as we would have liked. But a sister always knows a sister. And Carol and I knew she would have never left her children. On the other hand, we knew that Lewis was a mean drunk who often beat her. He threatened to kill her many times. And, in the back of my mind, I knew the day would come when he would kill her."

"It's a shame she didn't get away from him before he did it," said Taylor.

Suddenly, the back door opened and Detective Adams walked into the room. He and Ranger Taylor shook hands, and he spoke to Carol and me.

"How is your favorite prisoner?" I asked, looking up at him.

"Well, I've still got him," Adams replied, smiling. "And I aim to keep him."

"When he looks at you, I wonder if he remembers the times he insisted that you follow up on his leads, and demanded that you find her."

"Oh, Lewis not only did that to Adams," Taylor said. "He did it to me, too. He even came to my office in Brenham, and pounded on my desk, demanding to know just what I was doing to find his wife. He said she was at her sister's in Navarro County, and he wanted to know why I wasn't out there looking for her. He said it was my job to find her, and he accused me of not doing my job. I told him I was tired of his charade and that the day was coming when I would serve him with a warrant for murder."

"He thought he could outsmart everyone," I said. "But in fact, the more he lied, the more he gave himself away."

"You can say that again," Taylor went on. "Now, about the questions I want to ask you. Have you heard anything about a suicide note? Or a map?"

250

312

"No, sir, I haven't."

"Well, after Lewis was arrested, he said he had written a suicide note and drew a map showing where his wife's body could be found. He told us where he put the notes, in the house, but they weren't where he said they'd be, and we can't find them. Evidently, he wrote them the day he refused to keep his appointment for the polygraph test. I thought maybe you'd heard someone in the family mention them."

"No, I haven't. But my guess would be that someone else found them. Someone who was trying to protect him. And they may have hidden the notes in another place. I'm only speculating when I say that. But I think if you put the word out in the right direction, you may find them yet."

"Thanks, I'll remember that," Taylor replied.

"However, I do have a list of my own personal notes with me," I went on.

I then handed my notes to him, and he glanced over them.

"Do you mind if I keep these?" he asked.

"Not at all," I replied. "You're welcome to use them as you wish."

Ranger Taylor then left the room for a few moments. And the conversation continued with Detective Adams. James Larry Adams was a native Texan, forty-six years old. He was a graduate from Iola High School and attended college in Houston. He also served two years in the U.S. Army. He started his law enforcement career in 1969, in El Campo, Texas. Years later, he worked as an investigator for the Wharton County Sheriff's Department, where he achieved the rank of Lieutenant and was voted officer of the year in 1981. In 1986, he moved back to Grimes County, where he was now employed with the Sheriff's Department.

When Ranger Taylor returned, we stood up to leave.

"I want to thank you both for your help," he said. "You've helped us more than you know. And we appreciate it."

"That goes for me, too," Adams said. "And we'll see you again, at the trial."

We then asked where we could find Tracy Wright and Jackie

Siracusa.

Carol and I then left the Sheriff's office and drove across the highway to another office building. As we entered, we were greeted by a woman, around the age of thirty. She was of medium height, very pretty, with blonde hair and blue eyes. We told her we were looking for Tracy Wright and Jackie Siracusa.

"I'm Jackie Siracusa," she smiled. "Can I help you?"

"Yes. We're Patricia Crocker's sisters, and we understand that you worked on that particular case. We want to thank you for your help."

"Well, I appreciate your thoughtfulness," she replied. "I did some work on the case, though not as much as some of the other officers. But I went out to the house several times, during the investigation. And after Lewis was arrested I witnessed the statements given by the daughters, and others. I've worked eight years as a dispatcher. I am also a deputy, and I've seen a number of murder cases come through this office. But the Crocker case was definitely the worst."

Deputy Siracusa then led us down the hallway to talk with Investigator Tracy Wright.

Tracy Wright was of medium height with broad shoulders, brown hair and blue eyes. He was twenty-eight years old, and already had ten years experience in his law enforcement career. His father, Tommy Wright, was also in law enforcement, in Montgomery County, and he too, was involved in the Crocker case. Tommy Wright had been with the team of divers who had searched the stock ponds on the Jim Pierce ranch.

"I understand that you worked rather extensively on the case," I said to Tracy.

"Yes ma'am, I worked quite a bit on it," Tracy replied. "It was a very disturbing case. I was one of the investigators and I was at the house several times during the investigation. It hit me the first time I went there."

"What was that?"

"Murder. You could smell it. The whole house reeked with the scent of soap and blood. You know, like someone had done a half way job of trying to clean it up. But couldn't get the scent out of it. Speaking of overpowering scents, Lewis even took a bunch of fish heads out to the dump and spread them on the ground on top of where he had buried Patricia. I guess he thought the fish heads would disguise the odor of a decaying body."

"I understand that you were at the dump when her body was found."

"Yes ma'am, I was," Tracy said. "And I was also the one who retrieved her purse from the septic tank behind her house."

"Lewis was lying all the way through the investigation and I knew it. When he was offered the chance to take a polygraph test, he said he'd take it. I was hoping like heck that he would. But then he started making one excuse after another. Something always came up. One night, Larry Adams and I went to a Crime Stoppers banquet, in Navasota. Lewis was supposed to take a polygraph the next day. But he showed up at the banquet and said he'd changed his mind, again. Larry and I felt like knocking his head off. I'm glad we finally got him, though. And I hope he gets what he deserves."

"We hope so, too," I said. "And we appreciate everything you did to help. We won't forget it. We'll be at the trial and we hope to see you there."

"It was a pleasure meeting you," Tracy said.

"That goes for me, too," said Jackie. "Good luck."

"Thank you. We may need all the luck we can get before it's over."

It was late afternoon when we turned onto the highway again, for the drive back to Madisonville.

"I'd like to make one more stop," Carol said. "When we get to the ranch, I want to talk to Jack Thompson again."

"Okay, but it's getting late. What do you want to talk to him about?"

"I want him to take us to the dump and show us where that bastard buried Patricia's body."

"Oh, Carol, please don't do that to yourself. And to me. You know it's going to hurt us more."

"I don't care. I've got to know. I've got to see it for myself," she cried.

"And you may have a nervous breakdown when you do," I went on.

"I don't care. I'm telling you, I want to see where that sonofabitch put her. And if you don't want to go with me, I'll go by myself."

"Carol, you know darn well I'm not going to let you go there by yourself."

And so it was that when we came to the Jim Pierce ranch, once again, I drove through the main gate and stopped at Jack Thompson's house. And as we drove up, a short blonde haired lady wearing a flowered print dress and apron, came out to meet us. She was Helen, Jack Thompson's wife. She said Thompson was at the big barn, and that we could drive up there and talk to him.

At the barn, Thompson walked out to meet us, spitting tobacco on the way.

"Well, I didn't expect to see you girls again, so soon," he said. "Is there something I can help you with?"

"Yes, sir. We'd like your permission to go to the dump," Carol replied. "We want to see where Patricia was buried."

Thompson paused for a moment, looking into the distance toward the back part of the ranch. Then he rubbed his chin and spit tobacco again.

"Don't put yourselves through that," he said. "It won't help anything."

"What if it had happened to your sister?" Carol said, tearfully. "How would you feel? Wouldn't you want to know everything about it?"

"I don't know how I'd feel," he went on. "But I imagine I'd feel about the same way you do. All right. You can go. I'll get my jeep and you can follow me. But I want you to stay close behind me. Otherwise, you might get lost."

Thompson then walked behind the barn and returned in his jeep, motioning for us to follow him. I felt apprehensive about driving my car into the woods, especially after last night's rain, but the gravel road we were on appeared to be dry and solid. However, after we crossed the second cattle guard, about a mile from the barn, the gravel ended and we found ourselves on a long deep rutted road in the woods.

I followed the jeep slowly, trying to stay in its ruts while also trying to avoid the larger ones that were filled with water. Then, suddenly, I thought of the oncoming darkness and the dream in which I had searched for Patricia on a long deep rutted road. And, in the dark recesses of my mind, I thought I heard her call to me, again. *"Hurry, before it's too late. Hurry, before it's too late."*

Oh, God, I thought. This was the road in the dream. The deep ruts, the long road with the thick trees beyond it. It was the road where I had run so long and hard, jumping over ruts, calling her name, trying desperately to find her. Knowing she was somewhere among the trees, hearing her call to me, again and again. *"Hurry before it's too late. Hurry before it's too late."*

However, not wanting to further upset Carol, I said nothing about the road or the dream. And we continued following the jeep further into the woods. The road was rougher now, and since my car was a New Yorker and sat low to the ground, I wondered whether it would be damaged by the time our mission was completed.

"Well, you were right again," said Carol.

"What do you mean?" I replied.

"You were right when you said Patricia was buried on a deer lease," she said.

"Why do you say that? How do you know?"

"Well, don't you see the deer stands?"

"No. Where are they?"

"They're right in front of you. Can't you see them?"

"No," I answered, feeling embarrassed. "Carol, I've never seen a deer stand. I don't know what they're supposed to look like."

"Okay, I'll show them to you," she said. "Look to your right. Do you see those things that look like little tree houses sitting up in the trees?"

"Yes."

"Well, those are deer stands."

"Damn. Talk about a nightmare. This has got to be one of the worst ever."

About a mile further, Thompson stopped at a barbed wire gate and got out.

"I think we'd better leave our vehicles here and walk the rest of the way," he said. "It's over there by that last row of trees. You can see it from here."

We walked behind him a short distance further, toward the trees. Then he stopped and bowed his head, and looked back at us.

"Is this it?" I asked.

"Yes, ma'am, it is."

"Will you show us where she was buried?"

"He buried her right over there," said Thompson, pointing to an area near the trees. "See the far bank of the trench? He buried her right near that first patch of goat weeds. But we won't walk over there because the ground where the body was found hasn't settled yet."

Carol started crying, almost uncontrollably, and Thompson put his arm around her shoulder. I was also crying and I felt faint and nauseated.

"Now you know why I didn't want you to come here," said Thompson. "You're hurt even more now. I wish I could make it go away for you. But I can't. There's another thing you need to remember. Even if he goes to trial, he may be out walking the streets in a year or two. The prisons are overcrowded and first thing you know, some fool will say he's been rehabilitated, and they'll turn him loose. And when he gets out, he'll come after those who put him away."

"Well, I hope that doesn't happen. I hope the criminal justice system will keep him in prison for a very long time. Because, number one, he deserves it. And, number two, there's no doubt in my mind that he would kill again."

"I hope so, too. I'd hate to think he was anywhere around here," said Thompson, looking back toward the barbed wire gate. "Well, I expect we'd better be going back to the house. It's nearly dark and Helen might be worried about us. You're welcome to stop by for coffee. It might help settle your nerves."

"Thanks. But it's almost dark and we need to leave."

"Well, if you have any more questions, give me a call."

"Thanks. But I guess we've covered just about everything we can think of."

Thompson then closed the gate and waited for us, making sure we were in the car and ready to follow him.

On the way back, as we crossed the last cattle guard, we saw several barns and bales of hay.

"Of all the things to see," Carol said, tearfully. "Her makeshift grave at a garbage dump, and now a hay barn. And the sun has gone down. None of it seems real. It just can't be happening."

"But, honey, it is real. It's all real and there's nothing we can do to change it. We're going to have to deal with it the best way we can. Don't forget, she was my sister, too. And I have my special memories of her. I think of her every waking moment of the day, and at night. At times, I think I'm just not going to make it, day after day. You can see how I've changed because of it. It's made me hard and bitter. I don't trust anyone, any more. And I've got to where I cuss like a trollop. I think the only thing that keeps me from falling apart is vengeance. It's like this thing has all but swept my life away, and I'm refusing to let go until I see justice for her. Determination is what keeps me going.

"I know your childhood memories are very dear to you, and when you talk about them, it's as though I relive them through you. I see you and Patricia as little girls in school, or picking wildflowers or swimming, and the hundreds of other things you enjoyed. And in the evenings, when twilight comes, I see you both as children, sitting on top of the barn watching the sun go down."

"I just can't stand the thought of her body being thrown into a hole and Lewis standing over it, throwing shovels of dirt on her face," Carol cried.

"I know, Carol. I know. I think of it every day. But I try to believe, I have to believe, that God's arms reached out for her as her last breath ended. And I believe she is in heaven and that she sings with the angels. I think she knows how hurt we are and she knows how much we love her. But she is in a better world than we know. And I believe that someday we'll see her again. Those are my true feelings. And because of my faith that she is with God, I try to believe that she never felt the shovels of dirt that Lewis threw on her body, nor the weight of the rusty barrels and junk that he threw on top of her. Nor the long forty-four days and nights her body lay waiting to be found. We must trust in our faith, Carol. Our faith is all we really have."

The next morning, before we left the motel to go home, Carol and I called Aunt Margaret to say good-bye. She was glad to hear from us and relieved that we had survived our business meetings without getting hurt or into trouble. Then Carol and I said good-bye to each other.

"I'll see you in court," she called, waving good-bye from her car.

"I'll be there," I answered. "I'll be there with bells on."

CHAPTER 22

During the next session of the Grimes County Grand Jury, Lewis Marlin Crocker was indicted for the murder of his wife, Patricia Crocker. His court-appointed attorney was the locally famous Billy Carter, of Madisonville. And Carter had the reputation of being one of the best defense attorneys in Texas. I learned this new-found information in a phone call one morning from Mother.

"He pleaded not guilty," she went on. "And the trial will be sometime in February. Daddy and I are not going to be there. I don't think we could stand it. Besides that, I was told that it wasn't necessary for any of our family to be there, because the trial is only going to last ten or fifteen minutes. The judge is going to give Lewis a five year sentence, or maybe not even that much. He could get probation."

"Mother, who the hell told you that? Surely you know, if Lewis has a trial, his guilt or innocence will be decided there, and so will his sentence."

"Now, don't get huffy with me about it," she said. "I'm only telling you what I've heard."

"Well, you tell whoever told you that, not to hold their breath until the trial is over and the sentence is read. And tell them I plan to be there."

"Well, it's going to be wintertime and bad weather."

"So what? If I can drive in Alaska in winter, I can drive in Grimes County."

After the conversation was over, I called Tammie about a grave marker for Patricia's grave, knowing also that she would mention Lewis' indictment. She said Lewis pleaded not guilty. He said it was an accident. Carter said that the autopsy was questionable, and that he hoped to plea-bargain the case.

A few minutes later, I was on the phone again, this time with David Barron.

"Well, I don't know who is giving out that information," he said. "But I can assure you that that's not the way we're looking at it. I'm not interested in a plea-bargain because I don't think this case calls for that. We have a trial date on February 27. We are prepared to go to trial, and as far as I'm concerned, we're going to trial. And I'm looking forward to meeting you there."

And so it was that on February 27, 1989, Carol and I shivered in the morning coldness as we left the Best Western Motel in Navasota, for the ten mile drive to the courthouse in Anderson.

Alongside the curved and hilly highway, pastures were turning green again and in the distance farmers were cranking up machinery for spring planting.

Carol and I were nervous. We'd never attended a murder trial before. Our personal trial experience had consisted mostly of honoring jury summonses for jury duty. But still, we knew the criminal justice system worked. Even though it needed a little extra help, sometimes, it still worked.

"I want to hear what that bastard has to say for himself," said Carol. "And I want to be looking at him when he says it."

"Carol, I think now is as good a time as any to warn you that they're going to smear Patricia's name as far as they can smear it. Any way they can."

"They can't do that. Everybody who knew Patricia, knew she was a good woman."

"But Carol, that's not how the game is played. In a case where there is little or no defense, a defense attorney tries to put someone else other than his client on trial."

"But what about Lewis' confession?"

"Carol, the fact is that Billy Carter was appointed by the court to defend Lewis. Carter can't just walk up to the judge and say his client is a no good bum and throw him to the wolves. That wouldn't be a defense. And since Lewis has pleaded not guilty, more than likely, Carter will try to shift as much blame as he can on Patricia. Because he has to make Lewis appear as innocent as possible. That's his job."

"But it's not fair," said Carol. "Patricia didn't kill Lewis. He killed her."

"We know that. But that's not the way the game will be played in court."

As we drove down Main Street in Anderson, the long shadows of the towering old courthouse appeared once again, dark and imminent. Like the dark cloak of justice, they were waiting. And as we walked toward them, I wondered how many years they would be there, after our time was over.

After entering the courthouse, and not finding an elevator, I knocked on the door of the District Clerk's office.

"There are no elevators in the building," the dark haired man explained. "I'm Wayne Rucker, the district clerk. Perhaps I can help you."

"Yes. We're here for the Lewis Crocker trial."

"Oh, I see. Well, I was just leaving to go there myself," he went on. "It will be in the courtroom on the second floor. If you'd like to walk up with me, I can show you where to find it. Are you members of his family?"

"No. We're members of his victim's family. We're Patricia Crocker's sisters."

We entered the side door of the courtroom, then stood there a few moments wondering where we should sit. Rhonda, Virginia, Kimberly, Tammie and Garvin were sitting on a front row of benches. We smiled and nodded. Then the room began to fill as prospective jurors drifted in, handing their jury summonses to the clerk, and looking for empty seats.

I noticed a tall man with brown hair walking toward us. He was near the age of forty, and wore a brown jacket, brown tie and white shirt over jeans and boots. His long steps were sure and definite. His square jaw had the look of a lawman. And he stopped and spoke to us.

"My name is Patrick Page," he said. "I'm the investigator for the defense."

"Well, I'm afraid you're talking to the wrong people," Carol replied. "We're Patricia Crocker's sisters and we're really not interested in Lewis' defense."

"Well, did you know Lewis is illiterate?" Page asked.

"Oh, don't give me that," Carol replied. "He's not illiterate. I've known him for twenty-six years, and I know he can read and write."

Carol's blistering reply had obviously stunned Patrick Page, and he looked at me as though he expected me to defend his statement.

"Don't look at me," I said. "I'm her sister. And I'm not here to defend Lewis Crocker. I'm here to help hang him."

"But, if he gets twenty years, he may die in jail," said Page.

"So what? He's already lived longer than he let my sister live," I said.

"Well, just what do you want? Lethal injection?" he asked.

"That would be all right," I said. "Yes, I'd probably settle for that."

"Look, I know how you feel," he went on.

"No. You don't know how I feel," I said. "You'll have to wait until some bastard murders your sister and throws her body in a hole in a garbage dump, and lies about her, and when he's caught, he has the gall to plead not guilty. When that happens, then you can tell me how I feel."

"I'm sorry, ma'am," Page replied.

Our first fifteen minutes in the courtroom had already started with a bang, and within the next half hour, there was more to come.

I soon noticed a handsome man with dark brown hair, wearing a navy blue suit, a blue striped tie, white shirt, and black loafer shoes. He was near six feet in height, and I guessed him to be in his mid-thirties. His presence was striking, in the fact that when he walked by, everyone noticed. And when he spoke, they listened carefully. I thought of Walter Mitchell's description of David Barron, when he said Barron would come across as an Ivy League man. Clean cut, polite, but tough as a boot. The man I was now watching fit that description, and my eyes followed him as he walked over to Rhonda.

"Where is Donald?" he asked.

"I don't know," she answered, sharply. "I imagine he's at work. Why?"

"He received a subpoena, didn't he?" the man asked.

"Yeah, he got it," Rhonda answered.

"Then why isn't he in court?"

"I told you, I don't know why," she went on.

"Well, you tell him I said that he will be here tomorrow. One way or the other."

"Okay. Okay. Okay. I'll tell him," Rhonda replied.

Then the man walked to where Carol and I were standing.

"Mr. Rucker told me you were here," he said, extending his hand. "I'm David Barron, and I'm glad to meet you both."

"Thank you. I'm glad to meet you, too," I replied. "I see the courtroom is getting crowded. The case must have had a lot of media coverage."

"Yes, it has," Mr. Barron replied. "It's been in the newspapers and on TV. There are reporters here, today."

"That must explain the crowd then," said Carol.

"Well, I don't know about that," Mr. Barron went on. "I think most of the people here now are here for jury duty. We'll be selecting the jury today. And as soon as we've completed that, we'll start the trial. I don't know whether you've ever attended a murder trial before. But I know this one is going to be hard on you. Not only because of the murder, but you're also going to hear things about your sister that may be very upsetting. But I want you to know that I'm on your side all the way. And I hope to win it with flying colors."

Mr. Rucker then motioned to Mr. Barron, and as they both walked toward the judge's bench, I noticed another man coming in through the side door.

He was taller than Mr. Barron, and I guessed him to be in his mid-forties. He wore a dark pin-striped suit, white shirt and dark tie, and comfortable shoes. He had black hair and a short neatly trimmed beard, and he carried a briefcase. He had the look of a 'well-seasoned' attorney, one who had probably tried more cases than he could remember. He glanced at us and nodded hello. We smiled back, in greeting. Then as Rhonda and Virginia walked over to meet him, I knew he was Billy Carter, Lewis' defense attorney.

I was unable to hear the context of their conversation, but it appeared that he was a few minutes late, and was in a hurry to begin the jury selection. I glanced out into the main courtroom for a moment, and as I turned around, I saw him shake his head to one side and walk toward the judge's bench.

"Did you hear that?" Carol asked.

"No. I was watching the people take their places for jury selection," I said.

"The girls are wanting Carter to make us leave."

"Well, I don't think they can do that."

A few minutes later, David Barron returned and talked to the girls.

"Well, I'm sorry you feel that way," he said, half smiling. "But your aunts have as much right to be here as you do. If you don't want to take my word for it, feel free to discuss it with the judge. He's at his bench. Go ask him."

As Mr. Barron walked away, Virginia called out, "I'll go up there if I want to." But Barron kept walking. He had a jury to select and a case to try.

"Evidently, the girls think we have no rights whatsoever," Carol said.

"Carol, it doesn't matter what they think. This courtroom belongs to the State of Texas, and Lewis Crocker does not give the orders on how it is run. But if it's any consolation to you, I'm the one the girls are angry with. I'm the one who insisted on the Law getting involved in the first place, and I've helped as much as I could. I think I'd have been a sorry sister if I hadn't."

When the jury voir dire began, Carol and I moved to the back section of the courtroom and listened quietly to hours of legal words and phrases by Mr. Barron, Mr. Carter and Judge Ernst. Of course, we knew none of the potential jurors, nor did they know us. And we quietly blended in the background with the other spectators.

District Attorney David Barron was born in Bryan, Texas, on June 26, 1956. He graduated from Bryan High School. He received his undergraduate degree from Sam Houston State University in Huntsville, Texas, and his law degree from Baylor University in Waco. He then went into private practice in Bryan with his father, John Barron. John Barron was a former District Judge of the 85th District Court in Brazos County, and one of the first justices on the 14th Court of Appeals in Houston. David's brother, John Jr., was also an attorney. David continued in private practice with his father and brother until 1985. He then came to Grimes County as the Assistant District Attorney to Latham Boone. He served as prosecutor for Boone from 1985 through 1988. Then on January 1, 1989, David Barron became District Attorney for Grimes, Madison and Leon counties.

Today, February 27, 1989, was his fifty-eighth day in office as District Attorney, and Case Number 11,781, the State of Texas vs. Lewis Crocker, was his first murder case as District Attorney of Grimes County.

William Foster "Billy" Carter was born in Madisonville, Texas, on December 19, 1945. He was a graduate of Lon Morris College in Jacksonville, Texas, with an Associates in Arts Degree. He was also a graduate of Rice University with a degree in Business. He then graduated from University of Houston Law School with a Doctor of Jurisprudence in 1972, and was admitted to the State Bar of Texas in 1973. He later served as County Judge of Madison County from 1976 through 1979.

Billy Carter was indeed well seasoned. He knew the law like he knew the back of his hand. He was considered to be one of the best attorneys in the State of Texas.

The Honorable Judge Erwin G. Ernst, of Huntsville, Texas, retired and visiting, was on the bench in the courtroom. Judge Ernst was of medium height, with graying brown hair, and I guessed him to be in his early sixties. Today he wore a black suit, white shirt with a black string tie, and boots. As he approached the bench, he paused for a moment nodding hello to the jurors, the spectators, and to Barron and Carter. After he was seated, he introduced the court reporter.

"Ladies and gentlemen, this is Gary Harris. He is going to be our court reporter on this case. He will be taking down everything that is said on his machine. So, we want to remember that and show consideration for him."

District Clerk Wayne Rucker was also in his proper place near Judge Ernst.

The jury panel consisted of seven men and five women, all of various occupations. One worked in marine construction, one was a roofing contractor, another was a correctional counselor. One worked for the phone company, one was a veterinarian, another was a rancher. Two were nurses. Several were homemakers. Richard Bertrand, Sr., who was later selected foreman of the jury, worked for an electric co-op.

Suddenly, hushed whispers were heard throughout the courtroom as two sheriff's deputies escorted Lewis to the counsel table where Billy Carter was sitting. Then the deputies took seats nearby.

At the counsel table on Carter's right, David Barron sat glancing at his notes, and at his right, the jury was seated in the jury box, ready and waiting with full attention.

CHAPTER 23

For Lewis Crocker, the day of reckoning had begun. The Powers That Be were now in their proper places. Those who had come to find justice for the murder of Patricia Crocker. Those who had worked so diligently to find her body. Those who would now sit in judgment with the power to mete the punishment according to the law. And those who would defend him.

Judge Ernst cleared his throat and rapped his gavel. Court was now in session.

During opening statements, Barron told the jury that he intended to prove that Patricia's death was nothing less than murder.

Carter called it a crime of passion.

Brian D. Taylor, Texas Ranger, Company "A," stationed in Brenham, Texas, was the first witness for the State.

David Barron started with the State's Exhibit No. 1, the arrest warrant. Then questions and answers began, back and forth, sprinkled with Carter's objections, as Taylor gave his reasons for the warrant. He told of finding Patricia's body. His information concerning that was the same as what Jack Thompson had told us during our visit at the ranch. Then Taylor continued as he told of Lewis' arrest, and of Lewis saying at that time, "I killed her and I'm glad it's over with." Then came the subject of Lewis' taped confession at the Grimes County Jail. Taylor and Barron leaned heavily on the fact that the Miranda warning had been read to Lewis at the time of his arrest, and twice more before his confession.

Barron: "When did he tell you where the murder weapon was?"

Taylor: "It was the day of his statement on September 20."

Barron: "Was that after the reading of his Miranda rights?"

Taylor: "Yes, sir."

Barron: "And was that after he was magistrated by Judge Bobby McNew?"

Taylor: "Yes, sir. It would have been."

Barron: "Where did he tell you the murder weapon was?"

Taylor: "I already knew. Donald Bullion had the rifle and he told me about it previously. So when Lewis told me that was the rifle, I knew where it was at."

Barron: "Did you subsequently recover the rifle from Donald Bullion?"

Taylor: "Yes, sir, I did."

Barron passed the witness, and Carter cast his first attack, not on the subject of the rifle, but on the warrant.

Carter: "The only link you had to this being Patricia Crocker's body was a purse that some cadaver sniffing dog smelled of and then went to the property and found the body?"

Taylor: "There was a purse the dog smelled and also some other stuff that the trainer had. The dog searched the ranch and later went to the dump and that's where the dog detected the body."

Taylor knew the purse in question had belonged to Patricia, for Kimberly had given it to him, and told him it was Patricia's. In addition to the purse, Taylor had other evidence. Patricia's clothing, pieces of carpet, a blanket, and an empty beer can, the brand of which Lewis was known to drink exclusively, were also found with the body. Nevertheless, Carter was a defense attorney. He continued blasting Taylor with questions surrounding the arrest warrant and the following events of the day Patricia's body was found.

He went to the subject of the statement Lewis had blurted out: "I killed her and I'm glad it's over with." Lewis had said it to Larry Adams as Adams stood by the police car, moments after Lewis was arrested.

Carter: "All right. Do you know how much time elapsed from the time the Miranda warnings were given until Lewis made that statement to Larry Adams?"

Taylor: "No, sir. I don't."

Carter: "How long did you stay at the residence after you placed Lewis Crocker under arrest? Did you stay 10 minutes, 15 minutes, 20 minutes?"

Taylor: "Around 10 or 15 minutes. I couldn't give you the exact time."

Carter: "And the confession he gave that was recorded at the jail took place within two hours of the initial arrest under this warrant?"

Taylor: "Yes, sir."

Carter: "What did your report say that Larry Adams said Lewis Crocker said?"

Barron called Carter's last question 'triple hearsay.' The court called it 'repetitious.' But Carter wanted Taylor to look in his report for the answer.

Barron: "Your Honor, he is trying to befuddle my witness."

Court: "That's his job."

Carter: "So, I'm a befuddler."

And so it went, back and forth. Carter hadn't forgotten Charlie Lancaster either. Barron had previously entered the subject of the affair Patricia was to have allegedly had with Charlie and the guy named Bill. And Taylor had answered that he "still don't know who Bill is." Now, Carter was back on that.

Carter: "All right. You testified you knew about a relationship with Charlie Lancaster. Did that have any relevancy to the warrant or who did you receive that information from?"

Taylor: "Originally Deputy Adams."

Carter: "All right. I'd like to know about the actual arrest. When you got to the house, were you the one that gave Lewis his rights?"

Taylor: "Larry Adams read him his rights."

Carter was tough. But Taylor was not to be befuddled. He knew what he had going, and he was sending it straight into the minds of the jurors.

The testimony of Ranger Taylor seemed to last for hours as Carter continued trying to find loopholes in it. But Taylor was calm, collected and determined. He had done his homework well. And despite Carter's renowned talents, he was unable to shake the ranger.

Judge Ernst decided that everyone had heard enough for one day. He wished the jury a pleasant evening, then rapped his gavel and declared his court in recess until 9 o'clock the following morning.

On the second morning of the trial, as Carol and I walked up the steps of the courthouse, we noticed a white pickup in the parking lot. It wasn't as dirty as before, but we immediately recognized its double bumpers and the crack in the windshield.

"Keep your eye out for Lenny Compton," said Carol.

"Surely, he wouldn't be stupid enough to start anything in a court-room. But if he glares at me just once, I'll report him."

However, as we walked inside and sat on the row directly behind Mr. Barron, there was no sign of Lenny, nor anyone who resembled him. And as Judge Ernst rapped his gavel to begin the day's court proceedings, we focused our attention on the witness box.

Mr. Barron's next witness for the State was Doris Rawlins. She was of medium height, with brown hair and pleasant facial features, and I guessed her to be in her late thirties. She and Patricia had been co-workers at the school for approximately five years. And it was clearly obvious that she was still Patricia's friend. Tears rolled down her cheeks as she spoke, and she glanced at Lewis as though she would have enjoyed slapping him.

Barron presented the State's Exhibit No. 3, an 8 x 10 photograph of Patricia, and asked Doris Rawlins if she could identify it. In the midst of tears, she said it was Patricia, but that her face appeared fuller in the photograph than when she last saw her.

The photograph was a copy of a smaller photo that Patricia had sent to me the year before. It was a good likeness and I had given it to Mr. Barron.

Barron: "Did you have any occasion during those five years to see anything unusual about Patricia Crocker's appearance?"

Rawlins: "Yes."

Barron: "Would you tell the jury what that was?"

Rawlins replied that at least five times during those five years, Patricia had come to work with bruises on her face, eyes, abdomen and neck. And that Patricia was usually quite upset.

Barron: "When she had bruises on her face, would you see Lewis Crocker?"

Rawlins: "Sometimes."

Barron: "And would he have bruises on his face that you could

270

notice?"

Rawlins: "I've never seen any, no, sir."

Barron: "And when was the last time you saw Patricia?"

Rawlins replied that she last saw Patricia in town, back in June.

During cross examination, Carter asked Rawlins if Patricia had gone through a big weight loss during that time. And if she had taken diet pills to lose the weight. Rawlins replied that she had not seen Patricia take diet pills.

Carter: "So, this picture is not what she looked like in June?"

Rawlins: "She had lost a lot of weight and her face was slimmer."

I wanted to shout that I had also seen her in June, and the picture was a good likeness. It was a copy of the one the daughters had placed on her casket at the funeral home. I wondered if Carter preferred a picture of the autopsy.

Lily Tyler was the State's next witness. She was of medium height, and black, with a warm and friendly face. Patricia had been her manager at the school, and they had worked ten years together.

Barron: "During those ten years, did you ever see her come in with bruises or black eyes?"

Carter objected 'to the leading nature of the question, and asked that the jury be instructed to disregard it.' Judge Ernst instructed the jury. Then Carter asked for a 'mistrial because that particular instruction cannot cure the prejudicial effect.' But Judge Ernst overruled his motion, and Barron continued.

Barron: "Could you tell what was under the dark glasses?"

Tyler: "When she pulled them off, you could see bruises and her eyes black."

Barron: "And were you and Patricia friends?"

Tyler: "We were friends. That's the way we worked. Just all one big family."

Lucille Mayes was the third of Patricia's co-workers to testify. And she, too, had seen Patricia come to work with bruises.

Barron: "Would you describe those bruises for the jury?"

Mayes: "She would have fingerprints on her face or a scratch or something."

Barron: "How would she be emotionally on those days?"

Mayes: "She would be kind of nervous."

During cross-examination, Carter asked Lucille if Lewis had worked on her car and if he had eaten at the school cafeteria. She replied that he had.

The next witness for the State was Pauline Nicholson, tall and statuesque, wearing a fashionable brown suit and white bow tie blouse.

Pauline stated that Patricia had come to her shop three weeks before the alleged disappearance, and asked to borrow her car.

Barron: "Did you notice anything unusual about her physical features at that time?"

Nicholson: "She had bruises on her arms. And her face and neck were red."

Barron: "And what was her emotional condition?"

Nicholson: "Very upset. Very upset about the situation."

Pauline went on to say that Patricia spent the night at her home, and that Lewis came there wanting to talk, and was told to leave. She further stated that while Patricia was missing, Lewis came to her shop and asked whether she had seen Patricia or heard from her.

Carter was ready and waiting, and on cross examination, he showed no mercy.

Carter: "Was it in July that Patricia came to your shop with bruises on her?"

Nicholson: "Yes, sir."

Carter: "And did you know who Charlie Lancaster was?"

Nicholson: "Yes, sir."

Pauline stated that she had met Charlie at Claude and Betty's. Carter asked if Patricia was with her. Pauline replied that Patricia was not there. Then Carter pounced on the fact that Pauline and Patricia had gone to Fred's place one afternoon.

Carter: "And when you got to Fred's place, did Patricia say anything when you drove up out there?"

Pauline: "His truck was there."

Carter: "And what were you talking about?"

Pauline: "Just everything. We weren't talking about Charlie or anyone. We were just talking about my business."

I wondered if Carter knew that Lewis had chased Patricia down the highway intending to 'just shoot her tires out.' But Carter was now asking about a night Patricia had spent at Pauline's house.

Carter: "When Lewis came over, had he been drinking or could you tell?"

Pauline: "Yes, sir. I believe he had. I didn't see him."

Carter: "What made you think he was drinking?"

Pauline: "Because I know Lewis."

On redirect, Barron asked Pauline what she meant by that. Her answer was that every time she saw Lewis, usually he was drinking. Pauline was then excused from the witness stand. And Barron called his next witness.

Paybacks are hell, I thought, as the next witness walked toward the stand. He was six-foot-five and wore a dark suit, white shirt, dark tie and boots. And he had twenty years of law enforcement behind him. But on this case, he had run up against one of the biggest liars in his career. Not only had he been lied to, time and time again during the investigation, he had been sent on every wild goose chase he could think of. And he wasn't about to let anyone get away with that. Now, from the witness box, he glanced toward David Barron and also to Carol and me. Then Barron approached the stand with a half smile on his face.

Barron: "Would you state your name for the record and for the Court?"

Adams: "James Larry Adams."

Barron: "Deputy Adams, did you investigate a missing persons report on Patricia Crocker?"

Adams: "Yes, I did."

Adams stated that when he received the missing persons report, he went to Patricia's home, but no one was there. Then he went to the ranch and talked to Lewis. Lewis told him that he and Patricia had had an argument, and she had left walking. Adams then talked about the missing carpet and mattress, and of his various conversations with Lewis and other people.

Barron: "Did you have an occasion on September 20, 1988, to execute a search warrant at the residence of Lewis Crocker?"

Adams: "Yes, I did."

Barron: "And who was with you when you executed the warrant?"

Adams: "Texas Ranger, Brian Taylor."

Barron: "Who was the arrest warrant for?"

Adams: "Lewis Crocker."

Barron: "When you went to the house, who was present?"

Adams: "Lewis Crocker, one of his daughters and her friend."

Barron: "What did you advise Lewis Crocker at that point?"

Adams: "I advised him that he was under arrest for murder and I read him his Miranda warning."

Barron: "Did you read it off the card?"

Adams: "Yes, sir. I read it off the card."

Adams then stated that Lewis was placed in Ranger Taylor's car, and that he had waited by the car while Taylor went inside to inform the girls of what was going on. Adams also stated that as he waited beside the car, Lewis had blurted out the statement, "I killed her and I'm glad it's over."

Barron: "Do you remember him saying anything to you about a fight over a gun?"

Adams: "No, sir. Not on that day, or at that time. No, sir."

Adams stated that he and Taylor took Lewis to Judge McNew, and then to the Grimes County Sheriff's Office. At the office Lewis gave a taped confession.

Carter quickly objected to what he called the oral confession, as well as the taped confession. But Judge Ernst promptly overruled both objections. Then Carter cast his blow at Adams with a lengthy cross examination, beginning with Lewis' statement: 'I killed her and I'm glad it's over.' However, David Barron appeared to remain cool and collected, as though he may have been saying to himself: 'Go ahead, Billy. Be yourself. Give it everything you can. But I know what I've got and I know exactly what to do with it.'

Carter: "And just how soon after you placed him under arrest had he made that statement? Was it within seconds, minutes, or what?"

Adams: "It was after I arrested him, read him his rights, hand-cuffed him, and had him sitting on the inside of the car. I was standing on the outside. It could have been as much as ten minutes."

Carter: "Was the window up in the car?"

Adams: "No, it was rolled down."

Carter: "And when you went to the ranch to talk to him, I guess you had your gun on and everything else and said you wanted to talk to him?"

Adams: "I'm quite sure I had a pistol on my hip. All police officers wear pistols."

Carter: "In your investigation, did you uncover the name of a man named Charlie Lancaster?"

Adams: "Yes, I did."

Carter: "What did you find out about him?"

Adams: "That he had left Grimes County one week prior to Patricia's disappearance."

Carter: "Did you find out who he had left with?"

Adams: "Yes, I did."

Carter: "Who did he leave with?"

Adams: "I would rather not say. At that point he asked to remain anonymous."

Carter: "Well, who did he leave with?"

Adams: "I can't state the lady's name right now because I don't remember."

The cross examination of Adams continued, followed by redirect and recross, as the new District Attorney and the well seasoned Old Timer battled it out with the tough tall Law Man between them. But finally it ended. And Judge Ernst promptly recessed the Court for lunch.

As we were leaving the courtroom, Carol and I walked over to Larry Adams to say good-bye. He seemed pleased when we thanked him for his testimony.

"I'm sorry it took so long to find her. And I hope Lewis gets the maximum sentence," Adams went on. "But after the trial is over, I'd like to talk to you again. I've got to go now. I've got a meeting. But, ya'll take care and next time you're down this way, let us hear from you."

CHAPTER 24

After lunch we waited on the balcony of the courthouse until court began, hoping to catch a glimpse of someone near the white pickup. But no one walked near it. And, so far, we had not seen Lenny.

We returned to the courtroom and took our seats on the first row behind David Barron. And it was then that we noticed a change in the spectators. At the beginning of the trial, most of them had sat on the left side of the room, behind Carter. But now, they were crowded in the seats behind us, leaving the left side of the room empty, except for two news reporters.

A middle-aged woman, sitting behind us, leaned forward to make conversation.

"Why are the girls so hostile toward you?" she asked Carol.

"Why do you want to know?" Carol replied.

"Don't get me wrong," the lady said. "I was one of Patricia's neighbors, and I know Lewis was mean to her. I've seen her beat up, black and blue. I think they ought to take him out to the nearest tree and hang him by his balls."

David Barron heard her, and he glanced back at us for a brief second with a half smile on his face, then quickly looked the other way. Oh, Lord, he probably thinks I said that, I thought. Well, who knows, maybe he feels the same way.

David Barron's next witness for the State was Clarence Hudson, a retired civil service employee. He was of medium height with graying brown hair, and today, he wore a blue suit, blue shirt, red tie and western boots.

Mr. Hudson stated that he first met Lewis and Patricia at Fred's place on the day before Patricia's alleged disappearance. And that they came to his home the next morning to negotiate a sale for some hay. And that they met again that afternoon at three o'clock, at Fred's. He also stated that neither Patricia or Lewis appeared intoxicated at that time. He stated that Patricia became ill and went to the car, and that Lewis left later. Hudson said he also saw Lewis the next day, and that Lewis said Patricia had run off with another man and had "left him with all those kids." Hudson further stated that during the investigation, he had several conversations with Lewis.

Barron: "Did he say where Patricia might be located?"

Hudson: "Yes. He said she was at a lake in East Texas."

Barron: "Did he say anything about the investigation?"

Hudson: "He said he wasn't getting any cooperation from the law officials."

During cross examination, Carter apparently wanted Hudson to testify that Lewis and Patricia had been drinking before they went home.

Carter: "When you saw them at Fred's that day, were they intoxicated?"

Hudson: "Well, neither one of them was drunk. They had their faculties."

After Hudson was excused, Barron recalled Ranger Brian Taylor. Taylor was now on the stand giving further testimony of how the body was found. Taylor testified that he had contacted Bill Smith of the Internal Affairs Division of the Texas Department of Corrections, and that Bill Smith was in charge of the dogs of that unit, and that Smith had a dog that was trained in the detection of bodies buried or under water.

Taylor said that at daylight on the morning the body was found, the dog was given the scent of one of Patricia's purses, and that the dog searched several areas on the ranch before it located the body at the dump, and that the Crime Scene Unit from Conroe had then been called to exhume the body.

Taylor further stated that Ed Jordan and Troy Roberts, officers with the Crime Scene Unit from Conroe, had made a video and had also taken photographs of the grave site. Judge Ernst asked the jury to retire from the courtroom. Then the video was played for the Court and for the attorneys.

As the video played, Carol burst into tears and ran out of the courtroom. I sat there crying, frozen to my seat. I glanced at Lewis, hoping to see some sort of emotion. But he sat there, as rigid as steel.

Oh, damn him, I thought. Damn him to hell. How could he have done such a horrible thing?

The video became Exhibit No. 4, with Billy Carter fighting against it all the way. He objected to the video 'because of the gruesome nature' of it, and because 'the operator has not shown his training.'

Carter: "Ranger Taylor, you don't know if the operator knew how to operate a video or not, do you?"

Taylor: "No, sir."

Barron: "Was the person that took the video one of the crime scene officers?"

Taylor: "Yes, sir."

On and on the battle continued between Barron and Carter. Then Barron waved the autopsy photographs at Carter.

Barron: "Well, I guess we'll show the photographs if you'd rather have them."

Judge Ernst: "Are you talking to me?"

Barron: "No, sir. I'm talking to Billy."

After that, Barron proceeded questioning Taylor.

Barron: "Were there any changes, alterations or deletions made to that tape?"

Taylor: "No, sir. It appeared as it was at the grave site."

"Okay, one more for the hoop," said Barron.

Barron: "Ranger Taylor, was the video authentic and correct?"

Taylor: "Yes, sir."

Carter paced back and forth, pulling up his pants and perspiring profusely.

Carter: "Ranger, you don't know where the video has been prior to today?"

Taylor: "No, sir."

Carter: "So, if you haven't seen it prior to today, you don't know if there may have been some deletions or alterations?"

Taylor: "It was as it appeared."

Barron waved the photographs again toward Carter, and said: "Are you sure you wouldn't rather have these?"

Carter: "He's going to try to get them all in and I'm going to object."

Judge Ernst: "The video operator is competent. Objection overruled."

Taylor then stated that after Lewis' arrest, Lewis was taken to Judge McNew for his magistrate warning and for bond to be set, and then to the Grimes County Sheriff's Office.

Barron: "At that time, did you take a taped confession of him?"

Taylor: "Yes, sir. I did."

Barron: "Did he give this statement freely and voluntarily?"

Taylor: "Yes, sir. He did."

Barron then asked the Court to allow the tape to be played.

Carter: "Same objection."

Court: "Overruled. You may play the tape of the purported confession."

When the tape began to play, we listened carefully. We heard Lewis Crocker state his name, and that he knew his confession was being tape recorded. Then we heard Ranger Taylor's voice on the tape:

Taylor: "Lewis, before I go any further, I'm required by law to give you your rights and advise you of your rights as follows: It says under Texas law I'm required to inform you as follows: You have the right to remain silent and not make any statement at all and that any statement you make may be used against you at your trial. Any statement you make may be used as evidence against you in court. You have the right to have a lawyer present to advise you prior to and during any questioning. If you are unable to employ a lawyer, you have the right to have a lawyer appointed to advise you prior to and during any questioning. And you have the right to terminate the interview at any time. Mr. Crocker, do you understand and knowingly waive your rights?"

Crocker: "Yes, sir. I understand."

Taylor: "Do you knowingly and voluntarily waive your rights?"

Crocker: "Yes, sir."

Larry Adams had assisted Brian Taylor in taping the confession.

Taylor: "Deputy Adams, would you identify yourself for the tape?"

Adams: "James Larry Adams, for the Grimes County Sheriff's Office."

In the confession, Lewis said that he and Patricia had gone to Fred's place on the afternoon of August 7, 1988. He said they had some drinks there, and they left to go home around four o'clock. He said after they got home, they went to their bedroom and got into an argument. He said they were arguing about her leaving him, and that she had given their little girl to Rhonda. He said Patricia was tired of him and everything else. According to Lewis, Patricia said: "Mama and Daddy told me all my life what to do. I married you, and then you told me what to do. Now, the kids tell me what to do. And I'm sick of it." Lewis went on to say that one word led to another and they started fighting. And it wound up with a gun involved.

Taylor: "How did the gun become involved in it?"

Crocker: "I believe I picked the gun up."

Lewis stated that he had gotten the gun from their bedroom closet, and that Patricia started "screaming and cussing." He said they were fighting, "the gun went off, and Patricia was dead."

Taylor then asked if she fell or if he caught her. Lewis answered that she fell on the bed.

Taylor asked Lewis if he had put a cartridge in the chamber of the gun.

Lewis answered: "I don't recall." Lewis said they fought over the gun and it went off. He said the gun was a 308 Remington rifle, and that he later sold it to Donald. He said Donald wanted to use it to shoot coyotes.

Taylor asked Lewis what he did after Patricia fell on the bed. Lewis answered that he "jumped up, shut the door, then Rhonda drove up to get some clothes" for Jennifer. He said he was scared. Taylor asked if anyone was with Rhonda. Lewis said Jennifer was with her. Then Taylor asked if anyone else was with her. Lewis replied, "No. I didn't look out in the car. I don't know if there was anyone else with her or not." Taylor asked him how he knew Rhonda was at the house. Lewis replied, "I heard her drive up out front. I didn't know what to do. She came in there and said she had to get Jennifer some more clothes. But what she was wanting was in the front bedroom closet. She was in a hurry, so she left."

Taylor: "Did you ask her anything or tell her anything?"

Crocker: "Yes. I asked her if she'd seen her mother downtown. I was scared. I didn't want to tell her what happened right then. I don't know why I done what I done. I'm sorry I done it, but I did."

Taylor: "Then what did you do after Rhonda left?"

Lewis replied that he had "sat on the front porch until dark." Then he put Patricia's body in the trunk of the car. He said he "drug her off the bed and through the living room to the front porch." He said he "finally got her picked up and put in the trunk and closed it." He said he spread a blanket in the car trunk and, "laid her on it and wrapped her up in it."

Taylor asked him what he did after that. Lewis replied that he "went back and took the carpet up and carried it downtown and throwed it in the dumpster." Taylor asked Lewis if he had blood on his clothes. Lewis said he had blood on his pants. Then Lewis told of burying Patricia's body at the ranch. He said he had worked at the ranch about two months.

Taylor: "Did anyone see you go on the ranch?"

Crocker: "The foreman was there. I told him I was going in back fishing for a little while."

Taylor asked Lewis what day of the week that was. Lewis first replied that it was Sunday. Then he said it was the next day. "Monday. In the middle of the morning." Taylor asked him if he was supposed to work that day. Lewis replied that he was supposed to, but he "had a dentist appointment and didn't go."

Then Lewis said that after he got to the ranch, he drove down the road to the dump and, "backed the car up to that junk pile. I found that place was clean. I dug it up, cleaned it out some, put her in it, covered her up with that blanket, and then covered her with dirt and put some scrap, old rusty barrels and stuff there, by her."

Taylor: "But how did you lift her out of the car?"

Crocker: "I picked her up. I carried her over there and I just kind of slid down the bank with her and laid her down and covered her up with the blanket."

Taylor: "You didn't burn anything?"

Crocker: "The next few days I was cutting some pipe and them colored boys brought a bunch of pasteboard boxes and stuff."

Taylor: "What colored boys are you talking about?"

Lewis said he didn't know the men's names. Taylor asked "if the men knew she was there."

Crocker: "No. I was cutting some pipe and I told them not to burn the boxes because the welding machine was sitting there. I told them I'd burn them later."

Taylor asked him what he did after he buried Patricia. Lewis replied that he went home and drank. He also said that when he carried the body to the dump, he had forgotten to take Patricia's purse (the purse with her identification).

Crocker: "When I carried her over there, I forgot it. So, I just walked behind the house and throwed it in the septic tank."

Taylor: "What did you do with the mattress on your bed at the house?"

Crocker: "I rolled it up and carried it back over there the next day and throwed it on the pasteboard boxes and burned it."

Adams: "Have you ever pulled a gun on her before?"

Crocker: "She got a shotgun off the wall about seven years ago. It went off through a closet door. I should have got rid of all the guns then. But I didn't."

Adams: "Lewis, did you have an occasion to go looking for her a few months ago with a gun?"

Crocker: "Yes. I went looking for her. And I had the gun. I was just going to shoot the tires out of the car to stop it."

Adams: "Did you know her retirement check was in the mail?"

Crocker: "No, sir. I knew it was supposed to be, but I didn't know whether she had got it. I knew it was due to come."

Adams: "But you knew she was supposed to get it?"

Crocker: "Right. But I couldn't sign it. It ain't in my name."

Adams: "Didn't you go to the bank and attempt to cash it?"

Crocker: "No. When my daughter carried them up there, they

said we could not cash the check. I guess the check is still there. I don't know what the check was amounted for. I thought she got it the week before all this happened. I asked Kim if she got it. Kim said she didn't know and it came later."

Adams: "Lewis, do you or your wife have any life insurance?"

Lewis replied that Patricia had life insurance with the school. He denied knowing the beneficiary. But he said he believed it was Tammie.

Lewis was then asked if he wanted to add anything else to his statement. He replied that there was nothing he could think of. Then Taylor began the formality of ending it, asking Lewis whether he had been promised or threatened in any way to give the statement. Lewis replied that he had not. Therefore the statement from Lewis Marlin Crocker was brought to its conclusion, and was entered as State's Exhibit No. 2, in his trial for the murder of Patricia.

Carter: "Same objection I heretofore made."

Court: "Same ruling. Admitted."

Barron was now ready to present Exhibit No. 14, the murder weapon. The rifle was lying on Barron's counsel table, and as he walked toward it, a juror caught his attention and mentioned that the rifle barrel was pointed toward the jury.

"Oh, I apologize for not noticing that," said Barron, in pretended innocence.

"Point it toward Lewis," a spectator called out. "He's the one who needs to look at it." Judge Ernst quickly rapped his gavel, in warning that although he was friendly, he was not about to put up with any shenanigans in his courtroom. However, Barron did indeed turn the rifle around toward Lewis. Then he continued his questions to Ranger Taylor.

Barron showed the rifle and Taylor identified it as a "Savage Model 99E, 308 caliber Winchester A A 559124 lever action."

Judge Ernst asked Taylor to check the gun and see whether or not it was loaded. He said he'd had one gun go off in the courtroom and that was enough. Taylor checked the gun again and assured His Honor that the gun was not loaded.

Later, Barron presented a series of handwritten notes, which became the State's Exhibit No. 13, 13-A through 13-E. The notes were in Lewis' handwriting, and among them, was one upon which Lewis had drawn a map showing the location of where he had buried Patricia's body. The other notes merely rambled, one of which was his handwritten will.

However, during Taylor's testimony concerning the notes, I became more interested in the date that they were found, rather than the words they contained. For Taylor had found them on October 18, four days after our meeting at the Sheriff's office in Anderson. I wondered about him finding them so soon after our meeting. I had not mentioned the meeting to anyone. And until today, I had in fact seriously doubted that the notes existed.

Barron: "Did he give you the consent to search freely and voluntarily?"

Taylor explained that Lewis had given his consent, and that he had also read the Miranda warning again to Lewis. Then Barron passed the witness.

Carter: "Did you tell him you needed to go find some notes?"

Taylor explained that Lewis had told one of his daughters that he had left a letter in the living room under a chair, but Taylor couldn't find it. Taylor visited Lewis at the jail and asked him if he indeed wrote a letter. Lewis said he did. Lewis said it was under the carpet in the living room. Taylor found it slipped under the carpet seams.

The letter consisted of several pages, all in Lewis' handwriting. One page mentioned the mysterious "Bill." Lewis had written, "I could not have her no more. Now, Bill won't."

Judge Ernst declared a late afternoon break, "while we get these papers sorted out."

When we returned to the courtroom, Taylor was again on the witness stand, and Carter proceeded with another hard blow at the handsome ranger.

He fired questions about the high powered rifle, the location of the house, and the fact that a church and other houses were close to the house. He wanted to create the idea that the shooting had been accidental, and that one would not have intentionally fired such a high powered weapon in a close neighborhood.

But Carter didn't know Lewis' anger. He didn't know Lewis had been around guns all his life, and that he would have known how to prevent a loud noise. In his violent anger, he may not have cared if anyone had heard it. And had anyone came to investigate the noise, he would have denied it.

Carter continued on, leaving no stones unturned about the rifle, the location of the house, search warrants, making sure Lewis' rights had not been violated during the investigation or during the confession. And then, of course, there was Charlie Lancaster to be dealt with. Good old Charlie. Charlie, the ladies man. Goodtime Charlie. If only Carter could obtain proof that an affair between Charlie and Patricia had actually existed. He now proceeded to question Taylor about his interviews with Pauline, Claude and Betty, concerning Charlie.

Carter: "But in all your conversations with them you never uncovered anything that would lead you to think there was any type of affair between Charlie Lancaster and Patricia Crocker?"

Barron objected to the question, "based on hearsay," and was overruled.

Taylor: "I was told that Patricia was having an affair with Lancaster."

Carter's face brightened considerably.

Carter: "So then, Pauline Nicholson told you that?"

Taylor: "Let me find it in my report what she said."

Carter: "Okay. Pauline Nicholson mentioned something to you about that?"

Taylor: "Okay. My report says, 'Pauline Nicholson states Patricia would leave Lewis several times because of violent behavior.' "

Carter: "I'm asking you! Did Pauline Nicholson tell you anything about Charlie Lancaster and Patricia Crocker?"

Barron: "He (Carter) didn't like his answer."

Carter: "I object to his (Barron) sidebar remarks."

Court: "That will be sustained. D.A., you know better than that."

Carter: "Ranger, did you talk to Claude Hutchins?"

Taylor: "Yes, sir, I have."

Carter: "Did he mention anything to you about a situation existing between Charlie Lancaster and Patricia Crocker, if you remember?"

Taylor: "No, sir. I don't have anything in my report that he told me that."

Carter: "What about Betty Hutchins?"

Taylor: "I talked to Claude and her both."

Barron had two more questions for Taylor, concerning Charlie.

Barron: "Ranger Taylor, you never did uncover any kind of concrete evidence that Charlie Lancaster and Patricia Crocker were having an affair? It is all speculation, isn't it?"

Taylor: "As far as I'm concerned, yes, sir."

Barron: "And Patricia Crocker is not here to defend herself, is she?"

Taylor: "No, sir."

Well, that takes care of Charlie, I thought. But what about the guy named Bill? Carter had not asked a single question about Bill. Evidently, Lewis knew something about him. Why hadn't Carter raised cain about Bill, as he had about Charlie? It seemed to me that he would have been more upset over Bill. Lewis had not mentioned Charlie's name in the notes, but he had mentioned Bill. Now, I wanted to know who the hell was Bill. And where was he? But just as my thoughts on the infamous Bill shifted into high gear, Judge Ernst rapped his gavel and recessed court until nine a.m. the next morning.

Carol and I left quickly down the front steps of the courthouse, hoping to see the white pickup and its driver. But it was nowhere in sight. Talk about bad days, I thought. I had listened to Carter rip Brian Taylor most of the day, hoping to insinuate that my sister was no better than a whore, in his attempts to defend the lying bastard who murdered her. Now, the pickup was gone and I never knew when that monstrosity would suddenly appear behind me. Besides that, Carol had cried half the day and now I was crying. Enough is enough, I thought. Then it hit me like the sound of roaring thunder. It was really so simple. I was surprised I had not realized it until now.

In Lewis' confession, he had mentioned nothing about Charlie or Bill. Or that he suspected Patricia may have had a boyfriend. He said that he and Patricia had argued. And when Taylor asked him what they had argued about, Lewis had said, "Well, one thing, her leaving, and another thing, she gave her little girl away." No mention of boyfriends. And when Adams had asked him "why he got the gun out of the closet," Lewis said he didn't remember. When Adams asked if he thought the gun was going to settle the argument, Lewis had replied, "I guess. I don't know why I got it." Still, no mention of Charlie or Bill, or any other boyfriend. Also, after his arrest, as he was being transported to the Grimes County Sheriff's Office, Lewis told Adams and Taylor that he "wanted to tell his side of it." Still, no mention of boyfriends.

It was my opinion that as he struggled for an excuse for the murder, the question of boyfriends never entered his mind. Because they didn't exist. And the most damaging excuse he could think of was to say that Patricia had given Jennifer away. Of course he knew it was a lie. But the fact that Rhonda often kept Jennifer while Patricia worked, was something he thought he could use against her.

In a conversation with Mother, back in May, she said Patricia was upset because of Lewis' behavior and the effect it had on Jennifer. Patricia said that Jennifer would cry and scream, "Please don't fight. Oh, please don't fight." And that was the reason Jennifer was allowed to spend extra time away from home on weekends. I knew this was true because for a while after Patricia's death, Jennifer had said similar words to others.

Poor old Charlie Lancaster. Wherever he was, he probably didn't have the slightest notion that he had all but been crucified in a murder trial in Grimes County. And it was not over yet. I wished I knew how to contact him, and ask him to attend the trial. I would have enjoyed seeing the look on Lewis' face as Charlie took the witness stand. For I had overheard a remark that "old Charlie was a mean tough dude. He could have eat Lewis for breakfast." But Charlie was long gone, and it was my guess that Lewis knew it. That was the reason he had thrown old Charlie's name in the game to begin with. Also, Claude Hutchins had said "it seemed like all the single women and widow women in the area were going crazy over Charlie." From my point of view, I wondered just how many women Claude knew in the area, and by what method was he able to obtain such coveted information. Did all the single and widow women frequent his establishment? I sincerely thought not. But, nevertheless, Charlie had made a good scapegoat. He was said to be handsome and a smooth talker. He liked the women and they liked him. And he was a drifter. Ah, that was the key. A drifter, long gone. No one knew where. And, he'd probably keep drifting, never to return to Grimes County. So, of all people, who could possibly make a better scapegoat than Charlie Lancaster? Unless it was Bill.

The infamous Bill was another subject. Bill, the man that none of the investigators had been able to trace, for no one could recall knowing him or ever having met him. Not that there weren't any men in the area named Bill. But the trouble was, no one knew this particular Bill. Lewis probably realized that, too, when he wrote: "I could not have her no more. Now, Bill won't."

CHAPTER 25

That night, over dinner, Carol and I talked about the daughters' hostility toward us. Our show of concern for them had been returned with cold stares and silence. As though it was none of our business that their father had murdered our sister. Patricia was dead, and we were supposed to bow out of the picture. Each day during court recess, the daughters hovered around Lewis in a show of strength, determined to save his hide from prison. I felt like asking them to show their love for Patricia. She was their mother and she loved them. I hated Lewis so much for murdering her, I guess I wanted the daughters to hate him, too. But I had read somewhere that children's minds and personalities are conditioned by what they see and hear in their environment. And even though a child will know right from wrong, they sometimes think that the parent who has control over them is the parent who must be right. For that parent gets his way. He is always the winner. It was that way with Lewis. He had to have the final word, the final slap. No matter what. He had to prove that he was the winner and controlled the situation.

When the girls saw the blood in the house, they knew Lewis' finger couldn't have bled that much. And when they saw the carpet gone and the mattress missing, they should have known something had happened to Patricia. They knew Lewis' track record. What were they thinking? And now that Lewis was on trial for murdering their mother, how could they hover around him and cater to his whims, as though he was still in control of their lives?

The thought crossed my mind that if Lewis asked them, they might possibly slip something else into his coat pocket, other than cigarettes.

Carol and I arrived at the courthouse earlier than usual the next morning. When we started up the stairs, we met Rhonda and Virginia. And again our attempted smiles were met with cold stares as they hurried past us.

In Barron's office, I expressed my concerns about the security in the courtroom. The back doors in the courthouse were wide open and I thought how easy it would be for Lewis to dart through a door and disappear. He knew the country roads and he could easily be out of sight within minutes.

But when Court began, a half hour later, my fears were subdued. Deputies Willie Love and John Sebastian were seated on a bench near the defense counsel table. Deputies Jackie Siragusa and Tracy Wright were near the back door. And Sheriff Bill Foster watched it all from the front door.

Glenn Hightower and Patrick Page sat behind Carol and me. Hightower had been the investigator for the prosecution. Page had been the investigator for the defense. Both of them had interviewed hundreds of people and had presented their findings to David Barron and Billy Carter. But now they sat side by side, like two tired old warriors taking time out to rest between battles.

When I turned around again, Sheriff Foster was closing the door as Darlene and Patty Lynn hurried down the aisle to join us.

Judge Ernst nodded to the jury and rapped his gavel. Court was in session.

David Barron's first witness that day was Doctor Mack Leon Bennett III. He was tall with graying brown hair, and I guessed him to be in his early forties. He wore a tan jacket, dark brown trousers, white shirt and striped tie. Doctor Bennett was a dentist. His office was in Madisonville.

Doctor Bennett stated that he had been in practice since 1966. And that Patricia Crocker was one of his patients. He had extracted four of her teeth, the last two in December 1985, and another tooth was missing. He further stated that he had furnished her dental records to Dr. Arial Espanola, the Department Chief Medical Examiner for Harris County.

On cross examination, Carter glanced at the dental records, then did his best to confuse Dr. Bennett with a string of questions amounting to little or nothing about the extracted teeth. However, Dr. Bennett patiently explained that he used the Universal System and that his records were correct.

David Barron then called his next witness, Dr. Arial Espanola, Chief Medical Examiner for Harris County. Dr. Espanola stated that he had received his medical education at Manila Central University in Manila, Philippines. And that he had received his pathology internship, pathology residency and forensic pathology training in Detroit, Michigan. "I am board certified in anatomic, clinical and forensic pathology by the American Board of Pathologists and I am a licensed physician in the State of Texas." Dr. Espanola further stated that during the past eleven years, he had performed thousands of autopsies, and that he had performed the autopsy on the body of Patricia Crocker.

Barron: "Would you describe to this jury the state of her body when it arrived at the medical examiners office?"

Carter immediately objected to Barron's line of questioning, saying that it was elicited only to inflame the mind of the jury and that it had no probative value to any issues in this particular case, and that it "concerns an extraneous matter which is abuse of a corpse."

Barron's face turned red at the words: "abuse of a corpse." I agreed with Judge Ernst when he asked Carter if he wanted the jury to believe that Patricia had been buried in a "National Cemetery, somewhere in Washington."

Court: "Objection overruled," said the Honorable Judge Ernst.

Barron: "Doctor, would you describe to the jury the nature of the body when it arrived at the medical examiner's office?"

Dr. Espanola stated that he had received the body in an enclosed black crash bag, and that the body was partially mummified, partially skeletonized, measured sixty-three inches in length and had a residual weight of fifty pounds.

Barron: "If the body had been buried six weeks, would that be consistent to this decomposition?"

Carter objected again. His objection was overruled.

Barron: "Is there a difference in the rate of decomposition?"

Espanola: "As long as the body was underground, the decomposition would be the same. The face and the skull were mummified. And the chest was mummified. Also the neck bones were absent."

Barron: "The neck bones were absent?"

Espanola: "Yes."

Barron: "Doctor, what would be the reason for the neck bones to be absent?"

Espanola: "There are multiple explanations for that. One is … "

Apparently, Carter had been waiting for that question. And he quickly objected to it on the grounds that is was "sheer speculation."

Court: "If it is speculation, sustained. If it is based on reasonable medical probability, overruled."

Barron: "Doctor, can decomposition cause the absence of the neck bones?"

Espanola: "No, sir."

Barron: "So, there would be some other reason?"

Espanola: "That's correct."

Barron continued about injuries to the body.

Dr. Espanola stated that he had discovered a gun shot wound of entrance in the left side of the chest and the exit in back. That the bullet had entered one half inch left of the midline, thirteen inches from the top of her head, and exited sixteen inches below the top of her head. That the direction of the bullet was front to back, downward and forward to the left.

Barron: "Could someone survive for some time with a wound like this? So, it wouldn't necessarily be fatal?"

Espanola: "No, it is fatal. But I cannot tell you if it was instantaneous death or the person lived for a few minutes."

Barron: "There was a possibility that a person could live for a few minutes with a wound like that?"

Espanola: "Yes, sir."

Barron then asked about drug and alcohol tests. Dr. Espanola stated that he performed the tests. The results of both tests were negative. "There were no drugs in her system." Espanola further stated that there were rib fractures. He also said there was jewelry on the body: "A ring on her left ring finger."

Barron passed the witness.

Carter: "That particular type of gun shot wound would be more consistent, would it not be, with instantaneous death?"

Espanola: "I was not sure whether it was instantaneous because the only instantaneous death in the chest is if it involves the heart, but if it only involves the lungs it will not be instantaneous death."

Carter: "But from the pathway of that particular bullet, would it be more consistent with it hitting the heart?"

Espanola: "Not necessarily. The wound was in the left side going downward and the heart is in the middle of the chest. So, it is more likely that the injuries were confined to the lungs."

Later, in a private conversation, Dr. Espanola would say he believed that Patricia could have lived approximately twenty-nine minutes after she was shot. I would remember that conversation every time I thought of Lewis and Rhonda standing in the front yard talking for twenty or thirty minutes after her mother was shot. How I wished Rhonda had gone into her mother's bedroom when she went into the house to get the extra clothes for Jennifer.

Carter remained steadfast, on center stage, as he continued to question Dr. Espanola. He asked about the different positions Patricia and Lewis may have been in when the gun was fired. Were they standing or sitting down? Was he standing? Was she sitting down? Were they in bed?

Carter: "It would be consistent with the weapon being lower than the object?"

Espanola: "We don't know the position. If they were both standing up, then it will not be consistent, but if the victim was sitting down and the assailant was standing up, it may be consistent."

Carter continued on about the positions and the pathway of the bullet, leaving no stones unturned. Finally, he passed the witness back to Barron.

Barron: "However, if one was sitting down and the person that was shot was further away, it would be consistent?"

Espanola: "Yes."

Barron passed the witness.

On recross, Carter had only two questions for the doctor. And both were certainly relevant. But, had he reconsidered, he may have chosen to rephrase the last one.

Carter: "Doctor, how many feet away from someone would they have to be to make that particular angle in the body in someone if they were sitting down?"

Espanola: "I cannot give you an answer right now. I would have to calculate it. It would take time for me to do that."

Carter: Okay. You think it would be more than twelve feet?"

Espanola: "That would be too far."

Of course it would be too far, I thought. The entire bedroom was less than that.

Carter passed the witness. Barron announced that he had no further questions. And Judge Ernst excused the doctor from the stand.

David Barron paused for a moment, then rose from his counsel table to end the first half of the battle. "Your Honor, at this time the State of Texas rests."

During break, Patty and Darlene, and Carol and I sat on a bench in the hallway near the coke machine. A pretty black lady wearing a red dress and carrying papers stopped to chat with us. Her name was Brenda Williams. We later learned that she was Mr. Barron's executive secretary.

"I'm so sorry about your sister's death," she said. "Oh, my, how sad it was."

"Yes, it was," I replied. "We're still in shock over it. Did you know her?"

"No, I didn't. But I've met her daughters."

We chatted a few moments more about the case, the town and the weather. And she walked with us back to the courtroom.

"I'll say a prayer for you all," she said as we climbed the stairs.

"Thanks, I appreciate that. I've prayed so many prayers, I sometimes wonder if God hears them anymore."

"Of course He does," she went on. "God doesn't forget those who trust him. And He'll be blessing you when you least expect it. Just keep your faith. You'll see."

When we said good-bye in the courtroom, she reminded us again to "keep trusting in the Lord. He'll hear you."

Carol and I took our seats. As we sat down, Patrick Page leaned forward and said, "Ma'am, I just want you to know that of all the people I interviewed on this case, I didn't find anyone who didn't like Patricia. She was well liked and respected. And she was a hard worker."

"It's nice of you to say so, but we've always known that," I replied.

"Well, do you know anything about the Texas Criminal Justice System?"

"No, this is my first experience. But I know it's supposed to work."

"Well, if I can, I'd like to try to explain a few things about it," he said. "You know, Brian Taylor was the State's investigator for the prosecution on this case. That was his job. And, according to the law, the defense was also entitled to an investigator. It has to be that way. Otherwise it wouldn't be fair. You see, in a case where there is a court appointed attorney, there is also a court appointed investigator. That was my job."

I wondered why he chose to explain to me, his position in the case. But later, I reached the conclusion that he had wanted me to know that he was really a decent human being with moral principles and ethics. And that although there were times when he'd rather walk through a pasture of muck, nevertheless, he did his job. He further explained about the wheels of the criminal justice system. How they were put together. What made them turn. Why they worked and why sometimes they didn't. I also learned that he had an Undergraduate Degree in Criminal Justice and a Graduate Degree in Social Services. He was a licensed private investigator and a certified social worker. And as time went by after the trial, I would remember him with kindness and respect.

I glanced at David Barron, and the stack of papers on his counsel table. And at the rifle, the constant reminder, which lay in front of him. He appeared confident, but not overly confident. Prepared was a better word. As he hung his coat on the back of his chair, I got the impression that he may have been thinking: 'Okay, Billy, it's your turn. You're in the batter's box now. Come on, hit the ball and watch me catch it.' And I remembered Walter Mitchell's words: 'Barron knows what he's doing.' Well, so far, so good, Walter.

Rhonda Crocker Bullion, age 23, second oldest daughter of Lewis and Patricia Crocker, was the first defense witness. She stated that her husband was a farm hand, and that she sometimes worked exercising race horses.

Carter asked her to describe the marriage relationship between her mother and father. She replied that, from the time she could remember, there had always been a lot of hostility, anger and jealousy. And that weapons were often involved.

Rhonda was obviously nervous, which was understandable, but I wondered why she avoided looking at Carol and me. So far, she had said nothing that we didn't already know. But as she shifted from side to side in the chair, Carter seemed equally as nervous.

Barron: "Your Honor, could you ask Mr. Carter not to walk around so much? I can't see the witness."

Carter apologized and continued his questions to Rhonda.

Carter: "All right. Was there any drinking in this particular relationship?"

Bullion: "Yes."

Carter: "Would it be more by one parent or by the other or what were the circumstances of that?"

Bullion: "In the first years when the children were all young, she wouldn't drink as much, and not very many guns and weapons were pulled out. But in the last six months she drank just as much as he did."

Carter asked Rhonda if Patricia was seeing a doctor for weight problems, and if she had noticed a change in Patricia's personality.

Rhonda answered, "yes," to both questions. Carter: "What type of change in her personality did you observe?"

Bullion: "Before the pills, she wasn't drinking like that. She would care about her family and at the end of the six months prior to her death, she thought about her, I mean, herself. She was first and it was never that way. Her family was always first and, then, come her, but at the end it was her and, then she worried about her family."

Carter: "Rhonda, how do you think your father felt about your mother?"

Bullion: "He loved her very much. He worshipped the ground she walked on and she did the same for him. He would send her flowers for different occasions."

Carter: "How do you explain the fights?"

Bullion: "Jealousy and fear. They would fight over anything."

Carter then asked Rhonda about Kimberly's motorcycle accident.

Kimberly, whom I thought was the most beautiful of the four grown daughters, graduated from Madisonville High School in 1986, and landed a job at one of the local banks. Patricia financed a new car for her. Kimberly's future was bright. She had a good job and she was in love. Her boyfriend often took her riding on his motorcycle. But, in October of that year, while on a motorcycle ride on a gravel road, the motorcycle skidded and hit a bridge embankment. Kimberly was critically injured with a head injury which also paralyzed the left side of her body. She was hospitalized the rest of the year. Her injuries were permanent. Her speech was now slow and careful. However, she did not lose her memory or her intellectual abilities.

Carter asked Rhonda how things were after Kimberly came home from the hospital. "Everyone waited on her," Rhonda said. "I mean, my mom. She was there. When Kimberly hollered, Mom came."

Carter then led Rhonda to the day of August 7, 1988. The day Patricia was killed. Rhonda explained that she was visiting a friend in Bedias, around noon that day. And that Lewis and Patricia brought Jennifer over to see her.

Carter: "So you picked up Jennifer and you told your mother and father you are going to come by their house later on that Sunday?"

Bullion: "Yes."

Rhonda then stated that she and Donald, their daughter and Jennifer, had gone to the house that evening around "seven to eight o'clock."

Carter: "Who went into the house?"

Bullion: "Myself and my father."

Carter: "And where did you go then?"

Rhonda said she picked up some clothes for Jennifer, and went into the kitchen and drank a glass of water, then she and Lewis went back outside. And, quote: "Stood in the yard, laid up against the back of the car and my father and I were talking and he was talking to me and my husband and I left." Unquote.

Evidently, Rhonda didn't know that in Lewis' confession, he had stated that Jennifer was with her. But that he didn't look out in the car. And he didn't know if anyone else was with her or not. He said he heard her drive up and that she came into the house and got some more clothes. He said she was in a hurry and left. Nor did Rhonda know that Donald had said they had talked twenty or thirty minutes.

I wondered what they talked about during those twenty or thirty minutes. And I shuddered to think what might have happened if, during that time, the small children had wanted to use the bathroom, or wanted to go in the house for a toy or something to drink. For when Rhonda was in the house drinking a glass of water at the kitchen sink, she was approximately twelve feet from her mother's bedroom door.

My guess was that when Lewis heard Rhonda drive up, he knew he was going to send Jennifer back home with her. And he had quickly moved some of Jennifer's clothing to the front bedroom, so Rhonda would have no reason to look in her mother's bedroom. Rhonda said Lewis followed her through the house. I wondered if she smelled the gun powder, and what she thought as Lewis followed her. I knew I would never know all the answers. But I was most certain of one thing: It took a cold-hearted sonofabitch to stand in his front yard talking to his daughter while her mother lay in the house dying from gunshot wounds.

Carter's next question to Rhonda was whether Lewis had the occasion to stay at her home between August 7, and September 20, the day he was arrested. She stated that he did. Carter asked how he would act when he was there. She replied that he was lonely and hurt.

Barron interrupted to complain that Carter was pacing the floor again.

Carter: "I'm sorry Judge. I have a difficult time not walking. Can I just go stand over there?"

Judge Ernst: "Can you live with that, D.A.?"

Barron said he could live with that.

Carter got back to his questions again about Lewis' emotions during the times he stayed with Rhonda. Rhonda said she could hardly ever get Lewis to eat, and that he sat in a chair a lot. "He mostly just was by himself." And she, quote: "felt that he had a lot of guilt and anger. Not anger, but loneliness."

I wondered what the people at the beer joints he had frequented between August 7, and September 20, could say about that.

But Carter passed the witness and Judge Ernst declared that it was lunch time.

After lunch, David Barron wasted no time in beginning his cross examination of Rhonda Crocker Bullion. It was straight and to the point. His first question was to remind her of the formal statement she had given to Brian Taylor, on September 21, the day after Lewis' arrest. He asked if she remembered giving the statement. She said she did.

Barron then went back to August 7, and to Rhonda's arrival at her parents' home. She said she arrived there about 7 or 8 o'clock, and that Donald, and their daughter and Jennifer were with her. She said she was there to pick up some clothes. She walked up on the front porch and knocked on the door.

Barron: "And did your father respond?"

Rhonda replied that he did, and he told her to "hold on a minute."

Barron: "Was the front door locked?"

Bullion: "Yes, and that's not unusual."

Barron: "You know now that you arrived shortly after your father shot your mother?"

Bullion: "Right."

Barron asked Rhonda what Lewis did when he opened the door. Rhonda replied that he walked out on the front porch and pulled the door behind him.

Barron: "Did he ask if you had seen your mother?"

Bullion: "Yes. He asked me if I had seen my mother and I told him, 'no.' "

Barron: "How was your father dressed?"

Bullion: "He had a pair of men's black slacks on and he did have a shirt on."

Barron: "Did your father seem to be upset in any manner?"

Bullion: "Would be kind of like in a panic that I drove up at the time I did, like, "What are you doing here at this time?"

Barron: "Did he seem angry?"

Bullion: "No. He was like he was in a shock."

Barron: "Was he in a rage?"

Bullion: "Not at that time."

Barron asked Rhonda if she saw anything unusual about the way her father was acting. Rhonda replied, quote: "he was like when you have done something and somebody pulls up when you're not expecting them." Unquote.

Barron asked if she went into the house, and if the door to her parents' bedroom was open or closed. She said the door was closed, and "there wasn't anything unusual about that."

Barron asked if Lewis appeared to have been drinking at that time.

Bullion: "He acted like he had drank two or three beers but he wasn't intoxicated if that's what you're asking."

Barron asked her again if Lewis was intoxicated. She answered, "No."

Barron: "Was any of the carpet removed from the house at that point?"

Bullion: "No."

Barron: "A few days after this or a couple of weeks after this did you find some blood in the house?"

Bullion: "Yes."

Rhonda stated that she had found blood on the bottom of a dresser in her parents' bedroom.

302

Barron: "What did you do when you found the blood?"

Bullion: "Well, okay. I got a piece of toilet tissue and wet it and wiped the spot off. There were two spots on there and it could have been anything."

Barron: "Was the carpet off at that time?"

Bullion: "Yes."

Barron: "Did that strike you as unusual?"

Bullion: "No. Because they had talked about it two or three weeks before."

Barron: "Did the blood strike you as unusual?"

Bullion: "Yes."

Barron: "And you knew your mother had disappeared?"

Bullion: "Yes, sir. That's why it struck me as unusual."

Barron: "You suspected your father as having something to do with her disappearance?"

Bullion: "Yes."

Barron: "How long after this time did you report her missing?"

Bullion: "I did not report her missing."

Barron: "How long was it until she was reported missing?"

Bullion: "About a week."

Barron: "Why was it that it took so long for her to be reported missing?"

I doubted that she would have ever been reported missing, had I not learned of her disappearance, and insisted on getting the law involved in it.

Bullion: "Because it was not unusual for her to go and stay gone."

Stay gone? Come on, Rhonda, give us a break. Every time she left, Lewis tracked her down within a day or two, if not sooner.

Barron: "Did she leave because of the arguments with your father?"

Bullion: "Yes."

Barron: "What kind of mother was Patricia Crocker?"

Bullion: "My mother was always a loving and understanding mother."

Barron: "And really the only criticism of her being the fights she would have with your father?"

Bullion: "Did I criticize her?"

Barron: "Would that be the only criticism you would have of her?"

Bullion: "No. It would be that when she drank."

Barron: "Do you drink?"

Bullion: "Occasionally. Maybe once or twice a month."

Barron: "Had she ever had an opportunity since she was a young lady to do really what she wanted to do?"

Bullion: "No."

Barron asked Rhonda if Patricia worked regularly. And if she also worked extra jobs in the summers. Rhonda answered "yes," to both questions.

Barron: "Not really caring about herself or doing things she wanted to do?"

Bullion: "Right."

Barron: "Do you know if she had plans to go back to school to further her education?"

Bullion: "Well, this is just hearsay that she told us she was going to go in January and get her nursing license to be an L.V.N."

Barron: "She was thinking more of herself, thinking better of herself?"

Bullion: "Yes. She wanted more than just working at the school."

Rhonda stated that Patricia had given her resignation at the school.

Barron: "Do you know if she was expecting a retirement check from the school district?"

Bullion: "Yes."

Barron: "When did that check arrive?"

Bullion: "The end of August or the first of September."

Barron: "But it was after her death?"

Bullion: "Yes. Two to three weeks after her death."

Oh, come on, Rhonda, I thought. Stop sitting there lying your little buns off. You know the check arrived a few days after her death. You know Lewis took it to the First City National Bank in Madisonville, the week after her death. Furthermore, you know one of his daughters also went to the bank.

Evidently, Rhonda knew that if the State could prove that Lewis had murdered Patricia for her retirement money, he might possibly be charged with capital murder. A charge that could carry the death penalty. Now, Barron's questions leaned in that direction.

Barron: "Did your father know she was expecting that check?"

Bullion: "Yes, everybody knew it. The whole family knew it."

Barron: "Did you assist him in trying to cash that check at the bank?"

Bullion: "No, he didn't want to cash it."

Barron: "Do you know if he took the check to the bank?"

Bullion: "Yes, because they had loans there and she was behind on a note or had gotten behind since her disappearance. Her banker called and said he needed some money, so my father took the check to him and told him to hold it."

Barron: "You say the note got behind when your mother disappeared?"

Bullion: "Well, he was one ... . Her note was due. Her note was set up at the bank, She got paid on the 25th. Her checks went automatically to the bank. They took her notes out of her paycheck and the rest was put into her account."

I noticed how quickly Rhonda shifted from the word, "he" to "her," in her answer. Evidently, wanting the jury to believe that the note was not really Lewis' responsibility. Stop it, Rhonda, I thought. Stop trying to protect him. Look at the jury. Tell them how he abused your mother. Tell them about the bloody beatings and the guns. Cry for her, Rhonda. She would cry for you.

Barron: "Did the money benefit both of them?"

Bullion: "I don't know. I don't know how much the note was or anything."

But you can bet your little buns that whatever it was, he got his share, I thought. And if the retirement check had been deposited in the bank, he would have had that, too, wouldn't he? After all, if he was only interested in paying the note that was due, why didn't he pay it out of his own salary?

Barron then asked Rhonda about her parents' home. Did they own it, and who owned it now. Rhonda replied that all five girls now owned it. "After this accident or whatever it was happened, we had him put the house in our name."

Barron: "Did any of your father's other property go to you all?"

Bullion: "They have a bus that is a camper and a boat that was given to me years ago. I was told that when they broke up housekeeping or both died, that that was mine. They have two cars that were divided. But the home belongs to all of us."

But Rhonda, I thought. Did you know that on August 7, Lewis tried to sell the bus to Fred? Why would he try to sell the bus on that particular day? And, just a few days before your mother's body was found, he tried to sell it to Clarence Hudson. He told Clarence he needed the money to go north to find your mother.

Barron asked Rhonda if she knew the range of punishment for murder. Carter quickly objected to the question, as being totally irrelevant. But Barron said it went to the motive. Judge Ernst overruled the objection. Then Barron asked it again and waited for Rhonda's answer.

Bullion: "I don't know. I never learned it in school. It could be lethal injection, I don't know."

Barron: "You haven't discussed that with Mr. Carter?"

Rhonda replied, "No." Then Barron asked if she knew the range of punishment for voluntary manslaughter. Carter placed a running objection to anything regarding punishment. Judge Ernst overruled the objection. And Barron continued.

Barron: "Did you hear me say murder carries with it five to ninety-nine years and voluntary manslaughter carries two to twenty years?"

Bullion: "Yes, but I do not know it by reading it. I know it by hearsay."

Barron: "Do you question whether this is accurate or not?"

Bullion: "I'd like to read it in the law books. That way I'd know for certain."

Barron passed the witness.

On recross, Carter asked whether the house had been deeded to the girls. Rhonda replied that it had.

I wondered when Lewis deeded the house to the girls. And whether he deeded it before or after he had obtained a court-appointed attorney who would be paid by the taxpayers of the State of Texas.

Judge Ernst turned to Rhonda and said, "Young lady, you are excused." Then Rhonda left the stand and smiled at the jury. She had done her best to save her father's hide and she wanted the jury to believe her testimony. But as she walked across the room looking like a little girl dressed in grown-up clothes, I felt an added emptiness. She was her father's daughter.

THE DARK SIDE OF TWILIGHT:

CHAPTER 26

Carter's next witness for the defense was Virginia Crocker, age 20, second youngest daughter of Lewis and Patricia Crocker. Virginia was blonde with wide set eyes like Lewis. Her height and build was petite like Patricia.

Virginia and her two children had, at various times, both before and after the murder, lived in Lewis and Patricia's home in Bedias. However, neither she nor her children were there on August 7, 1988.

Carter: "When was the last time you saw them prior to that date?"

Virginia: "About two weeks before then."

Carter: "Were you living in Bedias at the house at that time? And what were the circumstances of that?"

Virginia: "I was there and they had been arguing a lot that whole week."

Carter: "Could you tell the jury what you observed about their relationship during that week period? As far as the arguments and those kind of things?"

Virginia: "I don't know. I know she wanted to leave."

Carter: "Did you see any weapons at that particular time?"

Virginia: "Not that week. I don't think I did."

Carter: "Did you do anything to try to stop the arguments?"

Virginia: "One time they were in the kitchen and I thought they were going to start fighting and I got between both of them and she told me to move."

Barron objected to the hearsay. "Sustained," said the Honorable Judge Ernst.

Carter asked Virginia if she was able to stop the fight. She answered, "No."

Virginia stated that she did not see Lewis and Patricia on August 7, 1988, but that she did see Lewis in Navasota on August 8th.

Carter asked Virginia if she lived in the house in Bedias after

August 7th. She replied that she and her children lived in the house about three or four weeks after August 7th.

Carter: "Could you describe for the jury your father's behavior during the time you were at the house these three weeks after the shooting?"

Virginia: "He'd come home about nine o'clock or so and he would never sit in the living room. He would sit at the kitchen table for a few minutes and then he would go to his bedroom and sit on the side of the bed."

Carter: "When you say: 'He would come in and sit in the bedroom,' what would he do?"

Virginia: "Just sit on the side of the bed. Smoke a cigarette and drink beer."

Carter: "How long would he sit?"

Virginia: "For an hour or an hour and a half or so, then he would lay down."

Carter: "Would he move around or just sit there the whole darn hour?"

Virginia: "He would move by going to the bathroom or going to get a beer out of the refrigerator."

Carter: "Would he do anything else? Did he watch T.V. or anything?"

Virginia: "No."

Listening to Carter's questions, I got the impression that he was hoping Virginia would suddenly blurt out some sort of earth-shaking answer. Anything that could show Lewis had been remorseful. But, so far, I believed Virginia's answers. I could visualize Lewis coming home late, sitting in his bedroom, drinking, then sleeping in the same bed that he and Patricia had shared. "That wasn't unusual," as Rhonda might say. "Cold," was what Brian Taylor would have called it. I thought, "Sorry, Carter. You may try but you can't change it."

But, indeed, Carter trudged on, trying his best to change it.

Carter: "Virginia, I'd like to get your impression of what you thought your father thought about your mother?"

Virginia: "I know he loved her. And he was always very jealous of her."

Carter: "And what about your mother's feelings toward your father?"

Virginia: "I know she loved him as far as being jealous."

Carter then passed the witness. And, as Barron began his cross examination, we noticed an immediate change in Virginia's attitude. She had answered Carter's questions with a barely audible voice, as warm and cuddly as a newborn kitten. But now, for Barron, her voice was stronger and her eyes flashed.

Barron: "Virginia, why was your mother jealous of him?"

Virginia: "What do you mean, 'why was she jealous'?"

Barron: "I don't know any other way to ask it. You said she was jealous of him and I wondered why?"

Virginia: "Because of the lady that worked at the store. I've seen my mom walk through the store while my daddy was there to see what they were doing."

Barron: "Was he having an affair with her?"

Virginia: "No."

Barron: "When you were staying at your father's house for those three weeks, did you notice some unusual things about the house that weren't there before?"

Virginia replied that she noticed a mattress and some carpet was missing.

Barron: "Did you notice a bloody handprint on the front door?"

Virginia: "Yes, sir."

Barron: "And putting all that together I assume you became suspicious of your father?"

Virginia: "Not so much that he had killed her."

Barron: "You say during that time he looked depressed and wasn't very active?" Virginia's answer was, "No."

Barron: "Of course, now you know he was depressed over the shooting incident?"

Virginia: "I wouldn't say he shot her because I don't think he did."

Barron: "Why would he confess to doing it then?"

Virginia: "I don't think he shot her to mean to do it."

Barron: "How often would your parents fight when you were growing up?"

Virginia: "I would say once a week."

Barron: "Did you ever see any firearms pulled by either party?"

Virginia: "Yes, sir."

Barron: "On how many occasions?"

Virginia: "Five times out of ten they were fighting the gun was involved."

Barron: "On August 8 of last year did you ask him where your mother was?"

Virginia replied by nodding yes.

Barron: "Did he ask if you had seen her?"

Virginia: "Yes, sir."

Barron passed the witness back to Carter for redirect.

Carter: "What makes you think they were fighting over the gun?"

Virginia: "Because I've seen it happen."

Carter: "What would you say happened?"

Virginia: "Maybe one of them had their hand down and he would be just like that and sometimes they would be closer and the gun would be between them."

Virginia, stop trying to cover for him, I thought. Weren't you the one who called the sheriff the night he chased her down the highway to shoot her tires out? She wasn't fighting with him over the gun that night, was she? She was running to get away from him as fast as she could, wasn't she? And you feared for her life, that night, didn't you? Now, why do you think the night he killed her was any different, other than the fact that he did kill her before she could get away from him that time? Remember, Lewis said he took the coil wire off of her car so she couldn't leave that afternoon. And the other car was at Tammie's house. He said your mother was sick, and after they got home from Fred's, she went to bed. And wasn't it convenient that the girls were gone for the weekend? Tell the jury how many times the sheriff was called to the house because of your father's violent behavior. Tell them how he controlled your mother with guns and beatings. Tell the jury how he still controls his daughters.

On recross examination, Barron went straight to the heart of what I thought were the true motives behind the testimony of both Rhonda and Virginia.

Barron: "Virginia, do you know the range of punishment between murder and voluntary manslaughter?"

Virginia: "Yes."

Barron: "What is the maximum punishment your father could get if he is found guilty of voluntary manslaughter?"

Virginia: "Twenty years."

Barron: "And if it is murder?"

Virginia: "Ninety-nine years to life."

On recross, Carter asked Virginia how she felt about her father. She replied, "I still love him. I don't know why but I don't hold any anger."

Carter then passed the witness. Barron had no further questions. Judge Ernst excused her, and granted the jury a ten minute break.

During break, Darlene and Patty went out into the hallway. When they returned a few moments later, Darlene's face blushed with excitement.

"I overheard them say that Lewis is going to testify," she said.

"Good," I replied. "I'm sure his testimony will be interesting."

"Well, I don't know if I can stand to look at him," Carol said.

"Carol, I feel the same way. But please promise me that no matter what he says, you won't let it upset you. At least not in the courtroom."

"I don't know if I can promise that, or not," she went on.

"You've got to promise. Remember, we're here for Patricia. And David Barron needs us. And Mother and Daddy are depending on us. We can't afford to let them down. We've got to stay calm and keep our heads on straight."

"Okay. I'll try my best," said Carol. "But what about you?"

"Don't worry. I'll be fine. Just remember, Patricia and Barron."

So, once again, when the Powers That Be, in the case of the State of Texas vs Lewis Crocker, were all in their respective places, Judge

Ernst rapped his gavel. Court was again in session.

Carter's next witness was the defendant, himself, Lewis Marlin Crocker, age 47. He was married 26 years, 10 months and 9 days to Patricia Lavon Crocker. Now he sat in the witness chair to defend himself on the charge of murdering her.

Lewis stated that he was born in Madisonville, and had dropped out of school in the seventh grade to work as a farm hand. And at the age of twenty, he was employed as a forklift operator by the United Salt Corporation. And, also at the age of twenty, he had met and married Patricia.

During the following years, he held various jobs, farm and mechanic work. And at one time, he owned a mechanic shop in Richards, near Anderson. Later, he was employed as a mechanic for school buses at Madisonville High School. After an injury there, he returned to ranch work and worked on several ranches in Grimes County. And in June of 1988, he was employed at the Jim Pierce ranch.

Carter: "Lewis, how did you feel about Patricia when you married her?"

Crocker: "I loved her."

Carter: "And if I asked if you were a jealous husband, would you say you were or you weren't?"

Crocker: "Yes, sir, very jealous."

Carter: "Was she a good mother?"

Crocker: "Yes, sir."

Carter: "Did you ever leave her at any time like she'd leave you?"

Lewis replied that he had never left Patricia. He wanted to but never did. Carter asked him why he didn't.

Crocker: "I could never leave that woman. I was going to leave about two weeks before this happened. I was really going to leave."

Carter: "Why were you?"

Crocker: "It was just getting on bad, her talk and stuff. We kept fighting and I told her we needed to do something. She wasn't the same person no more."

Carter asked him what he meant by that.

Crocker: "She got where she didn't care no more. She didn't care about our baby. She wanted to give her away. She said so, several times."

Suddenly, those words hit me like a bolt of lightning. How dare that lying bastard say that about Patricia. I quickly jumped up to face him. "Oh, that's bullshit!" I called out. "That's lying bullshit and you know it." I wanted to slap his face. I wanted to tear into him with all my might. Damn him! Damn his lies! Damn him to hell! But instead, after my outburst, I started walking out of the courtroom. Well, never mind, Carol. I was the one who blew it. And not only did I expect Judge Ernst to reprimand me for it, I also expected to hear boos from the spectators. However, to my utter amazement, the courtroom was completely quiet, and as I walked down the aisle toward the front door, I heard only the sounds of my shoes on the wooden floor. I opened the door and closed it behind me. Then I stood on the balcony and burst into tears.

"Hey, Ms. Lasell, are you all right?" a voice called from below.

As I turned around, Brian Taylor ran across the street toward me. And I ran to meet him. "No, I'm not all right," I cried. He placed his arm around my shoulder. I burst into tears again and told him what happened.

"Lewis Crocker is on the stand lying his head off," I cried. "And watch what I tell you, the jury will believe him."

"No, they won't," Taylor replied. "Trust me, they won't. They'll have the evidence to convict him. We'll get him."

"No, they won't," I cried. "They'll believe his lies. They'll let him walk out of there a free man. He said he'd get out of it. And his daughters are already planning a vacation trip to Las Vegas."

"Well, it's going to be a long time before Lewis goes to Las Vegas."

"But you're not on the jury," I said, wiping my tears from his jacket.

"That's true. But I did my homework," he replied, smiling. "Give me credit for that."

"I do. You know I do. But I'm worried that the jury will believe his lies."

"Well, we'll get him. Trust me, we'll get him. The only place he's going is right back over to the jail. Now, try to calm down, and when you feel better, go back in the courtroom. Just remember that I told you, we'd get him. I've got to leave now, to go to Columbus, but I'll see you again tomorrow."

I returned very quietly to the courtroom, half expecting Judge Ernst to ask me to leave. However, he appeared not to notice me, at all, as I quietly took my seat by Carol. Well, thank you, your Honor, for not scolding me, I thought. Then, I glanced at the jury, hoping they had also forgiven my outburst. One of the jurors half-smiled at me. But I dared not smile back in return. I had already pushed my luck to the limit.

Lewis was still in the witness chair, trying to appear as pitiful as possible.

Carter: "Lewis, did you suspect there was anything going on with her and other men in 1988?"

Crocker: "Yes, sir."

Carter: "What made you suspect that?"

Crocker: "Well, she got to where she would go off. She'd leave sometimes for no reason. She would be gone for two or three days. Two occasions I went to her sister's. One time her and her sister both was gone. And the kids were by themselves."

Carter, leading his witness, asked which kid was there. Lewis referred to Frances' kids and grandkids. Carter asked why that concerned him.

Crocker: "They left that evening and got back at one or two in the morning."

Carter" "Where were you?"

Crocker: "I was sitting there waiting for them to come in."

Then, referring to Patricia, Lewis said, "She told me she had been over there at a beer joint partying."

At that, Darlene's face turned red and she whispered: "Why that liar! Mama and Daddy and Aunt Pat went out for dinner that night, and they were home long before any one or two o'clock. I ought to know. I was at Mama's house. Besides that, all of Mama's kids are grown. And Aunt Pat took Jennifer with her. Just wait. I'm going to tell Mama what he said!"

Carter: "What was going on in the relationship in 1988 that was leading up to August 7, 1988? Why were you all fighting?"

Crocker: "Another man."

Carter asked Lewis if he knew who the other man was. Lewis replied that he knew who it was. It was Charlie Lancaster.

Carter: "Would she stay gone a lot or what were the circumstances of that during the summer of 1988?"

Crocker: "She never did go and stay a whole lot. Mostly in the daytime while I was working she'd go off and tell me she'd been different places putting in job applications for jobs."

Carter's questions then led to the day of August 7th.

Lewis stated that he and Patricia got up early that morning and went to Navasota to look at some hay. Then they took Jennifer to see Rhonda, who was visiting a friend in Bedias. After that, they drove Kimberly to Tammie's house.

But, Lewis, I thought. Don't you want to tell the jury that Patricia's eyes were swollen when you and she arrived at Tammie's? Tell us why her eyes were swollen and why she had been up all night crying, after working all day.

Carter's questions continued, and Lewis stated that he and Patricia went to Fred's Place for the turkey shoot. He said he thought Patricia was in the bathroom, but Clarence Hudson told him she was in the car. Lewis went outside. He said she was walking in front of the car, and she said she wanted to go home. Lewis wasn't about to say that he told Larry Adams that Patricia was so sick she lay her head on his lap on the way home.

Carter wanted to hear more about Charlie Lancaster.

Carter asked Lewis if he had any other problems with her in relationship to Charlie Lancaster prior to this time. Lewis replied, "Yes, sir."

Carter: "Did you suspect anything else?"

Crocker: "Well, he wouldn't talk across the table. He would go around and whisper in her ear. Several people seen it."

For Heaven's sake, Lewis, I thought. Give us a break. How many women's ears did you whisper into? Knowing you, if old Charlie had whispered in her ear, you would have hit him.

Carter continued. And Lewis told about the time he went to Pauline Nicholson's house, back in July. Patricia had gone to Pauline seeking refuge after Lewis chased her down the highway, trying to shoot her tires out.

Carter: "And why did you go there?"

Crocker: "I just wanted to talk to her. Try to get her to come back home."

Carter's questions had become increasingly nauseating. And I removed several candy mints from my purse.

Carter: "Lewis, how were you feeling about all this stuff?"

Crocker: "I don't know. Can't explain it. I just hurt because she left. I always go look for her."

Carter's questions then went back to the day of August 7th. And Lewis was trying to explain what happened after he and Patricia arrived home from Fred's.

Crocker: "She jumped on me because of the night before."

Carter: "The night before, on August 6th, had you gone somewhere together?"

Crocker: "No, she was working."

Lewis stated that he picked Patricia up from work. And they were supposed to meet some friends, but they didn't. Patricia wanted to go home.

Lewis and Patricia argued on that Saturday night. Patricia accused him of being with another woman. He denied it. And the fight continued.

The next day, her eyes were swollen. She told Tammie that she had been up all night crying. After her body was found, Tammie said to me, quote: "I'll bet the autopsy report will show that he beat her before he shot her." Unquote.

Carter's questions now continued. And, Lewis stated that after he and Patricia arrived home from Fred's, around five o'clock that Sunday evening, the argument continued. He said he sat on the porch ten minutes, and then went back inside and sat in the living room.

Carter: "What happened then?"

Crocker: "She was in the kitchen."

Carter: "How did you wind up in the bedroom? Did ya'll go in there or what?"

Crocker: "Yes. She wouldn't cut the air conditioner on. It was hot."

Carter: "Where was the gun located?"

Crocker: "Right inside the door as you go inside the bedroom. A closet."

Carter then moved a portable chalk board close to the witness stand and drew an outline of the bedroom as Lewis explained it to him.

Carter: "Okay. Now when you went in the bedroom where was your wife? Were you all standing up arguing or what?"

Crocker: "We were sitting on the bed."

Carter: "What happened then?"

Crocker: "Well, she was at the foot of the bed."

Lewis stated that they were sitting on the bed talking, and got into a fight.

Carter: "Got in a fight over what? What were you all fighting about?"

Crocker: "Charlie Lancaster. She told me, 'I don't want what we got,' and a bunch more. I was lashing out or something. I told her it was no worse than him sliming around on her, and I don't know what happened."

Carter: "What did you do then?"

Crocker: "I got the gun. I had to get it out of the closet."

Carter: "Then what happened?"

Crocker: "I don't know. Well, it was so fast."

Carter: "Tell the jury what you all were doing with the gun before it went off, shoving like this?"

Crocker: "Jerking. I had to have my hand on the trigger. It happened so fast."

Carter, leading his witness again, asked, "She fell back across the bed?"

Crocker: "Yes, sir."

Carter asked Lewis what caused him to get the gun. Lewis replied that he was angry, mad, and hurt.

Carter: "After the gun went off, what did you do?"

Crocker: "I grabbed her. Hollered at her not to die. I held her and cried. I don't know how long I sat there and held her."

But, Lewis, I thought. How long could you have held her? Have you forgotten that you said you thought Rhonda and Donald heard the shot? They drove up, Rhonda got out of the car, ran upon the porch, tried to open the front door. But the door was locked. And you told her to "wait a minute." It was near a hundred degrees outside, and your air conditioner was off. Who locked the door, and why?

Why was Patricia at the foot of the bed, near the bedroom door, when she was shot? Was she trying to escape, again? She was running from you the night you chased her down the highway with a loaded gun. Of course, you said you were "just going to shoot her tires out," that time. But was she also trying to escape when she was shot? Was she pushed or knocked down trying to get out of the bedroom? You're only six inches taller than her. How long is a 308 deer rifle? If you were both standing up, how could she have been shot from such a downward angle? Why did you get the gun out in the first place? You must have intended to use it. Otherwise, why was your finger on the trigger? You did remember that part. Now, tell us whether the gun was usually kept loaded. Common sense says it was not, because of Jennifer and the grandchildren who lived in the house. You would have had to load the gun. And when you loaded it, you must have intended to use it. Tell us, also, how the gun stock got busted. The experts said it was caused by a swinging motion, similar to swinging a baseball bat. Another question: If there was a struggle, why didn't you have blood on your clothes? The blood splattered, didn't it? She was shot in the chest. You said you held her and cried. If you held her, how did you prevent getting blood on you then? And don't forget that during that time, Rhonda was still waiting for you to open the front door. And when you opened the door, why didn't you have blood on you? And where were the tears you cried? How could you turn them off so quickly? And when you asked Rhonda if she had seen her mother, why didn't Rhonda see your tear-stained grief-stricken face? She has testified under oath that everything seemed normal. And nothing appeared "unusual."

Lewis, I thought. If you were so bereaved, why didn't you come out of the house screaming and crying for Rhonda and Donald to call an ambulance to try to save Patricia's life. At least that would have looked like an effort. Why did you lie and say that Patricia had given Jennifer to Rhonda, and that Rhonda had come to pick up Jennifer's clothes? When the truth was that Rhonda had come to the house only to bring Jennifer home from an afternoon visit. Isn't it true that Rhonda told Patricia earlier that day that she had to work the next day? And isn't it a fact that it was only after Rhonda returned to the house that evening, and after you told her that Patricia had left you, that she in fact told you that the best thing to do was for her to take Jennifer home with her, and that she would need to get some clothes for her? But you knew Rhonda would have to come inside the house to get the clothes. So, you told her that Kimberly had moved some of the clothes into a front bedroom. Did Kimberly move the clothes? Or, did you? I will always wonder if perhaps as Patricia lay dying behind the closed door of her bedroom, she heard you and Rhonda talking while Rhonda was in the house getting clothes for Jennifer.

Carter's questions resumed. He was at the point where Rhonda came to the house. Lewis shifted from side to side in the witness chair. Carter asked Lewis why he didn't tell Rhonda what happened. Lewis replied that he was scared. Carter asked him why he didn't call the law. Lewis said he was scared.

Carter: "You took the body out to the ranch and buried it, is that correct?"

Crocker: "Yes, sir."

Carter: "And what did you do with the mattress?"

Crocker: "I carried it out there later. Throwed it on some boxes and burnt it."

Carter: "What about the carpet? Where did you take it?"

Crocker: "Throwed it in the dumpster."

Carter: "How were you feeling about this now, Lewis. The next day?"

Crocker: "I don't know how to explain the feeling. I was still scared."

Carter: "In your confession I think you said that once before you went looking for her with a gun, is that correct?"

Crocker: "Yes. I was going to shoot the tires out of her car and stop her. I knew she was drinking."

Carter: "I think in your confession you also said you put the body of your wife in the trunk of the car, is that right?"

Crocker: "Yes, sir."

Carter: "When did you bury her?"

Crocker: "It was on a Monday that next morning."

Carter: "And when the officers asked you where your wife was, you didn't tell them the truth, did you?"

Crocker: "No, sir. I didn't tell them the truth."

Carter: "When you made the statement, 'I killed her. I'm glad it's all over,' what did you mean by that?"

Crocker: "I don't remember saying that. I could have said it. I was nervous."

Finally, Carter passed the witness.

It was the moment David Barron had been waiting for. And as he walked toward the witness stand to begin cross examination, Lewis shifted from side to side in the chair as though to brace himself as much as possible.

Barron: "Who is Tyrone Jones? Who is Tyrone Jones? You know a black man named Tyrone Jones who used to work at the Jim Pierce ranch?"

Crocker: "I know him. I don't know his last name."

Barron: "Do you recall having a conversation with Tyrone Jones the first week of August 1988 at the Jim Pierce Ranch when you told him you would kill your wife because you had a girlfriend in Roans Prairie, and you could go to her anytime? You didn't say that?"

Crocker: "No, sir, I didn't."

322

Barron: "So, if Tyrone Jones comes in this courtroom tomorrow and says you did say that, he wouldn't be telling the truth?"

Crocker: "No, sir."

Barron: "Do you know Marcell Nelson? A black man named Marcell that used to work at the Jim Pierce Ranch?"

Crocker: "He was out there. I didn't know him. I didn't work around him."

Barron: "Do you recall bragging to Marcell Nelson about all the women you have? Did you tell him you have a black girlfriend in Madisonville?"

Crocker: "No, sir."

Barron: "None of that happened either? So, if Marcell Nelson comes in this courtroom tomorrow morning and testifies, he wouldn't be telling the truth?"

Crocker: "The only black person I mentioned was Beverly Webb. I worked on her car. We was all talking one day. I don't know what led to it. I said you all know Beverly. I told him she worked with my wife."

Barron: "You didn't claim she was your girlfriend in Madisonville? You continually bragged to Marcell Nelson about that?"

Crocker: "Lord, no."

Barron: "Charlie Lancaster?"

Crocker: "I know him."

Barron: "Charlie Lancaster. What is interesting to me, Mr. Crocker, September 20, when you were arrested and you gave this taped confession to the Texas Ranger, you didn't mention Charlie Lancaster, did you?"

Crocker: "No, sir."

Barron: "You didn't mention that your wife was leaving you for another man?"

Crocker: "No, sir."

Barron: "And it is only since you have been appointed a lawyer and prepared your defense that Charlie Lancaster and another man has come into your story?"

Crocker: "No, sir."

Barron: "Why didn't you tell the Ranger about Charlie Lancaster? Why didn't you tell the Ranger your version of the events you just told this jury today?"

Crocker: "I don't know. I didn't want my daughters to know what kind of man their mother was going to live and run around and sleep with."

Barron: "She's not here to defend herself. You took care of that, didn't you?"

Crocker: "No, sir."

Barron: "So, you're telling the jury under oath that you didn't tell Brian Taylor about Charlie Lancaster or another man to protect your daughters, is that what you're telling these people?"

Crocker: "No, sir."

Barron: "Well, what are you telling them? I didn't want my daughters to find it out? I'm ashamed they found it out now?"

Crocker: "Right."

Barron: "You lied to your daughters? You lied to the police officers? Lied to your friends and now you expect this jury to believe you under oath? You don't expect that, do you?"

Crocker: "I don't know."

Barron: "You don't say anything in your confession about her saying you were washed up and no good, you don't say anything about that in your statement?"

Crocker: "No. I was ashamed of it. I didn't want nobody to know it."

Barron: "You weren't ashamed to say you buried your wife in a garbage dump, but you were ashamed to say your wife called you some bad names?"

Crocker: "I wasn't going to be around."

Barron: "Charlie Lancaster. Is he the only man you were jealous of?"

Crocker: "Here lately, yes."

Barron: "Well, do you remember being at Fred's Place the day your wife was killed, and making the statement in front of Clarence Hudson, that, 'if I catch Fred fucking my old lady, I'll kill him'?"

Crocker: "No, sir."

Barron: "If Mr. Hudson comes in here and says you did, he would be lying?"

Crocker: "Yes."

Barron: "And this so-called suicide note of yours you have written, 'I could not have her no more. Now Bill won't.' "

Crocker: "That's what I called him instead of Charlie."

Barron: "Why did you call him 'Bill'?"

Crocker: "I didn't want them to know who it was. That's why I put the name Bill down there. There never was a Bill that I know of."

Well. Well. Well, I thought. So, now we know the truth about the mysterious Bill. He was just another typical Lewis Crocker lie. Made up, Crocker style.

Barron: "Why didn't you want anybody to know who it was? It says your wife had an affair with somebody?"

Crocker: "Yes, but they wouldn't know it was an ex-convict."

Barron: "But Charlie Lancaster didn't materialize in your story until today?"

Crocker: "It has been going on for a long time."

Barron: "But this is the first time you told anybody?"

Crocker: "Right."

Barron: "And it sure makes your defense a lot better if the jury believes you?"

Crocker: "I don't know."

Barron: "It will help you with that voluntary manslaughter defense, won't it?"

Lewis shook his head.

Barron: "You told Larry Adams you had beaten your wife in the past. How often did you do that?"

Crocker: "Not too often. She would hit me. I'd hit her back."

Barron: "It was in self-defense?"

Crocker: "Sometimes. I guess you could call it that. Yes."

Barron: "You remember the ladies who worked with her at the school? They saw her when she was beat up and you didn't have a scratch on you. Were you just a better fighter?"

Crocker: "I don't know."

Barron: "Well, how did it make you feel to hit a woman?"

Crocker: "It don't make me feel good."

Barron: "You have a history of doing it?"

Crocker: "I just never filed any charges or complaints on her for hitting me."

Barron: "That's awfully big of you. So, are you now trying to say you are a battered husband? And every time you hit her was in self-defense?"

Crocker: "No."

Barron: "Sometimes you just slapped her around for the fun of it?"

Crocker: "No. We would be arguing."

Barron: "Did you ever black her eyes and choke her?"

Crocker: "No, never choke her."

Suddenly, I thought Carol was going to jump out of her seat. And I grabbed her hand in warning. "That lying bastard," she whispered. "He always went for her throat. That's probably why her neck bones were missing."

Barron: "Well, you heard Pauline Nicholson's testimony that your wife came to her house and had scratches on her neck. How did that happen?"

Crocker: "I don't know. She had left. She had been off that day. Maybe she got them somewhere else."

Barron: "Where would you suggest she got them?"

Crocker: "Probably with Charlie."

Barron: "Charlie Lancaster. Mr. Crocker, if we hadn't found your wife's body out on Jim Pierce Ranch you wouldn't be here today, would you?"

Crocker: "Yes."

Barron: "You would be here?"

Crocker: "Right. I couldn't take it no more. I had to tell some-body where she was at."

Barron: "But you didn't tell anybody where she was at, did you?"

Crocker: "No, sir. But I was going to."

Barron: "When were you going to do it? The day you got arrested?"

Crocker: "That same morning. I had gotten ready to come down."

Hold it, Lewis, I thought. When you saw Brian Taylor and Larry Adams stop in front of your house, the afternoon they arrested you, why did you tell Kimberly to tell them you were not at home?

Barron: "Well, why didn't you come down that morning? You weren't arrested until the afternoon?"

Crocker: "I don't know. I had to sit there and think."

Barron: "You're telling this jury under oath that you were going to come down to the sheriff's department the day you were arrested and turn yourself in?"

Crocker: "Right."

Barron: "You lived with it for six weeks without telling anybody? Looks like you were doing pretty well."

Crocker: "It was running me crazy. I had to tell somebody."

Barron: "In your confession you just mentioned one time that you pulled a weapon on your wife. Was it more than once?"

Crocker: "It had been more than once. Yes. We had both pulled weapons."

I grabbed Carol's hand again. "That liar!" she whispered. "If Patricia had ever pulled a weapon on him, he would have killed her then."

Barron: "Mr. Crocker, I want you to come out and demonstrate to me how this so-called struggle happened."

Carter was quick on his feet objecting to Barron's sidebar remarks. Barron had used the word, "so-called struggle." Judge Ernst sustained the objection. And Barron re-phrased the question. Then Lewis stepped down from the stand for the demonstration and Barron picked up the rifle.

Barron: "Okay. I'll be your wife. Now, were you struggling over it like this? Were her hands on like this? Show me in slow motion how it went off when I jerk it. You jerked it like that and it went off right square in her chest? Did you have it up over her head?"

Crocker: "No, I didn't have it over her head. I don't know."

Lewis then returned to the witness chair, and Barron's questions continued.

Barron: "Okay. And you didn't tell Rhonda when she came up to the house because you were scared to death?"

Crocker: "Yes."

Barron: "How did you know your wife died that minute or did you know?"

Crocker: "I grabbed her."

Barron: "You did what?"

Crocker: "I jumped over and then grabbed her and raised her up off the bed."

When Lewis said, quote: "I jumped over and then grabbed her," he had, in my opinion, just admitted to cold-blooded murder, and destroyed his defense that he and Patricia were struggling over the gun when she was shot. For, had they been struggling, with only the gun between them, why did he say he "jumped over and then grabbed her"? What did he jump over?

His story had been that she was standing at the foot of the bed, and when she was shot, she fell back across the bed. So, why did he have to jump over anything? And if he grabbed her, why didn't his clothes have blood on them?

Barron: "You heard the doctor's testimony that, if it didn't hit her heart, the likelihood was that she could have lived for a while?"

Crocker: "She was dead. No pulse, at all."

Barron: "In your statement, you said the first thing you did was get up and shut the door and, then Rhonda drove up. She could still have been alive in that room when you were talking to Rhonda?"

Crocker: "No."

Barron: "She just died instantly?"

Crocker: "It was an hour probably, before Rhonda came."

But, Lewis, I thought. Remember, you said you thought Rhonda heard the shot?

Barron: "Here's a question from your statement to Larry Adams and Brian Taylor: 'Okay. After she fell on the bed at the house, what did you do?' You answered: 'I jumped up, shut the door and then my daughter drove up.' "

Crocker: "I was sitting on the bed for a long time when Rhonda drove up and I shut the door."

Barron: "It's different than it is in your statement, just like there is no Charlie Lancaster in your statement?"

Crocker: "Yes, I guess it is."

Barron: "Then you decided after Rhonda left to wrap her up in a blanket?"

Crocker: "It was at night after I covered her up with a sheet."

Barron: "Covered her up with a sheet, wrapped her up in a blanket, drug her out, stuck her in the trunk of your car? Did you close the trunk?"

Crocker: "Seems like I did."

Barron: "You drove to the Jim Pierce Ranch, and saw Jack Thompson there that morning?"

Crocker: "Yes, it seemed like I did."

Barron: "You told him you were going to go fishing in the back, did you not?"

Crocker: "Yes, I told him I was going fishing or something."

Barron: "And you went back there? Where did you get the shovel to bury her?"

Crocker: "I don't remember."

Barron: "You go to the dump, dig a shallow grave, take her out of the trunk, throw her in a hole, and covered her up with dirt. Is that the way it happened?"

Crocker: "No. I picked her up out of the trunk and took her over there."

But, Lewis, I thought. Remember, at the house, you couldn't pick her up. That's why you had to drag her through the living room. That's why you had to remove the carpet. So, at the dump, supposedly some twelve hours later, how were you able to pick her up out of the trunk of the car? Did anyone help you? You were seen in Navasota that morning. You were also seen in Roans Prairie at 8:30 that morning, already drunk. And you said you were at the ranch in the middle of the morning. Are we to believe that you traveled all those miles with the body in the trunk of the car, before you went to the ranch and buried it?

Barron: "And you threw her in the hole?"

Crocker: "No. I slid down the blanket and wrapped her up."

Barron: "And covered her up with dirt. Did you say any last words over her body, a little prayer or something?"

Crocker: "I think so."

Barron: "Then you piled the trash back on top of her grave?"

Crocker: "I don't remember."

Barron: "Had you been drinking any beer out there?"

Crocker: "No."

Barron: "If this was an accident, why did you have to cover up your accident?"

Crocker: "I don't know, sir."

Barron: "The fact of the matter, is Mr. Crocker: This was a murder and you told Tyrone Jones a week before it happened that you were going to kill her?"

Crocker: "I did not."

Barron: "You came after her with your gun about three weeks before this?"

Crocker: "I had a gun in the car, yes."

Barron: "Claude Hutchins took the gun away from you, didn't he?"

Crocker: "I gave it to him. I had been drinking and he took me home."

Barron: "You were going to shoot the tires out on the car your wife was driving?"

Crocker: "Yes."

Barron: "Were you angry that day?"

Crocker: "Some angry, yes."

Barron: "Is this the gun that has been marked into evidence the gun that you used to kill your wife?"

Crocker: "Yes."

Barron then questioned Lewis about the fact that he had sold the gun to his son-in-law, a couple of days later. Barron asked him why he sold the gun.

Crocker: "He wanted to borrow it and I loaned it to him. Later he bought it."

Barron: "Of course, you didn't suspect that the police might be coming around your house asking to see the gun? That wasn't your consideration, was it?"

Crocker: "No."

Barron: "And you weren't trying to get rid of evidence? Just like you weren't trying to get rid of evidence when you buried your wife?"

Crocker: "No, sir."

Barron: "And then you carried on a charade for six weeks pretending to look for her, didn't you?"

Crocker: "Just didn't seem like she was gone."

Barron: "All five of your daughters were worried sick about their mother those six weeks, weren't they? And you put them through hell, didn't you?"

Crocker: "I'm sure I did."

Barron: "When you and your wife would have arguments, she would be the one to leave, wouldn't she?"

Crocker: "Yes. Here lately you could say anything and she would leave."

Barron: "Let's assume that she planned to leave you for good. Could you blame her with the kind of life you gave her? Could you really blame her?"

Crocker: "She wasn't no angel either. It wasn't all my fault."

Barron asked the question again. Lewis replied, "I don't know."

Barron passed the witness. Carter had no further questions. Barron then announced that he would have rebuttal witnesses the next morning.

Judge Ernst: "All right folks. We'll see you at 9:00 o'clock in the morning."

THE DARK SIDE OF TWILIGHT:

CHAPTER 27

The following morning, at precisely 9:20, David Barron called Clarence Hudson back to the stand as his first rebuttal witness.

Barron: "I believe you testified earlier that you were at Fred's Place on August 7th of last year. On that day, who did you see at Fred's Place?"

Hudson replied that he saw a lot of people, including Lewis and Patricia. Barron asked if he overheard a comment made by Lewis, at Fred's Place. Hudson said he did.

Barron: "Who was present when this remark was made?"

Hudson: "There was his wife, Fred, Fred's mother and myself, and other people."

Barron: "To the best of your recollection, what did Lewis Crocker say?"

Hudson: "He said if he caught Fred fooling or fucking his wife, he'd kill him."

Barron passed the witness.

Carter asked Hudson if Lewis had directed the remark to the table in general. Hudson replied, "No." Then Carter asked if it just came out of his mouth. Hudson replied, "He was facing me."

Carter passed the witness back to Barron. But Barron had already made his point, and Hudson was excused.

Barron's next rebuttal witness was Marcell Nelson. Nelson was tall and black, around the age of thirty. Today, he wore a three piece navy blue suit, white shirt, striped tie and black boots. He had been one of Lewis' co-workers at the Jim Pierce Ranch.

Nelson stated that he had worked six weeks with Lewis Crocker.

Barron: "Would you tell the jury what his drinking habits were when he was on the job?"

Nelson: "Beer."

Barron: "Did you ever have a conversation with him about

women?"

Nelson: "Yes."

Barron: "What did he tell you?"

Nelson: "He said he had a couple of them in Madisonville."

Barron: "Did he say they were black or white?"

Nelson: "Black. He had one black."

Then Barron passed the witness, and Carter began his cross examination.

Carter: "Is this the first time you've told anybody about this statement being made by Lewis Crocker?"

Nelson: "No, sir."

On redirect, Barron came back for more.

Barron: "Marcell, while you were working at the ranch, did you have any problems with Lewis Crocker?"

Nelson: "No. I never had any problems with him. He just drank a lot."

Marcell Nelson was then excused from the stand. He had come to make a point, and he made it well.

Barron's last rebuttal witness was Tyrone Jones, age thirty-three, tall and black, wearing a gray suit, white shirt, blue tie, and gray western boots. Jones had also been one of Lewis Crocker's co-workers at the Jim Pierce Ranch.

Barron asked Jones about a conversation he had had with Lewis, during the first part of August 1988.

Barron: "And what did he tell you?"

Jones: "He said, 'You know my wife and I are having a few problems.' And he said he had a woman that he messed around with and he had a lady up here in Roans Prairie. He said, 'If she pushes me too far, I will kill her.'"

Barron: "If she pushes me too far I will kill her?"

Jones: "Yes, sir."

Barron: "This was the first part of August?"

Jones: "Yes, sir."

Barron: "Did you give a statement to Sheriff Ed Fannin in Madison County about what was said?"

Jones: "Yes."

Barron: "And did you give that in the summer?"

Jones: "Yes, sir."

Carter objected, loud and clear. "It goes to the motive," said Barron. "Objection overruled," said Judge Ernst. And Barron continued.

Barron: "Tyrone, do you have anything personal against Lewis Crocker?"

Jones: "No, sir."

In the cross examination of Tyrone Jones, Carter batted what he hoped was a home run. But it sailed with flying colors right into David Barron's hands.

Carter: "When did you give that statement to Ed Fannin? Was it in the summer?"

Jones: "Yes, sir."

Carter asked if the statement was made sometime in August. Jones said yes.

Carter: "Do you know when it was in August?"

Jones: "It was the early week in August."

Carter passed the witness.

On redirect, Barron had one more question for Tyrone Jones.

Barron: "You were subpoenaed to be here, weren't you?"

Jones: "Yes, sir."

Barron passed the witness back to Carter. Carter had no more questions. Barron stood up again, squared his shoulders and glanced at the jury. Then, to Judge Ernst, he said, "Your Honor, the State rests and closes." Judge Ernst declared that both sides had rested and closed. Then he granted a fifteen minute break for the jury.

Darlene and Patty, and Carol and I walked downstairs to the soft drink machine on the main floor. And we noticed that the back door leading out of the courthouse was open.

"That wind is so cold," said Carol, shivering. "It probably blew the door open. I'm going to close it."

I would later wonder if the wind and open doors may have been an omen for Carol and me. For as we reached the doorway and looked out into the cold gray morning, we saw the white pickup, parked behind the courthouse.

"Do you see what I see?" Carol asked.

"Yes, I see it," I replied. "And I wish I knew who parked it there."

"Well, I don't know about the white pickup," said Carol. "But the one parked in front of it belongs to the Crocker family. I'd know it anywhere. And isn't it strange that both trucks were also parked together the other morning?"

"Well, maybe it's just a coincidence. I hope that's all it is."

"I'm telling you, I don't trust them," Carol went on, as we walked back up the stairs. "You don't know these people, but I do."

As we returned through the side door of the courtroom, Brian Taylor and Patrick Page walked through the front door. As we walked to our seats, they nodded hello, then sat in the seats directly behind us.

After the jury was led in, and seated, Judge Ernst made a folksy little comment, something about seeing the light at the end of the tunnel. Then he cleared his throat, a signal which meant that it was time for serious business. Game time was over. The cards had been dealt. Now, it was time for decisions. Facing the jurors, he then began reading the charge:

"The Defendant, Lewis Crocker, stands charged by indictment with murder, alleged to have been committed on or about the 7th day of August, 1988, in Grimes County, Texas. To this charge the Defendant had pled not guilty. Our Law provides that a person commits the offense of murder if he intentionally causes the death of an individual." Judge Ernst then went on to define the law of involuntary manslaughter, sudden passion, and voluntary manslaughter.

"If you find and believe from the evidence beyond a reasonable doubt that the Defendant, Lewis Crocker, did intentionally or knowingly cause the death of Patricia L. Crocker, by shooting her with a firearm, and that the Defendant, in so acting, was not acting under the immediate influence of sudden passion arising from an adequate cause, then you will find the Defendant guilty of murder as charged in the indictment."

His Honor went on to further define the law of murder, voluntary manslaughter, involuntary manslaughter, sudden passion, criminally negligent homicide, and also the impeachment of witness testimony. And he further reminded the jury that: "A grand jury indictment is the means whereby a defendant is brought to trial in a felony case. It is not evidence of guilt nor can it be considered by you in passing upon the question of the guilt of the Defendant. The burden of proof in all criminal cases rests upon the State throughout the trial and never shifts to the Defendant.

"The Defendant is presumed to be innocent until his guilt is established by legal evidence beyond a reasonable doubt, and in case you have a reasonable doubt as to the Defendant's guilt, after considering all the evidence before you and these instructions, you will acquit him. You are the exclusive judges of the facts proved, the credibility of the witnesses and the weight to be given their testimony.

"After you retire to the jury room, you should select one of your members as your foreperson. You may communicate with the Court in writing through the officer in charge. Whatever your question is, sign it and give it to the bailiff and I'll answer it if under the law I'm allowed to. Just put it in writing."

When it was time for closing arguments, David Baron waived his right to open and reserved his right to close.

"Very well, Billy. It's your turn," said the Honorable Judge Ernst.

Billy Carter, the old warrior, loosened his tie and adjusted his coat. Then he walked over and faced the jury.

"Ladies and gentlemen of the jury," Carter began. "I want to remind you about the rules of argument. The arguments of myself and Mr. Barron are not evidence. We are arguing positions to you, taking the charge and arguing the facts that relate to the charge. It is your responsibility to fit the facts to the law.

"I guess the thing that troubles me most about this case is the fact that I'm afraid that the burying of the body will so cloud the total situation that took place on August 7th that it will prejudice you or inflame you to a degree that you may not consider all of the charge. That would be a travesty.

"The TV News was talking about this case, last night. They said there was a murder charge in Grimes County and there was a burial of a body. I thought to myself, 'Boy that sounds bad.' And it does. But, when you go back to make your decision, I want you to look at the state of mind of this Defendant, Lewis Crocker, on August 7th. Not only his state of mind, but what was going on when this shooting took place. I want to urge each of you to think about this. If you were going to commit a murder, an intentional, cold blooded murder, you would do it a little different than this. I wouldn't do it in my home. And I sure wouldn't take the body of the person I killed to the place I worked. I'm not going to do it in my bedroom where there is blood and I have to cut the carpet up, and I have to take the body out of the house. That does not lend itself to murder."

But, Mr. Carter, I thought. If Lewis had killed her somewhere else, he might have been seen. No one was at the house, and the gun was in the closet. As for the carpet being cut out, the girls knew Patricia had planned to remove it. And as for burying the body where he worked, what better place to hide it than at a garbage dump in the woods, on private property, where he would have the opportunity to check on it, and see that it remained buried.

"There are two intentional acts in this charge," Carter said. "One is murder, but voluntary manslaughter is also an intentional killing. The only difference in murder and voluntary manslaughter is that they are both intentional, but voluntary manslaughter is done under the influence of sudden passion brought on by an adequate cause."

Barron quickly objected to that, saying it was a misstatement of law. "There is a difference in range of punishment between the two," he yelled.

"This is the guilt or innocence phase," Carter yelled back. "The punishment has nothing to do with that." Judge Ernst, with a stern look, said, "Very well."

"Voluntary manslaughter is what you call a crime of passion," Carter went on. "Remember what Ranger Taylor said? In family violence, you always have anger, hatred and emotion. What more profound place do you find family violence among husband and wife than in the bedroom? You know it is easy for us to sit here in judgment. We weren't there that night."

Carter's voice grew louder. And he paced a little faster, back and forth before the jury. He was dealing the "crime of passion" card for Crocker's defense.

"And what about the remorse of Lewis Crocker, the remorse he felt?" Carter went on. "No one has said he hasn't felt it. You can consider that. The Ranger said two or three times during the confession he became emotional, almost like he was going to cry."

Remorse? I thought. Hold it right there, Mr. Carter, I thought. I'd like to tell you what my family knows about Crocker's remorse. We know that one of his daughters said, quote: "It didn't seem to bother him." Unquote. Remorse? Where was his remorse when he sat at Frances' house, for two hours, telling lies about how Patricia just walked off and left him, knowing damn well that her body was rotting in a garbage dump where he had left it? Where was his remorse when he sat in the beer joints in Grimes County telling filthy lies about Patricia and her non-existent boyfriends? That she had been located in Ennis. That she was at a lake in East Texas. And how the law refused to help him find her. Where was his remorse as he continued to work at the ranch, and worked within thirty feet of her decaying body? Where was his remorse when he stood in his yard talking to Rhonda, within minutes after he had shot her mother? She didn't see any blinding tears, did she? And his emotions when he was arrested? He told the news media that he was scared. Did he shed any tears then?

Carter was now on the subject of the notes Lewis had written.

"Take those notes that he wrote," Carter said. "These are not the notes of a murderer. They are notes of pain and sadness. When Lewis Crocker was arrested, he told Larry Adams, 'I killed her. I'm glad it's over with.' Then an hour after that he's confessing to it. He signed the consent to search, to go back to the house to get the notes. The notes of a man who told the officer he had left a note telling where the body was."

Oh yes, the notes, I thought. But Mr. Carter, the body had already been found. And the notes were not where Lewis said they were. He said they were under a chair. But the officer couldn't find them. It wasn't until October 17th, that the note showing the location of the body was found. That particular note was hidden in another area. But perhaps you are referring to the note which read: "I can't have her, now Bill won't". Lewis testified that there was no Bill that he knew of. So, what does that tell you? I know what it tells me.

"Also, you have a charge on criminal homicide," Carter went on. "And you have a charge on accident. If you think this was an accidental killing under all this evidence, as the Court explains it to you, you may bring back a verdict of not guilty, even though he buried the body.

"You know, I think it's sad that these two people fought. They have five children. And they fought in front of them, fought with fists and guns. I'm sure it has marked the children of that marriage forever and that's sad. I don't know how it is to fight with a weapon with somebody you love. But they did. And I wouldn't know how it would be when one of those weapons went off. But they did. And how tragic that was. The saddest thing is, I think these people loved each other. I think from the testimony of their children, I believe Lewis Crocker worshipped her. But they just fought all the time. See where the evidence and common sense leads you."

Carter continued on, leaving no stones unturned on his side of the arena. Then he thanked the jury, and returned to his counsel table.

"All right, Mr. D.A., you have forty minutes," said the Honorable Judge Ernst.

"I'll give you back some of your time, Your Honor," Barron replied.

David Barron picked up the 8x10 color photograph of Patricia, and walked over to the jury. He showed the photo to the jury, and then placed it face up on the railing of the jury box and left it there, hoping they would glance at it while they listened.

"Patricia Crocker married Lewis Crocker when she was sixteen years old," Barron told the jury. "She raised five daughters, and, as the children grew up, she began working full time and raising five daughters. As time went on a trouble developed between Lewis Crocker and her. Beatings occurred. She was beaten up, bruised, given black eyes. Later, she probably joined her husband in drinking just to fit in.

"As time went on, weapons became involved in the fights. Sometimes she would stand up for herself. But the evidence shows that most of the times she was beaten up and forced to leave her home.

"In 1988, Patricia Crocker decided she wanted something better from life. She wanted to escape the hell that she had been living in. She began improving her personal appearance and she wanted to become an LVN or a nurse. She wanted more out of her life.

"The end of July she turned 42 years old and she saw that her youth was running out. And she wanted a change. I think sometime in 1988, she made up her mind to leave him finally after 26 years. Finally leave an alcoholic wife beater and do something different for a change. Make herself happy for a change. It was building long before August 7.

"I think she was going to leave him. But I don't think she was going to leave him for another man. You haven't heard any concrete evidence that she was having an affair with anybody. But if she was, could you really blame her? Remember, she is not here to defend herself. She is not here to answer those allegations. Her name has been drug through the mud in this case and she can't answer back. She can't answer back.

"She was going to leave him eventually and he knew it and he wasn't going to let it happen. And on August 7th of last year, he did something about it. You will see the beginning of intentionally and knowingly in this charge.

"I'd like to read the definition of knowingly to you because the State has to prove murder or voluntary manslaughter. A person acts knowingly or with respect to a result of his conduct when he is aware that his conduct is reasonably certain to cause the result.

"If someone points a deer rifle at you and pulls the trigger, I submit to you that that's reasonably certain to cause someone's death and that's knowingly. That's what we have to prove to get to murder and to voluntary manslaughter. And I think clearly, under the facts of this case, we have proven that. So if you believe this action was done knowingly, you will not consider criminal negligent homicide or involuntary manslaughter. From the beginning the defendant has put all his eggs in one basket.

"Why is this a murder and not voluntary manslaughter? I'd like to go over a few things in evidence that I think will prove that it was a murder and not an act of sudden passion arising from an adequate cause."

Barron pointed to Lewis' taped confession, and continued. "This confession! On September 20, 1988, he gave this confession. And in this confession, nowhere is rage mentioned. Nowhere is terror mentioned. Nowhere is Charlie Lancaster mentioned. You see, Charlie Lancaster is his ticket to voluntary manslaughter. Charlie Lancaster is his defense. And Charlie Lancaster is not mentioned in this confession. On the witness stand, he said that he was ashamed to mention the fact that his wife was having an affair with Charlie Lancaster. But ask yourselves does it make sense to you that a man that is not ashamed to say he buried his wife in a junk pile is ashamed to mention that his wife is having an affair with an ex-convict? It just doesn't make sense.

"Listen to the confession, because that was given before he formulated a defense. I'd like to play you an excerpt from the tape about the shooting. In it, he says, 'We got to talking and arguing about first one thing and then another.'

What were you arguing about, Lewis?

Well, one thing her leaving and another thing she gave her little girl away.

Who did she give her girl away to?

Her daughter, Rhonda Bullion.

Are these your daughters, too?

Right. My wife, she just got tired of me. She said, 'my momma and daddy told me all my life what to do. I married you, and you told me what to do. Now the kids tell me what to do.' She said she was tired of it all. One word led to another and we got to fighting. And it wound up with a gun involved.

How did the gun become involved?

I believe I got it. I picked the gun up.

From where?

Sitting in the closet.

In the closet? Where?

In our bedroom. We got to fighting. The gun went off. She was dead.

"No anger, no rage, no frustration in that statement. No Charlie Lancaster."

"My wife was talking about leaving me." Did he say for another man? No, he did not. But Charlie Lancaster is his ticket to a lesser charge and that's what he's going with.

"He knew his wife was leaving him and I think he knew that for sometime before August the 7th. It wasn't sudden passion arising from any cause. He was insanely jealous of her, as you heard. You also heard what Clarence Hudson said that he said at Fred's Place the day she was killed. Jealous of Fred, but not jealous of Charlie Lancaster. He was jealous and he wasn't going to let anybody else have her. And in this so-called suicide note, 'I could not have her no more. Now Bill won't.' Does that tell you something about his intent?

"Also his demeanor after the shooting. He says in the confession, question: "Okay. After she fell on the bed at the house, what did you do?"

Answer: "I jumped up, shut the door, and then my daughter drove up."

"He sees his daughter, Rhonda, within seconds after killing his wife in what he calls a crazy rage and how does he act? Nothing really out of the ordinary. Not angry. Not crazy. Is that consistent with someone who is in a rage? His own daughter didn't recognize it seconds after he killed his wife. That should erase any reasonable doubt as to whether or not this was an act committed in sudden passion. And further evidence of his intent to kill her is the statement he made to Tyrone Jones that he denied under oath yesterday. He told

Tyrone Jones, within a week of this murder, that, 'If I catch my wife fooling around, I'll kill her.' "

Carter: "I object to that. Tyrone Jones' testimony was this morning and it was, 'If she pushes me, I will kill her.' I object to misleading the witness."

Court: "Very well. The jury will judge the facts."

For a second, Barron looked as though he wanted to smile. And I couldn't help but think that he had deliberately misquoted Tyrone's statement, knowing Carter would hit the floor with an objection. Thereby reinforcing the words, "If she pushes me, I'll kill her," into the minds of the jurors. Another one for the hoop, I thought. And Carter had bought it, hook, line and sinker. Now, looking serious, again, Barron faced the jury and continued.

"He was thinking about killing his wife in the first part of August and he carried it out on August the 7th. That should erase any reasonable doubt as to whether or not this was murder or voluntary manslaughter.

"We know that two or three weeks earlier he had gotten the same gun out and put it in his car and went looking for her. Is this sudden passion arising from some kind of adequate cause? What's he going to do? Shoot her tires out he says. Shoot her tires out?

"Intent to use that gun was evident three weeks earlier. Again, that should erase any reasonable doubt as to whether or not this is a murder.

"Mr. Carter says burying the body clouds the issue. To me it makes the issue a lot clearer. Him burying his wife's body in a trash dump tells you something about the way he felt about her that day.

"And I can tell you one thing, if it wasn't for Ranger Brian Taylor and if it wasn't for that cadaver sniffing dog, Lewis Crocker would be home right now in Bedias, halfway through a 12 pack. And we wouldn't be here today and Patricia Crocker's family wouldn't have justice today and Patricia Crocker wouldn't have justice today, because he would be free.

"If you want to believe him when he says, 'I was going to turn myself in that very morning,' you can believe it. But I don't think you do and that should tell you something about this man's credibility.

"The only version of the facts of this shooting that we have heard is from his mouth. And can you believe him under oath? I submit to you that you can't.

"We know that yesterday under oath he said, 'No. I didn't discuss my girlfriend with Marcell Nelson.' He said, 'No. I didn't say anything about killing my wife to Tyrone Jones.' He said, 'No. I didn't make this statement about Fred Reynolds to Clarence Hudson.' Well, Marcell Nelson, Tyrone Jones and Clarence Hudson got on that stand and lied?

"You are a liar, Lewis Crocker!" Barron shouted toward Lewis. "You're a liar if you will lie to these people." Then, turning back to the jury, Barron continued.

"Don't you think he will lie under oath to save his own skin? But you don't have to believe a word he says about the incident. Not a word. And I hope you don't. Judging from the credibility of a witness, you look at what they have to gain or lose. Lewis Crocker had a lot to gain and he's got a lot to lose. If you convict him of murder, he's looking at a life sentence. I don't think he's worthy of being believed.

"You know, if this was an act of sudden passion, he was living sudden passion for 26 years. You heard his daughters testify that on the average of maybe once a week they would get into a violent argument. Was it sudden passion every time? Or is it just sudden passion when he finally killed her?.

"A defendant in a criminal case has a lot of rights. They have the right to remain silent. They have the right to have a lawyer appointed to represent them if they can't hire a lawyer. They can get an investigator appointed to help them prepare their case. They can make the State prove beyond a reasonable doubt that they are guilty. But, Patricia Crocker has rights, too. And foremost of those rights is that she be allowed to live with dignity and to die with dignity. And she couldn't do that because of him.

"I ask in your deliberations to keep in mind Lewis Crocker, certainly. But also keep Patricia Crocker in mind, because she wasn't here to defend herself. She wasn't here to answer the slanderous allegations of the defense.

"We don't know much about her, other than she was a 42 year old mother of five, lived in Bedias and worked in Madisonville schools, apparently well liked by the people she worked with and the people she knew."

Barron paused for a moment and looked at Carol and me. Then he extended his hand toward us, and said: "And ladies and gentlemen, Patricia Crocker has family over here that loves her. And believe me, they are interested in this case.

"You know Lewis Crocker is getting his rights under our Constitution. He's getting a jury trial of 12 citizens. But Patricia Crocker was not that lucky; because he was the judge, he was the jury, and he was the executioner of her. And he was also the grave digger."

Barron then paused for a moment and glanced back at Lewis, allowing time for the jurors to think about those words. Then in a soft emotional voice he would likely have used in church, he faced the jury again, and continued.

"I just wonder," said Barron. "I just wonder what kind of little prayer he said over her grave."

Then, in a rising voice clearly meant for everyone to hear, Barron cast his final plea to the jury.

"Under the facts of this case, ladies and gentlemen, Lewis Crocker is guilty of murder as charged in the indictment. Under the facts of this case, any verdict less than murder will be a victory for Lewis Crocker. And under the facts of this case, Lewis Crocker doesn't deserve a victory."

After that, Barron returned to his counsel table. He had fought a good fight, and fought it honorably.

"All right folks," Judge Ernst said, addressing the jury. "We're going to have you retire, now. You need to remain together as a group and the Sheriff will be close by, should you need anything. When you reach a verdict, knock and we will receive your verdict."

The jury filed out of the courtroom to a room across the hall for deliberations.

CHAPTER 28

Patricia's daughters walked outside and sat on the balcony to wait for the verdict. As they walked by, I wanted to tell them how much I loved their mother, and that I loved them, too. But we were on opposite sides of the trial, and I couldn't change the way I felt about Patricia's murder. The pain and bitterness was almost more than I could cope with. However, I hoped that in years to come, the girls would someday understand that I was not their enemy. And that, on the road of life, we must all stand by our principles and have the courage to act upon them. We must listen to our conscience and refuse to be intimidated. We must have the courage to protect and defend our loved ones. Otherwise, we have failed ourselves.

"The sun is out. I think Patty and I will sit outside, too," Darlene said. "Be sure to call us when the jury comes back."

As Darlene and Patty stood up to leave, I glanced briefly across the aisle, thinking perhaps most everyone else had left. For all the seats behind the defense table were empty, except for news reporters writing notes. However, as I glanced behind me, my eyes met with a sea of faces crowded close together in a show of moral support for the prosecution. And, still sitting directly behind Carol and me, were the now familiar faces of Brian Taylor and Patrick Page.

I wanted to stand up and tell them all that I appreciated their thoughtfulness. But, instead, I quietly turned back around to watch the clock.

Approximately half an hour later, the jury sent a note to Judge Ernst, requesting to re-read the testimony of Rhonda Crocker Bullion. The request was granted.

Judge Ernst then leaned back in his chair and closed his eyes, as though he may have been wishing for an afternoon nap. Carter was sorting through papers and writing something on a legal pad. Lewis

THE DARK SIDE OF TWILIGHT:

looked as nervous as a cat behind a rocking chair on a hard-waxed floor. David Barron was walking back and forth shooting rubber bands at a small object on his counsel table. The object appeared to be a tiny bottle of liquid paper and, so far, each time he had aimed for it, he had missed it. But, seemingly oblivious of the spectators who by now were all watching him, he continued without emotion, as though he were alone.

The courtroom scene remained that way for the next half hour, without interruption. Judge Ernst appeared to enjoy a well deserved nap. Carter did paperwork, Lewis shifted nervously in his chair. And Barron shot rubber bands. Then the jury sent in another request. They wanted to know how tall Lewis was.

Judge Ernst, now fully awake and rested, asked Lewis how tall he was.

Lewis replied that he was five-feet nine inches. Then the officer left again.

The quiet courtroom scene continued, until at last, with a well aimed, strong rubber band, David Barron finally hit the small object, knocking it over. When it fell, the spectators cheerfully applauded him. And, with an astonished look on his face, he looked at them and smiled. Then he bowed to them and sat down.

An hour and fifty minutes later, the jury sent the officer back with another message to the Court. The jury had reached a verdict.

Several spectators whispered softly as I glanced around the room. And, Patricia's neighbor, who had made the comment that Lewis should be hanged, was standing in the doorway calling to those who waited outside.

"The jury has reached a verdict," she called. "Hurry. The jury is ready."

Within minutes, the outside spectators returned to the courtroom and were quietly seated. Billy Carter sat very still. Lewis bowed his head. David Barron loosened his tie. Carol reached for my hand. Judge Ernst looked out across the courtroom, then turned to the officer and asked that the jury be led in.

As the jurors were seated, I glanced at them, trying to read their

348

emotions. But they looked straight ahead, showing no emotion. Suddenly, I wondered if the whole damn thing had gone downhill. And if Lewis Crocker had been right when he said, 'when I tell the Judge why I had to kill her, I'll walk out of that courtroom a free man.' Surely, these twelve intelligent jurors who had heard the evidence and decided his fate, were not going to just let him go. I looked away from the jury. But a moment later I turned back to face them.

Judge Ernst declared that the "Court was ready."

Court: "All right, Mr. Foreman, have you reached a verdict?"

Richard Bertrand, Sr., the selected jury foreman, stood up and replied," Yes, sir. We have."

Judge Ernst: "All right. Kindly pass it to the bailiff, sir."

The bailiff carried the verdict to Judge Ernst to be read. And Judge Ernst read it precisely: "All right. We the jury find the Defendant guilty of murder as charged in the indictment. Signed by the foreman."

"Mr. Foreman, was this a unanimous verdict?"

The Foreman: "Yes, sir."

Court: "All twelve agreed to that verdict?"

The Foreman replied that all twelve jurors had agreed to the verdict.

Court: "Very well. The verdict will be received and filed. The jury is excused. Mr. Crocker has elected to take the second phase to the Court."

Carol leaned over and whispered to me: "I'm glad he got what he deserved."

Virginia must have been watching, for she called out from across the room.

"Well, I'm glad, you're glad," she screamed. "I'm glad, you're glad!"

"Ignore it, Carol," I said. "We've got what we came for. Let's go talk to Barron. I'd also like to thank the jury, but I don't know if that's proper."

As Carol and I stood up, Brian Taylor and Patrick Page stood up with us.

"Congratulations," said Page, shaking my hand.

"I told you we'd get him," Taylor said, putting his arm around my shoulder. "You didn't think we would, but we did. See, I told you I did my homework."

"Yes, you did," I said, in tears. "Thank you so very much."

"It was just part of my job," he said, glancing around the room. "Looks like your sister's daughters are a little upset. Do you think you'll be all right?"

"We'll probably be okay. We'll be leaving in a few minutes."

"Well, then I'll say good-bye, and good luck to you both. Next time you're down this way, stop in and say hello."

Texas Ranger Brian Taylor then placed a pinch of Skoal in his mouth and waved good-bye. He left not knowing that he would forever be my hero.

"I've got to leave, too," said Patrick Page. "It was nice meeting you both."

"Thank you," I said. "And thanks for telling us the nice things you learned about Patricia."

"She was a good woman," he replied. "There was no getting around that."

Brian Taylor and Patrick Page then went their separate ways, and so did we.

Carol and I were standing near the jury box talking to David Barron, when suddenly we heard another commotion. Rhonda had said something to the jurors as they were leaving. And I heard Judge Ernst say, "We don't need any of that." Then Virginia yelled at Carol, and I turned around facing her.

"Did you hear that?" said Carol. "They're threatening us."

"This is not the end of it," Virginia called to us. "This is not the end! This is just the beginning! We'll be waiting for you outside!"

Judge Ernst immediately rapped his gavel to quieten her.

"Listen young lady," he said, sternly. "Unless you want to go to jail with your father, you'll leave this courtroom, now."

Virginia turned to leave the courtroom, but as she reached the door, she looked back and called to us, again. "This is not the end of it!"

Carol was visibly shaken by the outburst. I was stunned and embarrassed that Patricia's daughters would behave that way. But David Barron didn't seem surprised at all.

"There was no reason for that," he said. "And I intend to bring it to the Court's attention."

Minutes later, Darlene, who had been outside during the outbursts, walked back into the courtroom to tell us that she and Patty were going home.

"Patty and I have to leave," she said. "Rhonda and Virginia are not going to do anything to us. They said they just want you and Aunt Carol."

"That's fine. Be careful going home," I replied.

"Well, I'm not leaving without police protection," said Carol. "I know those girls, and I know what they're capable of doing."

I saw the concern on Barron's face, and Judge Ernst's, as well as the two deputies standing close by. Judge Ernst then phoned the Sheriff's Office and asked that we be escorted to our motel in Navasota.

My God, this can't be happening, I thought. Why did the girls hate us? We had done nothing wrong. Their father had murdered our sister, who was their mother. He had buried her in a garbage dump. Carol and I had gone through hell to help find the body. He lied about her, and we went through hell again trying to disprove his lies. Certainly she deserved a decent burial and to have her murderer convicted. He was given a fair trial in a court of law and was convicted by a jury. Surely the girls did not believe that he should have gotten away with it. Did they think he was above the Law? Was it because he was Daddy and Daddy was supposed to always win? Was he now lashing out at us through his daughters?

He was not only a murderer. He was a thief. He robbed our family of a beloved daughter and sister. He robbed his children of their mother, his grandchildren of their grandmother. He robbed Patricia's friends and neighbors of their relationship with her.

Lewis Crocker was an alcoholic wife-beater. And Patricia had probably lost every fight she ever had with him. But thanks to David Barron and a jury of seven men and five women, Patricia had won the last and final fight.

Judge Ernst and David Barron remained in the courtroom with Carol and me, until Deputies John Sebastian and Willie Love arrived to escort us to Navasota. Mr. Barron then followed us as we walked to my car.

"Be sure to call my office and let me know if you have any more problems," said Barron. "If I'm not in the office, call me at my home."

David Barron waited on the courthouse steps as we pulled away from the parking space and onto the street. It was a picture that I would long remember. He was a good and decent man. His kindness had given us hope throughout the trial. His strength and courage were the wings of our victory.

Carol and I would always remember him as a friend. A true friend.

We had first come to Grimes County, alone and afraid, seeking justice for Patricia's murder. Now, our debt of gratitude to Judge Ernst, David Barron, Brian Taylor, Larry Adams, Tracy Wright, and others was more than we could ever repay.

As we left Anderson, I followed John Sebastian and Willie Love followed me.

We were about three miles west of Anderson when we saw the white pickup parked on the roadside waiting with its brake lights on and its motor running.

"I'd like to know who's sitting in that truck," Carol said.

"I would, too," I said. "But I'm not going to stop to find out."

As we passed the white pickup, Carol tried to see who was in it, but its windows were still dirty. As I looked through my rearview mirror, the pickup made a wide U turn and headed back toward Anderson.

About a mile further we noticed another pickup parked on the roadside, waiting. It was dark blue and larger than the white pickup.

"There they are," said Carol. "I knew they'd do something like this."

"Are you sure that's their truck?"

"Sure, I'm sure. I'd know it anywhere. I've seen it at Mother's. Turn on your lights, or pull over. Let the police know about it. Otherwise, they'll run us off the road. Police cars and all."

"They wouldn't be that crazy."

"Are you kidding? What do you think they're waiting for?"

I flashed my lights at John Sebastian, and to Willie Love, in the car behind me. As we passed the pickup, its windows were down. And Rhonda and Virginia stared back at us. A short distance further, Willie Love stopped and waited.

"Of all the stupid stunts. Did they have the window down for a better aim at my tires, in case they didn't hit my car hard enough to wreck it?"

"That wouldn't surprise me," Carol replied.

John Sebastian escorted us to our motel, then notified the Navasota police.

"We recognized the truck," he said. "That's why Willie stopped, in case it tried to come any further. The Navasota police will patrol this area tonight."

After Sebastian left, Carol and I went to the coffee shop, next door. Over coffee, we remembered Jack Thompson's advice: "Ya'll be careful. There's a strange breed of people in this area." Now we knew what he meant by that.

CHAPTER 29

The punishment phase of the trial of Lewis Crocker lasted barely half a day.

Mack Wilson, husband of Rosa Wilson, took the stand and testified in a manner that I thought was an attempt to make Lewis appear as saintly as the Angels at Heaven's Pearly Gates.

Wilson stated that he and Rosa had known Lewis and Patricia about seventeen years, and, "They were our best friends and they got kids the same age as ours." He stated that they spent most weekends together in the summer, and did things together as families. They hunted together and fished a lot. And they took trips together.

"I thought they were a nice couple," said Wilson. "They loved each other and they were fun to be around. That's what my opinion was."

Carter: "During that time period, did you ever see or witness any real problems between them?"

Wilson: "No."

Carter: "Did they ever argue, fight or anything like that?"

Wilson: "I saw them argue, but well, like everybody does. Not mean arguments. Just I want to do this and I don't want to do that. If we would go camping and the women started doing something, he'd say, 'Wait, I'll go do that myself.' I would let them do it. Like get the wood and stuff."

Carter: "All right. When you heard what had happened and all the testimony that came out at the trial, what was your feeling about that?"

Wilson: "I couldn't believe it when I heard what happened."

Carter asked Wilson how he felt about Lewis Crocker today. Wilson replied that Lewis was his friend. They were best friends and were still friends.

Carter: "And why were you so shocked about this thing?"

Wilson: "Well, you would think people would be mad at each other before something like that would happen."

Carter: "Did Lewis drink around you-all?"

Wilson: "Yes."

Carter asked Wilson if he felt that Lewis had a drinking problem. Wilson said he couldn't really judge that.

Carter passed the witness.

Barron: "Would you say Lewis worshipped the ground she walked on?"

Wilson: "Yes, I would."

Barron passed the witness back to Carter.

Carter: "Mr. Wilson, why would you say that?"

Wilson: "Because they was together all the time. If you saw one of them, you would see the other one. He bought her clothes and stuff like that so she would look nice. I mean, it takes a lot for somebody to go follow a woman around a mall and buy her clothes."

Carter: "Did you observe that?"

Wilson: "I didn't go with them, but I know they had been and come back with clothes."

Carter asked Wilson if he had ever done that with his wife. Wilson replied, "A few times. Not voluntarily."

Carter had no more questions for Wilson. But David Barron did.

Barron: "You ever buried your wife?"

"Your Honor, I object to that!" Carter called. "Sustained," said His Honor.

Barron: "This man that you are talking about that you say worshipped the ground she walked on is the same man that killed her and buried her in a garbage dump?"

Wilson: "They say that."

Barron: "Yes. That's what she says."

After that, Wilson was excused from the stand.

The next witness, called by the Defendant, was Rosa Wilson. Rosa stated that she and her husband lived in Navasota. She further stated that for the past two years, she and her husband saw Lewis and

Patricia, "Just about every weekend and maybe once or twice during the week. And before that we would spend weekends out camping. I mean hunting with them or whatever. We were always camping out somewhere."

Carter: "This proceeding and this conviction for murder against Lewis Crocker, were you surprised, shocked, or what was your feeling about what happened between them, based on the observations of their relationship?"

Rosa: "I was surprised."

But why were you surprised? I thought. In the seventeen years that you knew them, how many times did you see Patricia with black eyes and bruises. How many times did you see Lewis hit her? Or could it be that only her family, and the people she worked with, her neighbors and all of her other friends saw her that way.

Carter: "And why were you surprised?"

Rosa: "I feel that he wasn't in his right mind when all of this happened."

Carter: "And why would you say that?"

Rosa: "Because of the way he acted right after it. He didn't act right and I think if they hadn't taken him when they did take him, I don't think he would be here."

Really? I thought. Where would he be? At Fred's Place? I wondered how she knew how he acted, 'right after it.' During the forty-four days that Patricia's body lay buried at the dump, didn't she have at least one occasion to go to Patricia's home with one of the girls? And from her own thinking, didn't she suspicion the truth about what had happened? Didn't she make the comment to Claude Hutchins that she thought Patricia's body was in a stock pond on the Jim Pierce Ranch? And asked him not to repeat her comment?

Carter asked Rosa how she felt about Lewis today. Rosa replied that she felt sorry for him. Carter then passed the witness to Barron.

Barron: "How do you feel about Patricia today?"

Rosa: "I miss her very much."

Barron: "Okay. While they were looking, when Patricia was still a missing person, did Lewis Crocker tell you what happened?"

Rosa: "No, sir. He never did."

Barron: "Now, you are under oath. Did you make a statement to Claude Hutchins when he asked you, 'What do you really think happened to Patricia,' did you say, I think I know. She's in the lake on the Jim Pierce Ranch?"

Rosa: "I made the statement. I can't remember the exact words. I know I felt that she could be out there at Jim Pierce Ranch."

In early September, Claude Hutchins told an investigator that he had asked Rosa what she thought had happened to Patricia. Rosa replied, "I don't think. I know. She is in the lake on Jim Pierce Ranch. Don't say anything to Mack because he will kill me." Whether Rosa had made the comment as an idle remark of pure speculation, or whether she had actual reason for saying it, was a question in my mind that I would not soon forget.

Barron continued the cross examination of Rosa.

Barron: "Why did you feel that way?"

Rosa: "I don't know. I just felt it. I don't know why. I felt that she could be out there or that ranch he worked at before in Bedias."

Barron: "Before her body was found, you knew he had buried her?"

Rosa: "I felt it."

Barron passed the witness. Carter stated he had no further questions.

But as Rosa's testimony ended, I thought back to the day of Patricia's funeral. On that day, she introduced herself to our family as, 'Patricia's best friend. Her very best friend.' Now I wondered about the true meaning of being a best friend.

Virginia Crocker was Carter's next witness.

Carter: "Virginia, you realize your father has been convicted by a Grimes County jury for murder, don't you? And you understand that we are here today on the punishment hearing in front of the Judge?"

Virginia: "Yes, sir."

Carter asked Virginia what her feelings were today about her father. Virginia replied, "He's still my dad and I still love him. But he needs to be punished for what he done. But I don't think he needs to be for the rest of his life."

Carter: "You say you feel he needs to be punished. Why do you say that?"

Virginia: "Because he buried her."

Virginia was then excused.

The next witness was Tammie Allen, age 25, the oldest daughter of Lewis and Patricia Crocker. During questioning, by Carter, Tammie stated that when Lewis was drinking, "He was like the Devil himself."

Carter: "What impression did you get about the way your father felt about your mother?"

Tammie: "He loved her with a possessive love. He wanted to possess her. He loved her to death."

Carter: "How do you feel about your father now?"

Tammie: "I love him. He's my father and nothing is going to change that."

Carter: "How do you feel about your mother?"

Tammie: "I loved my mother and I still do. I haven't really accepted the reality that she's gone."

At the end of the questioning by Carter, Tammie asked the Court to show mercy for Lewis. Then David Barron began cross examination.

Barron: "Tammie, you saw your mother the day that she was killed, didn't you?"

Tammie: "Yes."

Barron: "Do you remember her telling you that she had been crying all night?"

Tammie: "Yes."

Barron: "Why had she been crying all night?"

Tammie: "I don't know. She just said that. I said, Momma, what is wrong with your eyes?" She said, "I'm allright. I've just been up crying all night." She just kind of shrugged it off."

Barron: "If your father was to walk out of this courtroom today, he wouldn't stop drinking, would he?"

Tammie: "Probably not."

After that, there were no more questions for Tammie.

The next witness on the stand was Dr. Wendell Dickerson. Dickerson was a practicing psychologist from Bryan, Texas. And other areas.

Carter: "You have testified as an expert witness in this state on numerous occasions, haven't you?"

Dickerson stated that he had "testified in court on many occasions."

Carter: "Did I ask you to examine Lewis Crocker?"

Dickerson: "Yes."

Dickerson stated that he saw Mr. Crocker on two or three different occasions 'over a week ago.' And that he had talked with two of his daughters. He also stated that he had the benefit of a hospital record from Mr. Crocker's brief stay in a Bryan hospital approximately three to three and a half weeks after the death of Mrs. Crocker. And he had the benefit of whatever other information that had been available to Mr. Carter.

Carter: "And from the information you had available to you, Doctor, did you give him any type of tests?"

Dickerson: "Yes. I gave him a reasonably comprehensive battery of tests."

Carter: "You feel comfortable in whatever observations you can give the Court now based on the data and the information provided to you?"

Dickerson: "Yes. I believe I have a satisfactory amount of knowledge and information available to me that would enable me to draw conclusions consistent with commonly approved practices."

Carter: "Did you find, in your observations and opinions of Lewis Crocker, his behavior to be consistent with that of someone with alcohol problems?"

Dickerson: "Oh, yes. I think alcoholism is the primary diagnosis in this case."

Carter: "And, Doctor, did you find that Lewis Crocker feels any remorse or is he dispassionate or cool about what happened?"

Dickerson: "It is my opinion that Mr. Crocker has been profoundly affected by the death of his wife. He is clinically depressed, even to the extent of there being some suicidal ideation there."

Carter: "How do you treat an alcohol problem of this nature?"

Dickerson: "The classic theory is that alcoholics have to climb out. They have to reach a point in their lives in which absolutely everything is coming to a roaring, screeching, screaming kind of disaster and at that point they begin to become accessible to the kind of things that will be useful to them in the future."

The Doctor went on to explain his point by analogy. "Man needs food to survive," he said. "It is not just food you put in your mouth, but also through your senses. Who we are, what we are, and what life is all about and this kind of stuff. These are important in feeding the entire man, the same way as cauliflower feeds the body. For people to recover from alcoholism, they have to emerse themselves in a psychological, emotional, spiritual will, if you will, kind of view that has been the great success of Alcoholics Anonymous because it emerses them in a different kind of substance for the spirit. There's a lot more to AA than a bunch of drunks getting together and saying I'm a drunk."

With all due respect to the Doctor, I wanted to tell him that based on twenty-six years experience as the sister-in-law of Lewis Crocker, my opinion was that there was a lot more to murder than just saying a killer was an alcoholic. And it was a safe bet that before today, all the wild horses in Texas could not have dragged him to an AA meeting. Liquor did not pull the trigger, Doctor. His daughter said he was not intoxicated. Murderers are not necessarily alcoholics. Alcoholics are not necessarily murderers. It is my opinion that murder has its own makeup. It can stem from not learning how to share, as a child; from not learning to respect others feelings as we would hope to have others respect ours. It may stem from insisting that one must always have his way. That he or she must always be right and must always win, regardless of the situation or the consequences. I think it stems from two things. Number one, never learning how to love. Number two, never learning how to let go.

The doctor continued a lengthy testimony. A good one I thought, as he told of the advantages of Alcoholics Anonymous.

Finally, Barron was up to bat in cross examination.

Barron: "Dr. Dickerson, you say he seemed suicidal?"

Dickerson: "To some extent."

Barron: "He had six weeks of freedom after he killed his wife and he didn't commit suicide."

Dickerson: "He didn't commit suicide."

Barron: "Okay."

Dickerson: "From what I gather, Mr. Barron, he was not taking very good care of himself. He had pneumonia from his inactivity and depression."

Barron: "Could part of his depression be that he has been in the Grimes County jail for nearly six months?"

Dickerson: I suppose part of it could be."

Barron: "Are you suggesting, Doctor, that the Court should mitigate Mr. Crocker's punishment because of his alcohol abuse?"

Dickerson: "I'm not sure what mitigation is, Mr. Barron. I think the people of the State have an interest and that needs to be addressed."

Barron: "What about the victim?"

Dickerson: "The victim's family has some. The victim, that is largely irrelevant because nothing makes any difference to them since she's dead. Her family has an interest."

Barron: "What about the punishment?"

Dickerson: "Justice must not only appear to be done. It must be done. I'm saying in terms of sentencing we have the issue of punishment, but we also have the problem of if this man is ever going to get out of the pen, can we get this business behind and constructively prevent further problems for all of us."

The last witness to take the stand, in the trial of the State of Texas vs Lewis Crocker, was none other than Rhonda Bullion.

Regardless of their previous behavior, my heart went out to all of Patricia's daughters. Their world was shattered by the loss of their mother. A mother's love that could never be replaced. I hoped they would seek counseling and rebuild their lives with dignity. Patricia would want that. And, someday, when the pain had partially lifted, I hoped to share with them childhood stories and photographs Patricia had shared with me so many years ago.

As Rhonda sat in the witness chair for the last time, Carter asked how she felt about her father after all that had happened.

"He's still my father and I still love him," she replied. She went on to say that when he was drinking, he was mean. "Like the Devil come out in him." She said she thought, "What happened, happened for a reason. And that he should be punished for what he did. But that she hoped the Court would show mercy.

Carter then passed the witness. Barron said, "No questions."

Carter said, "Your Honor, we will rest." Barron said he would, "waive the right to open and reserve the right to close." "Allright," said the Court. Then the last and final arguments began.

"Judge, there is not a lot I can say in this particular case," said Carter.

"I think that, number one, this whole thing is sad and it is tragic," Carter went on. "Lewis Crocker has been convicted of murder by a jury. In determining the punishment, we realize he's going to spend time in the Texas Department of Corrections. But I do think at times people can commit crimes and still not be a criminal. And we've seen many criminals come through the courtroom. I think a person can commit murder and be convicted of murder and still not be a murderer as you understand and David Barron understands murder. That's no excuse for what happened. But maybe it can serve as a reason for what happened. Not a justification.

"All of us have an evil and dark side and I think every day each of us walks a thin line between day and night. Between day and night, between good and evil, between good and bad. But that is not justification for what we do.

"Some of us are able to stay over the line and not step off and we are blessed by God if we are able to. But some people cannot. I don't think Lewis Crocker's stepping off the line into that darkness is as much an act of evil and wickedness as say other people that do. He spent days in the light, probably more in the light than in the darkness. We've seen some that spent all their time in the darkness and that's not the case with him."

Carter, the seasoned old warrior, was again living up to his reputation. But I could not agree with the poetic way he pleaded for his client. For it was my opinion that Lewis had crossed over to the dark side long before the murder. He was the dark side. He was the dark side of Patricia's life. He had proven that. And, as Tammie had said, "He was like the Devil himself."

"I think it is sad," Carter said. "Sad that he gets to a point in his life that he commits so horrible an act; and I just have to beg the Court, in determining what is best for him, to temper it with mercy.

"I really think, even though he was convicted of murder, even though he buried her body, I still think that this man, although he may not have shown mercy, does deserve mercy."

Carter, the old warrior, continued talking about mercy. He said he realized that Lewis was going to spend time in the Texas Department of Corrections.

"I just wish that in the time you assess that you would look at the whole thing. You know what the parole laws are. You know what the affirmative findings of deadly weapons are, how long he will spend on a certain sentence. You are aware of all that. So, I know he's going to spend time in the pen and probably a long time. I wish you would temper that time with a little mercy. I'm going to quote you something in closing on Clarence Darrow. I read it last night. They said that Judge Holly delivered this eulogy at Darrow's funeral and provided an epitaph at that time which fit the man exactly.

"He said, 'He loved mercy. We may not know what justice is. No judge who sentences a prisoner to the electric chair is more certain of the rightness of his judgment than the mob that hangs or burns its victim. Whether the offender is legally executed by the sheriff or illegally hanged by the mob, we cannot be sure it is justice or vengeance that is satisfied. But mercy is a quality we can all recognize. And in his heart Darrow was endowed with pity and mercy for the poor, the oppressed, the weak, and all races, colors, creeds, and all human condition. Clarence Darrow made the way easier for man. He preached no doctrine but love and pity, the only virtues that can make this world better.'

"Lewis Crocker is weak. I'm just asking the Court to show him some mercy in determining what is best for him and society and for his family. Thank you."

Carter sat down.

David Barron rose from his chair to cast the final blow in his fight for justice for Patricia.

"Your Honor, Clarence Darrow was never a prosecutor," said Barron. "He represented the people accused of crimes. My job is to represent the victims of crimes and speak for the Patricia Crockers.

"Billy Carter is probably right. Alcohol was a major problem in this problem between Patricia and Lewis Crocker. But on the occasion in question, from the people at Fred's Place to his daughter who saw him afterwards, said he was sober. So, I don't think alcohol has anything to do with this case.

"The cold fact is he murdered her.

"The jury found that and he showed his regard for her by burying her body at a dump site. And these daughters he loves, he put them through agony wondering where their mother was and all along he knew she was buried in a garbage dump on the Jim Pierce Ranch.

"If it wasn't for Brian Taylor and his investigation of the case, I don't think we would be here today. And these girls would probably still be wondering where their mother was.

"And I know it is easy to ask for mercy. But it is also easy for me to ask the Court for a life sentence and that's what I ask the Court to assess in this case."

Barron returned to his counsel table and sat down.

"Allright, gentlemen," said the Honorable Judge Ernst. "I tried my first murder case in 1950 and this is 1989. So, this case, based upon my experience, falls somewhere between 50 and 99 years. That's what traditionally this kind of case with these kind of facts would be.

"The judgment of the Court is 75 years confinement in the Texas Department of Corrections. Whenever you are ready we'll assess the punishment."

Carter stood beside Lewis and announced that they were ready.

The Court: "What if anything do you say why the sentence of law shall not be imposed against you?"

Carter: "We have nothing to say."

The Court: "Nothing to say in bar, it is the order of this Court that you be remanded to the custody of the Sheriff of Grimes County to be delivered to the director of the Texas Department of Corrections where you shall serve a term of 75 years under the rules and regulations of that Institution."

"One other thing," said David Barron. "The jury determined there was a deadly weapon."

The Court: "There was a finding of a deadly weapon by the Court."

Lewis was returned to jail for transfer to the prison in Huntsville. The courtroom was cleared. The echoes were silent. And at last, it was over.

CHAPTER 30

The next morning, as I drove past the Jim Pierce Ranch, glancing at the bare trees and frozen ground, I thought about taking another road to Interstate 45, on my way back to Dallas. But, in the recesses of my mind, I knew I would go to Patricia's house one last time.

Near the outskirts of Bedias, the freezing rain had shifted and passed on, leaving behind a mass of dark hovering snow clouds and cold gusty wind. The cold gray skies seemed fitting for my last visit here. And perhaps that was how it should be. It was better that way. For had it have been summer again, I might have thought that when I stopped at the small house at the end of the street, by some strange twist of fate, Patricia would be waiting for me.

I parked in front of the house, not knowing or caring whether or not anyone was watching. Nor did I care about the whispers behind the blinds and curtains in the houses nearby. Her neighbors had been at the trial and by now they knew most of the story anyway. So, there was no need to ask why I was here. They would know I had come to say good-bye.

The house looked cold and dark, inside and out. The tall frozen grass appeared not to have been mowed, probably since last September. A stack of roofing materials lay frozen on the driveway. Baskets of withered flowers still hung on the porch. The rose colored curtains hung awry in the windows.

The care Patricia had given her home was gone forever. Now it reeked of memories of beatings and the flash of gunfire. It echoed the sound of a trunk lid closing over her body. A car driving away in the darkness of night.

I vowed to never again think of the house as Patricia's home.

I would always love her and know that she loved me. I would always be thankful that we were sisters here on Earth. I would remember her with the love and respect that she deserved. The respect that was often denied to her by others.

I would recall the happy days of her childhood, and remember her beauty and intelligence. Her laughter and her smile. I would remember the good times we shared together as sisters. I would also remember her faith in God, and her prayers for the sick and the less fortunate.

Each time I visit her grave, I will try to remember the words to a favorite poem. Its magnificent author is unknown, but it reads, "Do not stand at my grave and weep; I am not there I do not sleep. I am a thousand winds that blow; I am the diamond glints on snow. I am the sunlight on ripened grain; I am the gentle autumn's rain. When you awaken in the morning's hush; I am the swift uplifting rush. Of quiet birds in circled flight; I am the soft star that shines at night. Do not stand at my grave and cry; I am not there; I did not die."

I know she would want me to keep the good memories. And I will keep them, along with my undying love for her. And I will cherish them with faith and with hope that someday, somehow, we'll meet again.